Cambridge International GCSE
Mathematics

Let's face it, Cambridge International GCSE Maths isn't easy... but this brilliant CGP guide has everything you need to be on track for exam success. Hooray!

It's full of clear study notes and examples, plus plenty of exam-style questions on each topic. Handily, you'll find fully worked answers for every question at the back.

We've also included two sets of practice exams — one for Core and one for Extended. So whichever course you're doing, you'll be ready to go on the big day.

How to access your free Online Edition

This book includes a free Online Edition to read on your PC, Mac or tablet. You'll just need to go to **cgpbooks.co.uk/extras** and enter this code:

0568 4599 7900 1303

By the way, this code only works for one person. If somebody else has used this book before you, they might have already claimed the Online Edition.

Complete
Revision & Practice
<u>Every</u>thing you need to pass the exams!

Contents

Section Four — Geometry and Measures

Section Five — Pythagoras, Trigonometry and Vectors

Section Six — Probability and Statistics

Extended

Some of the content in this book will only be assessed if you're taking the Extended version of the Cambridge International GCSE. We've marked up all the content that's only for the Extended course with purple brackets, like the ones around this text, or the example below:

Information or questions with a bracket like this are for the Extended course only.

Published by CGP

From original material by Richard Parsons.

Updated by: Sammy El-Bahrawy, Sarah George, Shaun Harrogate and Rosa Roberts

Contributors: Alastair Duncombe

With thanks to Alastair Duncombe, Simon Little and Glenn Rogers for the proofreading.

ISBN: 978 1 78908 474 0

Printed by Bell & Bain Ltd, Glasgow.
Clipart from Corel®

Order of Operations

Welcome to the wonderful world of maths. We're going to start off with something easy —
the order of operations like addition, subtraction and multiplication — also known as BODMAS.

BODMAS   BODMAS tells you the ORDER in which these operations should be done:

 KEY TERM

BODMAS: Brackets, Other, Division & Multiplication, Addition & Subtraction

> Work out Brackets first, then Other things like squaring, then
> Divide / Multiply groups of numbers before Adding / Subtracting.
>
> To decide between dividing and multiplying, or between adding
> and subtracting, just work from left to right.

This set of rules works really well, so remember "BODMAS".

EXAMPLES:

1.   **Work out $7 + 9 \div 3$**

1) Follow BODMAS — do the division first... $7 + 9 \div 3$
2) ...then the addition: $= 7 + 3$
   $= 10$

> If you don't follow
> BODMAS, you get:
> $7 + 9 \div 3 = 16 \div 3$
> $= 5.333...$ ✗

2.   **Calculate $15 - 7^2$**

1) The square is an 'other' so that's first: $15 - 7^2$
2) Then do the subtraction: $= 15 - 49$
   $= -34$

3.   **Find $(5 + 3) \times (12 - 3)$**

1) Start by working out the brackets: $(5 + 3) \times (12 - 3)$
2) And now the multiplication: $= 8 \times 9$
   $= 72$

4. $e = (f - 7)^2 + \dfrac{4g}{h + 1}$, **where $f = 4$, $g = 3$, $h = -2$.**
   Work out the value of e.

1) Write down the formula: $e = (f - 7)^2 + \dfrac{4g}{h+1}$

2) Put the numbers in: $e = (4 - 7)^2 + \dfrac{4 \times 3}{-2 + 1}$

3) Then work it out in stages: $= (-3)^2 + \dfrac{12}{-1}$

   $= 9 + \dfrac{12}{-1}$

   $= 9 + -12$

   $= -3$

Work brackets out first.

Around the top and bottom of a
fraction there are 'invisible brackets'.
You just have to imagine they're there.

Then other stuff — in this
case square the first bit.

Then divide.

Finally add or subtract.

Putting brackets round the
negative number makes it clear
that -3 is squared, not just 3.

Make sure you're confident with this before moving on

BODMAS comes up all the time, so it's really important that you can do it without getting confused.

Calculator Buttons

This page is really important — it's all about using calculators.

Know Your **Buttons**

Look for these buttons on your calculator — they might be a bit different on yours.

	The reciprocal button. The reciprocal of a number is 1 divided by it. So the reciprocal of 2 is ½.		The cube root button. You might have to press shift first.
	This uses your last answer in your current calculation — very useful.		Swaps your answer from a fraction to a decimal and vice versa.

BODMAS on Your Calculator

BODMAS questions can be packed with tricky decimals and maybe a square root and sin/cos/tan. You could do it on your calculator in one go, but you could lose precious marks if you make a mistake.

EXAMPLE: Work out $\left(\dfrac{64\cos 80°}{0.48 + \sqrt{0.79}}\right)^3$.

Write down all the figures on your calculator display.

$$\left(\frac{64\cos 80°}{0.48 + \sqrt{0.79}}\right)^3$$

You MUST write down the numbers as you go. That way, even if you mess up at the end, you may still get a mark.

$$= \left(\frac{11.11348337}{1.368819442}\right)^3$$

$$= 8.119027997^3$$

$$= 535.1950858$$

There are lots of slightly different ways of working out this type of calculation. Here's one:

1) Work out the bottom of the fraction: `0.48` `+` `√` `0.79` `=`
   Write the answer down and store it in the memory by pressing: `STO` `M+`

2) Now work out the top of the fraction: `64` `cos` `80` `=`

3) Do the division: `Ans` `÷` `RCL` `M+` `=`
   This gets the value of the bottom of the fraction out of the memory.

4) And cube the answer: `Ans` `x■` `3` `=`

NOTE:

1) On some calculators, a bracket opens when you use a trig function or the square/cube root function. So to enter something like tan 40° + 1, you have to close the bracket: `tan` `40` `)` `+` `1`
2) On some calculators, the cursor stays under the square root bar until you move it out by pressing the right arrow.

Check Your Answer Using **Brackets** `(` and `)`

Check your answer to a question like the one above by typing it into your calculator in fewer steps.

1) To work out $\dfrac{64\cos 80°}{0.48 + \sqrt{0.79}}$ you CAN'T just press `64` `cos` `80` `÷` `0.48` `+` `√` `0.79` `=`

2) The calculator follows BODMAS, so it'll think you mean $\dfrac{64\cos 80°}{0.48} + \sqrt{0.79}$.

3) You need to use the BRACKETS BUTTONS — the calculator will do the bits in brackets first. So you can press:

   `(` `64` `cos` `80` `)` `÷` `(` `0.48` `+` `√` `0.79` `)` `=` ← (Cube this to check the question above.)

Your calculator might need you to add an extra ")" here. See the note above.

You might also need an extra ")", or to move right one space here.

 EXAM TIP

Your calculator can save you time in the exam

Different calculators have different ways of doing things. Make sure you're familiar with how your calculator works before the exam — it might save you some marks as well as some time.

Place Value and Ordering Numbers

You need to be able to read big numbers, put numbers in order of size, and use symbols like > and ≤.

Always Look at **Big Numbers** in Groups of **Three**

EXAMPLE: Write the number 2 351 243 in words.

1) The number has spaces which break it up into groups of 3:

2 MILLION — 2 351 243 — And the rest
351 THOUSAND

2) So this is: Two million, three hundred and fifty-one thousand, two hundred and forty-three.

Putting Numbers in **Order of Size**

EXAMPLE: Write these numbers in ascending order:

12   84   623   32   486   4563   75   2143

Ascending order just means smallest to largest.

1) First put them into groups, the ones with fewest digits first:

2-digit	3-digit	4-digit
12 84 32 75	623 486	4563 2143

2) Then just put each separate group in order of size:

12 32 75 84	486 623	2143 4563

To put decimals into ascending order:
1) Order the whole number parts first, then the parts after the decimal point.
2) Group them by the number of 0s after the decimal point.
   The group with the most 0s at the start comes first.

If you were asked to put the numbers in descending order, the group with the fewest 0s would come first.

EXAMPLE: Write these numbers in order, from smallest to largest:

0.531   0.098   0.14   0.0026   0.7   0.007   0.03

1) These are all between 0 and 1, so group them by the number of 0s after the decimal point:

2 initial 0s	1 initial 0	no initial 0s
0.0026 0.007	0.098 0.03	0.531 0.14 0.7

2) Once they're in groups, just order them by comparing the first non-zero digits. (If the first digits are the same, look at the next digit along instead.)

0.0026 0.007	0.03 0.098	0.14 0.531 0.7

In decimals, like in whole numbers, the value of the digits decreases from left to right.

0.256
tenths
hundredths
thousandths

The inequality symbols are useful for showing if numbers are bigger or smaller than each other:

These ones aren't inequality symbols, but you still need to know what they mean.

> means 'Greater than' E.g. 2 > 1, 72 > 27	≥ means 'Greater than or equal to' E.g. 5 ≥ 3, 2 ≥ 2	= means 'Equal to' E.g. 9 = 9
< means 'Less than' E.g. 3 < 8, 0 < 44	≤ means 'Less than or equal to' E.g. 11 ≤ 13, 8 ≤ 8	≠ means 'Not equal to' E.g. 14 ≠ 41

Don't put your inequality signs the wrong way round

There's nothing too difficult about putting numbers into order of size — just remember the tips above.

Negative Numbers

Numbers less than zero are negative. You should be able to add, subtract, multiply and divide with them.

Adding and Subtracting with Negative Numbers

Use the number line for addition and subtraction involving negative numbers:

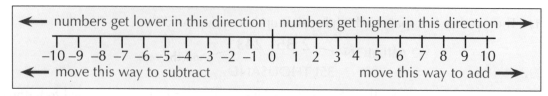

← numbers get lower in this direction numbers get higher in this direction →

–10 –9 –8 –7 –6 –5 –4 –3 –2 –1 0 1 2 3 4 5 6 7 8 9 10

← move this way to subtract move this way to add →

EXAMPLES:

What is –4 + 7? Start at –4 and move 7 places in the positive direction:

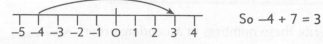

So –4 + 7 = 3

Work out 5 – 8 Start at 5 and move 8 places in the negative direction:

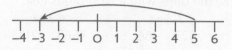

So 5 – 8 = –3

Find –2 – 4 Start at –2 and move 4 places in the negative direction:

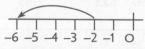

So –2 – 4 = –6

Use These Rules for Combining Signs

+	+	makes	+
+	–	makes	–
–	+	makes	–
–	–	makes	+

These rules are ONLY TO BE USED WHEN:

Multiplying or dividing

EXAMPLES:

Find: a) –2 × 3 ⌐(invisible + sign) – + makes – so –2 × 3 = –6

b) –8 ÷ –2 – – makes + so –8 ÷ –2 = 4

Be careful when squaring or cubing. Squaring a negative number gives a positive number (e.g. –2 × –2 = 4), but cubing a negative number gives a negative number (e.g. –3 × –3 × –3 = –27).

Two signs appear next to each other

EXAMPLES:

Work out: a) 5 – –4 – – makes + so 5 – –4 = 5 + 4 = 9

b) 4 + –6 – –7 + – makes – and – – makes + so 4 + –6 – –7 = 4 – 6 + 7 = 5

Number lines are useful when working with negative numbers

To multiply or divide negative numbers, you need to use the rules in the box above. Don't just learn them — make sure you know when you should use them too.

Special Types of Number

Before we go any further, there are a few different types of number that you need to know about.

Integers and Natural Numbers

 An integer is a whole number — it can be positive, negative or zero.
A natural number is a positive integer — not negative or zero.

Examples:

| Integers: | $-365, 0, 1, 17, 989$ |
| Not integers: | $0.5, 13\frac{3}{4}, \sqrt{7}, -1000.1, \pi$ |

| Natural: | $3, 56, 123\,456$ |
| Not natural: | $7.2, \frac{2}{3}, 0, -2$ |

Real, Rational and Irrational Numbers

 Rational numbers are numbers that can be written as fractions.
Irrational numbers can't be written as fractions.
Real numbers include every type of number — rational and irrational.

Most numbers you deal with are rational numbers. They come in 3 different forms:
1) Integers e.g. $4\ (=\frac{4}{1})$, $-5\ (=\frac{-5}{1})$, $-12\ (=\frac{-12}{1})$
2) Fractions $\frac{p}{q}$, where p and q are (non-zero) integers, e.g. $\frac{1}{4}, -\frac{1}{2}, \frac{3}{4}$
3) Terminating or recurring decimals e.g. $0.125\ (=\frac{1}{8})$, $0.333333...\ (=\frac{1}{3})$, $0.143143143...\ (=\frac{143}{999})$

Irrational numbers are never-ending, non-repeating decimals.
Roots of positive integers are either integers or irrational (e.g. $\sqrt{3}$ and $\sqrt[3]{2}$ are irrational, but $\sqrt{4} = 2$ isn't).

Square and Cube Numbers

 When you multiply a whole number by itself, you get a square number.
When you multiply a whole number by itself twice, you get a cube number.

Square numbers:

1^2	2^2	3^2	4^2	5^2	6^2	7^2	8^2	9^2	10^2	11^2	12^2	13^2	14^2	15^2
1	4	9	16	25	36	49	64	81	100	121	144	169	196	225

(1×1) (2×2) (3×3) (4×4) (5×5) (6×6) (7×7) (8×8) (9×9) (10×10) (11×11) (12×12) (13×13) (14×14) (15×15)

Cube numbers:

1^3	2^3	3^3	4^3	5^3	10^3
1	8	27	64	125	1000

(1×1×1) (2×2×2) (3×3×3) (4×4×4) (5×5×5) (10×10×10)

It will save you a lot of time in the exam if you can remember these square and cube numbers.

 ## Remember, an integer can be positive, negative or zero

It's really important that you know these different types of number and understand what they are — cover up the page and see how many definitions you can write down without looking.

Powers and Roots

You've already seen 'to the power 2' and 'to the power 3', but any number can be a power.
You also need to know the reverse of powers, which are called roots.

Powers are a very Useful Shorthand

1) Powers are 'numbers multiplied by themselves multiple times':

$$2 \times 2 \times 2 \times 2 \times 2 \times 2 \times 2 = 2^7 \quad \text{('two to the power 7')}$$

2) The powers of ten are really easy — the power tells you the number of zeros:

$$10^1 = 10 \qquad 10^2 = 100 \qquad 10^3 = 1000 \qquad 10^6 = 1\,000\,000$$

to the power of 6

6 zeros

3) Use the $x^\square$ or y^x button on your calculator to find powers,
   e.g. press 3 . 7 $x^\square$ 3 = to work out 3.7^3 (= 50.653).

Square Roots

'Squared' means 'multiplied by itself': $8^2 = 8 \times 8 = 64$

SQUARE ROOT $\sqrt{}$ is the reverse process: $\sqrt{64} = 8$

'Square Root' means
'What Number Times by Itself gives...'

EXAMPLES: **1.** **Find both square roots of 36.**

$6 \times 6 = 36$, so positive square root = 6

$-6 \times -6 = 36$, so negative square root = −6

All numbers also have a negative square root — it's just the '−' version of the normal positive one.

The $\sqrt{}$ symbol means the positive square root, not the negative one.

2. **Work out $\sqrt{16} \times 5^3$.**

$16 = 4 \times 4$, so $\sqrt{16} = 4$ $\qquad 5^3 = 5 \times 5 \times 5 = 125$

So $\sqrt{16} \times 5^3 = 4 \times 125 = 500$

Cube Roots

'Cubed' means 'multiplied by itself and then by itself again': $2^3 = 2 \times 2 \times 2 = 8$

CUBE ROOT $\sqrt[3]{}$ is the reverse process: $\sqrt[3]{8} = 2$

'Cube Root' means 'What Number Times by Itself and then by Itself Again gives...'

EXAMPLES: **1.** **Work out $\sqrt[3]{27}$.**

27 is a cube number.

3 times by itself and then by itself again gives 27:

$27 = 3 \times 3 \times 3$

So $\sqrt[3]{27} = 3$

2. **Calculate $\sqrt[3]{8} \times 2\sqrt{49}$.**

$2 \times 2 \times 2 = 8$, so $\sqrt[3]{8} = 2$

$7 \times 7 = 49$, so $\sqrt{49} = 7$

So $\sqrt[3]{8} \times 2\sqrt{49} = 2 \times 2 \times 7 = 28$

You can use your calculator to find any root of a number, using the $\sqrt[x]{}$ or $\sqrt[\square]{\square}$ buttons.

Make sure you know how to use your calculator to find roots — the buttons might be slightly different to these ones.

Use your calculator to make these questions really easy

If you can spot that a number is a square or cube number, you can quickly work out the root in your head.
Otherwise, you can just use your calculator — as long as you know where all the right buttons are.

Warm-Up and Worked Exam Questions

This stuff is pretty straightforward, but that doesn't mean you can get away without learning the facts and practising the questions. You should have learned the facts already — try these to make sure.

Warm-Up Questions

1) Find the value of: a) $15 - 12 \div 3$ b) $5 \times 2 + 3 \times 9$ c) $(3 + 5) \div 2 - 1$

2) Work out $\dfrac{\sqrt{8.67 - 4.94}}{4 \tan 87°}$. Write down all the figures on your calculator display.

3) Write the number 1 234 531 in words.

4) Choose from the numbers 1, 2.3, 3.2312, 10, –4, 7, $\sqrt{2}$, –5.1, $\frac{2}{7}$, 6π:
   Write down the numbers that are: a) integers
   　　　　　　　　　　　　　　　　b) irrational

5) The number n is an integer, and $3n$ is a square number between 10 and 50. Work out the value of n.

6) Write down the two square roots of 121.

Worked Exam Questions

Here are a couple of exam-style questions that have been worked out for you. Read them carefully, making sure you can follow them all the way through. Then have a go at the questions on the next page.

1　$d = \dfrac{3a^2 + 2b}{4(c + 3)}$, where $a = -2$, $b = 2$ and $c = -4$.
　Work out the value of d. Show all your working.

First, substitute the numbers in.

$d = \dfrac{3(-2)^2 + 2 \times 2}{4(-4 + 3)}$

Then follow BODMAS for the numerator and denominator separately — do the brackets and the squared number...

$= \dfrac{3 \times 4 + 2 \times 2}{4 \times (-1)}$

...then the multiplications...

$= \dfrac{12 + 4}{-4}$

...and finally, the addition.

$= \dfrac{16}{-4} = -4$

Then divide to get the answer.

$d = -4$

[2 marks]

2　Use your calculator to work out $\sqrt{\dfrac{12.71 + 137.936}{\cos 50° \times 13.2^2}}$
　Give your answer to 2 decimal places.

Use BODMAS.

$\sqrt{\dfrac{12.71 + 137.936}{\cos 50° \times 13.2^2}} = \sqrt{\dfrac{150.646}{0.642787609... \times 174.24}}$

$= \sqrt{1.34506182...}$

$= 1.1597680...$

1.16 (2 d.p.)

[2 marks]

Exam Questions

3 Use your calculator to work out the value of $\sqrt{\dfrac{7}{4^3} - (53 \div 2^4)^2}$.

Write down all the figures on your calculator display.

....

[1 mark]

4 Explain the difference between the integers and the natural numbers.

....

....

....

[1 mark]

5 Write these numbers in order, from smallest to biggest:

0.37   0.008   0.307   0.1   0.09   0.2

....

[1 mark]

6 Juliette thinks of a number between 1 and 10. She doubles it, then squares the answer.
   She then takes the cube root and gets back to the number she was thinking of.
   Work out the number that Juliette was thinking of.

....

[2 marks]

7 *x* and *y* are integers and $0 < x < y$.
   Write down two sets of values for *x* and *y* such that $6 = \sqrt{3x + 2y}$.

$x =$ .... , $y =$ ....

or $x =$ .... , $y =$ ....

[2 marks]

Prime Numbers

There's one more type of number that you need to know about — and that's prime numbers.

PRIME Numbers Don't Divide by Anything

 A prime number can only be divided exactly by two whole numbers — 1 and itself, e.g. 2 3 5 7 11 13 17 19 23 29 31 ...

E.g.   The only whole numbers that multiply to give 7 are: 1×7
The only whole numbers that multiply to give 31 are: 1×31

EXAMPLE: **Show that 24 is not a prime number.**

Just find another way to make 24 other than 1×24: $2 \times 12 = 24$

24 divides by other numbers apart from 1 and 24, so it isn't a prime number.

Five Important Facts

1) 1 is NOT a prime number.
2) 2 is the ONLY even prime number.
3) The first four prime numbers are 2, 3, 5 and 7.
4) Prime numbers end in 1, 3, 7 or 9 (2 and 5 are the only exceptions to this rule).
5) But NOT ALL numbers ending in 1, 3, 7 or 9 are primes, as shown here:
   (Only the circled ones are primes.)

How to FIND Prime Numbers — a very simple method

1) All primes (above 5) end in 1, 3, 7 or 9. So ignore any numbers that don't end in one of those.
2) Now, to find which of them ACTUALLY ARE primes you only need to divide each one by 3 and 7. If it doesn't divide exactly by either 3 or 7 then it's a prime.

This simple rule using just 3 and 7 works for checking numbers up to 120.

EXAMPLE: **Find all the prime numbers in this list:**   **71, 72, 73, 74, 75, 76, 77, 78**

1 First, get rid of anything that doesn't end in 1, 3, 7 or 9:   71, ~~72~~, 73, ~~74~~, ~~75~~, ~~76~~, 77, ~~78~~

2 Now try dividing 71, 73 and 77 by 3 and 7:

$71 \div 3 = 23.667$ $71 \div 7 = 10.143$ so 71 is a prime number
$73 \div 3 = 24.333$ $73 \div 7 = 10.429$ so 73 is a prime number
$77 \div 3 = 25.667$ BUT: $77 \div 7 = 11$ — 11 is a whole number,
so 77 is NOT a prime, because it divides by 7.

So the prime numbers in the list are 71 and 73.

Learn those five facts — they're important for a reason

A common mistake people make with prime numbers is saying that 1 is prime — it just isn't.
Don't forget that you can use your calculator to help you check if a number is divisible by 3 or 7.

Multiples, Factors and Prime Factors

You need to know what multiples, factors, primes and prime factors are — and how to find them.

Multiples and Factors

 KEY TERM The multiples of a number are just its times table.

EXAMPLE: **Find the first 8 multiples of 13.**
You just need to find the first 8 numbers in the 13 times table:

13   26   39   52   65   78   91   104

 KEY TERM The factors of a number are all the numbers that it can be divided by (to give a whole number).

There's a method that guarantees you'll find them all:

1) Start off with 1 × the number itself, then try 2 ×, then 3 × and so on, listing the pairs in rows.
2) Try each one in turn. Cross out the row if it doesn't divide exactly.
3) Eventually, when you get a number repeated, stop.
4) The numbers in the rows you haven't crossed out make up the list of factors.

EXAMPLE: **Find all the factors of 24.**

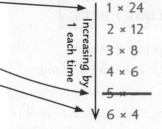

Increasing by 1 each time

1 × 24
2 × 12
3 × 8
4 × 6
5 ×
6 × 4

So the factors of 24 are: 1, 2, 3, 4, 6, 8, 12, 24

Finding Prime Factors — the Factor Tree

Any number can be broken down into a list of prime numbers all multiplied together — this is called 'expressing it as a product of prime factors'.

EXAMPLE:

Express 280 as a product of powers of prime factors.

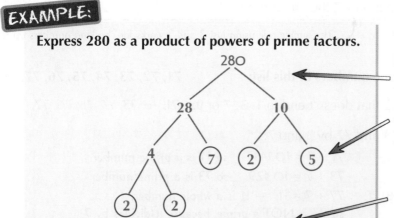

So 280 = 2 × 2 × 2 × 5 × 7 = 2^3 × 5 × 7

To write a number as a product of its prime factors, use the Factor Tree method:

1) Start with the number at the top, and split it into factors as shown.
2) Every time you get a prime, ring it.
3) Keep going until you can't go further (i.e. you're just left with primes), then write the primes out in order.
4) The question asks for powers of prime factors, so if a factor appears more than once you need to write it using powers (see p.6).

Factors and multiples are easy marks

Factor and multiple questions are simple multiplications and divisions, so there's no reason to lose marks. Practise doing them quickly and accurately and make sure you know what all the words mean.

LCM and HCF

Don't be put off by the names — they might sound complicated, but they're both quite easy.
This page covers the nice, simple methods for finding both of them.

LCM — 'Lowest Common Multiple'

 KEY TERM The Lowest Common Multiple (LCM) of some numbers is the smallest number that can be divided by all of those numbers.

METHOD: 1) LIST the MULTIPLES of ALL the numbers.
2) Find the SMALLEST one that's in ALL the lists.

The LCM is sometimes called the Least (instead of 'Lowest') Common Multiple.

EXAMPLE: **Find the lowest common multiple (LCM) of 12 and 15.**

Multiples of 12 are: 12, 24, 36, 48, (60,) 72, 84, 96, ...
Multiples of 15 are: 15, 30, 45, (60,) 75, 90, 105, ...

So the lowest common multiple (LCM) of 12 and 15 is 60.

HCF — 'Highest Common Factor'

 KEY TERM The Highest Common Factor (HCF) of some numbers is the biggest number that all of those numbers can be divided by.

METHOD: 1) LIST the FACTORS of ALL the numbers.
2) Find the BIGGEST one that's in ALL the lists.

EXAMPLES: **1. Find the highest common factor (HCF) of 24 and 42.**

Factors of 24 are: 1, 2, 3, 4, (6,) 8, 12, 24
Factors of 42 are: 1, 2, 3, (6,) 7, 14, 21, 42

So the highest common factor (HCF) of 24 and 42 is 6.

Extended

2. Find the highest common factor (HCF) of 36, 54, and 72.

Factors of 36 are: 1, 2, 3, 4, 6, 9, 12, (18,) 36
Factors of 54 are: 1, 2, 3, 6, 9, (18,) 27, 54
Factors of 72 are: 1, 2, 3, 4, 6, 8, 9, 12, (18,) 24, 36, 72

So the highest common factor (HCF) of 36, 54 and 72 is 18.

Extended

REVISION TIP ## LCM and HCF — learn what the names mean

LCM and HCF questions shouldn't be too bad as long as you know exactly what each one means.
Then you just multiply or divide to find the multiples or factors, exactly like on the previous page.

Warm-Up and Worked Exam Questions

Time for a quick few warm-up questions to make sure all that has sunk in. If you're not sure about any of them, take a look back at the previous pages. Otherwise, you can move on to the exam questions.

Warm-Up Questions

1) Find all the factors of 40.
2) Write down the multiples of 17 between 20 and 70.
3) Explain why 231 is not a prime number.
4) Write 40 as a product of its prime factors.
5) a) Find the lowest common multiple (LCM) of 9 and 12.
   b) Find the highest common factor (HCF) of 18 and 42.

Worked Exam Questions

Take a look at these worked exam questions. They're not too hard, but they should give you a good idea of what to write. Make the most of the handy hints now — they won't be there in the exam.

1   Express:

a)   210 as a product of its prime factors.

Draw a factor tree.

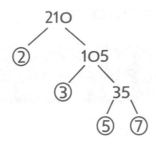

$$210 = 2 \times 3 \times 5 \times 7$$
....
[2 marks]

b) 105^2 as a product of its prime factors.

From part a), 105 = 3 × 5 × 7, so:

$105^2 = (3 \times 5 \times 7) \times (3 \times 5 \times 7)$

You could also write this as $105^2 = 3^2 \times 5^2 \times 7^2$

$105^2 = 3 \times 3 \times 5 \times 5 \times 7 \times 7$
....
[2 marks]

2   Find the lowest common multiple of 6, 8 and 10.

This method is useful, but you can also just list the multiples of 6, 8 and 10, as on p.11.

Write each number as the product of prime factors.

6 = 2 × 3
8 = 2 × 2 × 2
10 = 2 × 5

2 appears three times, so write it three times here.

Multiply the factors together to get the LCM.

So LCM = 2 × 2 × 2 × 3 × 5

120
....
[2 marks]

Extended

Exam Questions

3   a)   List all the factors of 30.

....
[1 mark]

b)   List all the factors of 48.

....
[1 mark]

c)   Write down the highest common factor of 30 and 48.

....
[1 mark]

4   Two remote-control cars start at the same time from the start line on a track.
One car takes half a minute to complete a circuit.
The other car takes 1 minute 10 seconds to complete a circuit.

Given that they started side by side, work out how long it will be before they are next side by side on the start line. State the units in your answer.

....
[2 marks]

5   Given that $25x^2 - 1$ factorises to give $(5x - 1)(5x + 1)$, write 2499 as a product of its prime factors.

This uses the 'difference of two squares' rule — you'll see this on page 52.

....
[3 marks]

Fractions

These pages show you how to do fraction calculations without your calculator or if you're asked in the exam to show all your working.

1) Cancelling down

> **KEY TERMS**
> The numerator is the number on the top of the fraction.
> The denominator is the number on the bottom of the fraction.

To cancel down or simplify a fraction, divide top and bottom by the same number until you can't any more:

EXAMPLE: Simplify $\frac{18}{24}$.

Cancel down in a series of easy steps — keep going until the top and bottom don't have any common factors.

$$\overset{\div 3 \qquad \div 2}{\frac{18}{24} = \frac{6}{8} = \frac{3}{4}}$$
$$\div 3 \qquad \div 2$$

2) Mixed numbers

> **KEY TERMS**
> Mixed numbers have an integer part and a fraction part, e.g. $3\frac{1}{3}$.
> Improper fractions are fractions where the top number is larger than the bottom number, e.g. $\frac{10}{3}$.

You need to be able to convert between these two different types of fraction.

EXAMPLES: 1. **Write $4\frac{2}{3}$ as an improper fraction.**

1) Think of the mixed number as an addition: $4\frac{2}{3} = 4 + \frac{2}{3}$

2) Turn the integer part into a fraction: $4 + \frac{2}{3} = \frac{12}{3} + \frac{2}{3} = \frac{12+2}{3} = \frac{14}{3}$

2. **Write $\frac{31}{4}$ as a mixed number.**

Divide the top number by the bottom.

1) The answer gives the integer part.

2) The remainder goes on top of the fraction.

$31 \div 4 = 7$ remainder 3

So $\frac{31}{4} = 7\frac{3}{4}$

3) Multiplying

Multiply top and bottom separately. It usually helps to cancel down first if you can.

EXAMPLE: Find $\frac{8}{15} \times \frac{5}{12}$.

8 and 12 both divide by 4

1) Cancel down by dividing top and bottom by any common factors you find in either fraction:

$$\frac{{}^2\cancel{8}}{15} \times \frac{5}{\cancel{12}_3} = \frac{2}{15_3} \times \frac{{}^1\cancel{5}}{3}$$

15 and 5 both divide by 5

2) Now multiply the top and bottom numbers separately:

$$= \frac{2}{3} \times \frac{1}{3} = \frac{2 \times 1}{3 \times 3} = \frac{2}{9}$$

Fractions

Here are some more methods for dealing with fractions.

4) Dividing

To divide one fraction by another, turn the second fraction upside down and then multiply:

EXAMPLE: Find $2\frac{1}{3} \div 3\frac{1}{2}$.

1) Rewrite the mixed numbers as fractions:

$$2\frac{1}{3} \div 3\frac{1}{2} = \frac{7}{3} \div \frac{7}{2}$$

2) Turn $\frac{7}{2}$ upside down and multiply:

$$= \frac{7}{3} \times \frac{2}{7}$$

3) Simplify by cancelling the 7s:

$$= \frac{1}{3} \times \frac{2}{1} = \frac{2}{3}$$

> When you're multiplying or dividing with mixed numbers, always turn them into improper fractions first.

5) Common denominators

This is useful for ordering fractions by size, and for adding or subtracting fractions.

You need to find a number that all the denominators divide into
— this will be your common denominator.

The simplest way is to find the lowest common multiple of the denominators:

EXAMPLE: Put these fractions in ascending order of size:

$$\frac{8}{3} \qquad \frac{5}{4} \qquad \frac{12}{5}$$

The LCM of 3, 4 and 5 is 60,
so make 60 the common denominator:

$$\frac{8}{3} = \frac{160}{60} \qquad \frac{5}{4} = \frac{75}{60} \qquad \frac{12}{5} = \frac{144}{60}$$

(×20)   (×15)   (×12)

So the correct order is $\frac{75}{60}, \frac{144}{60}, \frac{160}{60}$ i.e. $\frac{5}{4}, \frac{12}{5}, \frac{8}{3}$

Don't forget to use the original fractions in the final answer.

Don't get confused by mixed numbers

You can easily turn mixed numbers into improper fractions, like you did on the previous page. Finding a common denominator will often come in handy too — if you need a reminder on how to find the LCM, look back at p.11. You don't have to use the LCM, but if you don't then you might have to simplify later.

Fractions

6) Adding, subtracting — sort the denominators first

You can use this method to add or subtract any two fractions.

> 1) Make sure the denominators are the same (see previous page).

> 2) Add (or subtract) the top lines (numerators) only.

If you're adding or subtracting mixed numbers, it usually helps to convert them to improper fractions first.

EXAMPLE: Calculate $2\frac{1}{5} - 1\frac{1}{2}$.

1) Rewrite the mixed numbers as improper fractions: $2\frac{1}{5} - 1\frac{1}{2} = \frac{11}{5} - \frac{3}{2}$

2) Find a common denominator: $= \frac{22}{10} - \frac{15}{10}$

3) Combine the top lines: $= \frac{22-15}{10} = \frac{7}{10}$

> People usually find adding and subtracting fractions harder than multiplying and dividing — but it's actually pretty easy as long as you make sure the denominators are the same.

7) Fractions of something

> **Multiply the 'something' by the TOP of the fraction and divide it by the BOTTOM.**

It doesn't matter which order you do those two steps in — just start with the easier one.

EXAMPLE: What is $\frac{9}{20}$ of $360?

Start by dividing by 20, since that's easier. $\quad \frac{9}{20}$ of $360 = (\$360 \div 20) \times 9$
$$= \$18 \times 9 = \$162$$

8) Expressing as a Fraction

EXAMPLE: Write 180 as a fraction of 80.

Just write the first number over the second and cancel down. $\quad \frac{180}{80} = \frac{9}{4}$

You have to learn to handle fractions in these 8 situations

If you've learned how to find a common denominator (p.15), then adding and subtracting fractions should be pretty easy. To find a fraction of something, carry out the two steps in the order that's easier.

Fractions, Decimals and Percentages

Fractions, decimals and percentages are simply three different ways of expressing
a proportion of something — you need to know how to change between them.

This table shows the common conversions which you should know without having to work them out:

Fraction	Decimal	Percentage
$\frac{1}{2}$	0.5	50%
$\frac{1}{4}$	0.25	25%
$\frac{3}{4}$	0.75	75%
$\frac{1}{3}$	0.333333...	$33\frac{1}{3}$%
$\frac{2}{3}$	0.666666...	$66\frac{2}{3}$%
$\frac{1}{10}$	0.1	10%
$\frac{2}{10}$	0.2	20%
$\frac{1}{5}$	0.2	20%
$\frac{2}{5}$	0.4	40%

The more of those conversions you learn, the better — but for those that you don't know,
you must also learn how to convert between the three types. These are the methods:

Fraction $\xrightarrow{\text{Divide}}$ **Decimal** $\xrightarrow{\times \text{ by } 100}$ **Percentage**

E.g. $\frac{7}{20}$ is $7 \div 20$ $= 0.35$ e.g. 0.35×100 $= 35\%$

Fraction $\xleftarrow{\text{The awkward one}}$ **Decimal** $\xleftarrow{\div \text{ by } 100}$ **Percentage**

Converting decimals to fractions is awkward, because it's different for different types of decimal. There are two different methods you need to learn — one for terminating decimals and one for recurring decimals.

 KEY TERM ┃ Terminating decimals have an end — they don't go on forever.

The method for terminating decimals is fairly easy. The digits after the decimal point go on the top, and a power of 10 on the bottom — with the same number of zeros as there were decimal places.

$0.6 = \frac{6}{10}$	$0.3 = \frac{3}{10}$	$0.7 = \frac{7}{10}$	etc.
$0.12 = \frac{12}{100}$	$0.78 = \frac{78}{100}$	$0.05 = \frac{5}{100}$	etc. These can often be cancelled down — see p.14.
$0.345 = \frac{345}{1000}$	$0.908 = \frac{908}{1000}$	$0.024 = \frac{24}{1000}$	etc.

 REVISION TASK ## Practise changing between fractions, decimals and percentages

Any number can be written in any of these three forms. Write down some decimals, then try converting them into percentages and fractions. Use your calculator to check your answers.

Fractions and Recurring Decimals

The method for converting a recurring decimal into a fraction is a bit harder than for terminating decimals.

Recurring Decimals into Fractions

 KEY TERM — Recurring decimals have a pattern of numbers that repeats forever, e.g. $\frac{1}{3} = 0.333333...$

1) It doesn't have to be a single digit that repeats. You could have, for instance: 0.143143143...

2) The repeating part is usually marked with dots or a bar on top of the number. If there's one dot, then only one digit is repeated. If there are two dots, then everything from the first dot to the second dot is the repeating bit. E.g. $0.2\dot{5} = 0.2555555...$, $0.\dot{2}\dot{5} = 0.25252525...$, $0.2\dot{5}\dot{5} = 0.255255255...$

1) Basic Ones

EXAMPLE: **Write $0.\dot{2}3\dot{4}$ as a fraction.**

1) Name your decimal — I've called it r.   Let $r = 0.\dot{2}3\dot{4}$

2) Multiply r by a power of ten to move it past the decimal point by one full repeated lump — here that's 1000: $1000r = 234.\dot{2}3\dot{4}$

3) Now you can subtract to get rid of the decimal part:

$$1000r = 234.\dot{2}3\dot{4}$$
$$-\quad\ r = \ \ 0.\dot{2}3\dot{4}$$
$$999r = 234$$

4) Then just divide to leave r, and cancel if possible: $r = \dfrac{234}{999} = \dfrac{26}{111}$

2) The Trickier Type

If the recurring part doesn't come right after the decimal point, things are a bit harder.

EXAMPLE: **Write $0.1\dot{6}$ as a fraction.**

1) Name your decimal.   Let $r = 0.1\dot{6}$

2) Multiply r by a power of ten to move the non-repeating part past the decimal point. $10r = 1.\dot{6}$

3) Now multiply again to move one full repeated lump past the decimal point. $100r = 16.\dot{6}$

4) Subtract to get rid of the decimal part:

$$100r = 16.\dot{6}$$
$$-\quad 10r = \ \ 1.\dot{6}$$
$$90r = 15$$

5) Divide to leave r, and cancel if possible: $r = \dfrac{15}{90} = \dfrac{1}{6}$

 EXAM TIP — ## Practise converting both kinds of decimal into fractions

In the Extended exams, you could be asked to convert either terminating or recurring decimals into fractions. Luckily, your calculator will really help — <u>always</u> use it to check your answer.

Warm-Up and Worked Exam Questions

These warm-up questions will help to check that you've learned the basics from the last few pages —
if you're struggling with any of them, go and look back over that page before you go any further.

Warm-Up Questions

1) Work these out, then simplify your answers where possible:

a) $\frac{2}{5} \times \frac{2}{3}$ b) $\frac{2}{5} \div \frac{2}{3}$ c) $\frac{2}{5} + \frac{2}{3}$ d) $\frac{2}{3} - \frac{2}{5}$ e) $\frac{2}{5}$ of 120   f) $\frac{2}{3}$ of 120

2) a) Convert $4\frac{2}{5}$ into an improper fraction.   b) Convert $\frac{22}{3}$ into a mixed number.

3) Write down which percentage is the same as: a) $\frac{2}{5}$ b) $\frac{2}{3}$

4) Write down which decimal is equal to: a) $\frac{7}{10}$ b) $\frac{7}{8}$

5) a) Write down the fraction that is the same as 0.4.
   E b) Write down the fraction that is the same as 0.444444...
   c) Write down the fraction that is the same as 0.45454545...

Worked Exam Questions

Make sure you understand what's going on in these questions before trying the next page for yourself.

1   Francis has a bottle of fruit juice.

He gives $\frac{2}{15}$ of the bottle to Spencer and $\frac{5}{12}$ of the bottle to Jamie.

Work out what fraction of juice Francis has left.
You must show all your working and give your answer in its simplest form.

$$1 - \frac{2}{15} - \frac{5}{12} = 1 - \frac{8}{60} - \frac{25}{60}$$

Write over a common denominator

$$= \frac{27}{60}$$

$$= \frac{9}{20}$$

Remember to give your answer in its simplest form.

$\frac{9}{20}$
....
[3 marks]

2   Write $0.\dot{2}\dot{6}$ in the form $\frac{a}{b}$. Simplify your answer as far as possible, and show your working.

$$\text{Let } r = 0.\dot{2}\dot{6}, \text{ so } 100r = 26.\dot{2}\dot{6}$$

Multiply by a power of ten to get one full repeated chunk on the left-hand side of the decimal point.

$$100r - r = 26.\dot{2}\dot{6} - 0.\dot{2}\dot{6}$$
$$99r = 26$$
$$r = \frac{26}{99}$$

Extended

$\frac{26}{99}$
....
[2 marks]

Exam Questions

3   Dean has baked 550 muffins. $\frac{2}{5}$ of the muffins are chocolate, $\frac{3}{11}$ are lemon and the rest are strawberry. Find the number of strawberry muffins that Dean has baked.

....
[3 marks]

4   Work out the following calculations. You must show all your working and give your answers as mixed numbers in their simplest form:

a) $1\frac{1}{8} \times 2\frac{2}{5}$

....
[3 marks]

b) $1\frac{3}{4} \div \frac{7}{9}$

....
[3 marks]

5   If $a = \frac{3}{4}$ and $b = 2\frac{1}{2}$, find the value of $\frac{1}{a} + \frac{1}{b}$. Show all of your working.

....
[3 marks]

6   Show that $0.5\dot{9}\dot{0} = \frac{13}{22}$.

Hint: start by trying to get only the non-repeating part before the decimal point.

Extended

Extended

[2 marks]

Percentages

You're going to see 6 different types of percentage question on the next three pages.
The first few shouldn't give you too much trouble. Especially if you remember:

1) 'Per cent' means 'out of 100', so 20% means '20 out of 100' = $\frac{20}{100}$.

2) To work out the percentage OF something replace the word OF with a multiplication (×).

Six **Different** Question Types

Type 1 — **"Find x% of y"**

The normal method is to turn the percentage into a decimal, then multiply.

EXAMPLE: Find 18% of $4.

Change 18% to a
decimal and multiply.

18% of $4 ⟶ Replace 'of' with '×'.
= 18% × $4
= 0.18 × $4 = $0.72

However, you can also use this method, which might be useful if you can't use your calculator:

EXAMPLE: Find 135% of 600 kg.

1) Find 10% by dividing by 10:
2) Find 5% by dividing 10% by 2:
3) Use these values to make 135%:

100% = 600 kg
10% = 600 ÷ 10 = 60 kg
5% = 60 ÷ 2 = 30 kg
135% = 100% + (3 × 10%) + 5%
= 600 + (3 × 60) + 30 = 810 kg

You can also find 1% by dividing by 100.

Type 2 — **"Express x as a percentage of y"**

Divide *x* by *y*, then multiply by 100.

EXAMPLES:

1. **Give $36 as a percentage of $80.**

Divide $36 by $80, then multiply by 100: $\frac{36}{80}$ × 100 = **45%**

2. **Farmer Littlewood measured the width of his prized pumpkin at the start and end of the month. At the start of the month it was 84 cm wide and at the end of the month it was 1.32 m wide. Give the width at the end of the month as a percentage of the width at the start.**

1) Make sure both amounts are in the same units.   1.32 m = 132 cm

2) Divide 132 cm by 84 cm, then multiply by 100: $\frac{132}{84}$ × 100 = **157% (3 s.f.)**

Percentages are one of the most useful things you'll ever learn

Whenever you open a newspaper, see an advert, watch TV or do a maths exam paper
you will see percentages. It's really important you get confident with using them — so practise.

Percentages

Type 3 — **New Amount** After a **% Increase or Decrease**

There are two different ways of finding the new amount after a percentage increase or decrease:

1) Find the % then Add or Subtract.

Find the % of the original amount. Add this on to (or subtract from) the original value.

> **EXAMPLE:** **A dress has increased in price by 30%.**
> **It originally cost $40. What is the new price of the dress?**
>
> 1) Find 30% of $40:   30% of $40 = 30% × $40
>   = 0.3 × 40 = $12
> 2) It's an increase, so
>   add on to the original: $40 + $12 = $52

2) The Multiplier Method

This time, you first need to find the multiplier — the decimal that represents the percentage change.

> E.g. 5% increase is 1.05 (= 1 + 0.05)   26% decrease is 0.74 (= 1 − 0.26)

Then you just multiply the original value by the multiplier and you have the answer.

> A % decrease has a multiplier less than 1,
> a % increase has a multiplier greater than 1.

> **EXAMPLE:** **A hat is reduced in price by 20% in the sales.**
> **It originally cost $12. What is the new price of the hat?**
>
> 1) Find the multiplier: 20% decrease = 1 − 0.20 = 0.8
> 2) Multiply the original value by the multiplier: $12 × 0.8 = $9.60

Type 4 — **Simple Interest**

> Compound interest is covered on page 24.

Simple interest means a certain percentage of the original amount only is paid at regular intervals (usually once a year). So the amount of interest is the same every time it's paid.

> **EXAMPLE:** **Regina invests $380 in an account which pays 3% simple interest each year.**
> **How much interest will she earn in 4 years?**
>
> 1) Work out the amount of interest earned in one year: 3% = 3 ÷ 100 = 0.03
>   3% of $380 = 0.03 × $380
>   = $11.40
> 2) Multiply by 4 to get the total interest for 4 years: 4 × $11.40 = $45.60

Learn how to solve these simple question types

If you learn how to answer "finding *x*% of *y*" questions then simple interest will be easy. The only difference is that for simple interest you also have to multiply by a number of days/months/years.

Percentages

Watch out for these trickier types of percentage question — they'll often include lots of real-life context.

Type 5 — Finding the **Percentage Change**

1) This is the formula for giving a change in value as a percentage — LEARN IT, AND USE IT:

$$\text{Percentage 'Change'} = \frac{\text{'CHANGE'}}{\text{ORIGINAL}} \times 100$$

2) Typical questions will ask 'Find the percentage increase/profit/error'
or 'Calculate the percentage decrease/loss/discount', etc.

EXAMPLE: **Tariq buys a plain plate for $2. He paints it, then sells it at a craft fair for $3.75. Find his profit as a percentage.**

1) Here the 'change' is profit, so the formula looks like this: $\text{percentage profit} = \frac{\text{profit}}{\text{original}} \times 100$

2) Work out the profit (amount made – original cost) $\text{profit} = \$3.75 - \$2 = \$1.75$

3) Calculate the percentage profit: $\text{percentage profit} = \frac{\$1.75}{\$2} \times 100 = 87.5\%$

Type 6 — Finding the **Original Value**

This is the type that most people get wrong — but only because they
don't recognise it as this type, and don't apply this simple method:

> 1) Write the amount in the question as a percentage of the original value.
> 2) Divide to find 1% of the original value.
> 3) Multiply by 100 to give the original value (= 100%).

EXAMPLE: **A house increases in value by 10% to $165 000. Find what it was worth before the rise.**

Note: The new value, not the original value is given.

1) An increase of 10% means $165 000
represents 110% of the original value.

2) Divide by 110 to find 1%
of the original value.   ÷110

3) Then multiply by 100.   ×100

$165\ 000 = 110\%$
$1500 = 1\%$
$150\ 000 = 100\%$

If it was a decrease of 10%, then you'd put '$165 000 = 90%' and divide by 90 instead of 110.

So the original value was $150 000

Always set them out exactly like this example. The trickiest bit is deciding the top
% figure on the right-hand side — the 2nd and 3rd rows are always 1% and 100%.

Extended

Learn the 6 different types of percentage question

REVISION TIP If you learn how to use the percentage change formula then you'll find those questions much easier. To find the original value, remember to divide to find 1% and then multiply to find 100%.

Compound Growth and Decay

One more % type for you... Unlike simple interest, in compound interest the amount added on changes each time — it's a percentage of the new amount, rather than the original amount.

The **Formula**

This topic is simple if you LEARN THIS FORMULA:

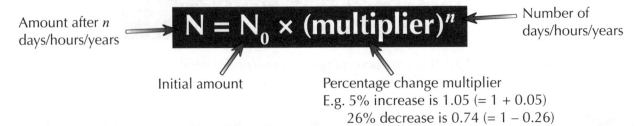

Amount after n days/hours/years

$$N = N_0 \times (\text{multiplier})^n$$

Number of days/hours/years

Initial amount

Percentage change multiplier
E.g. 5% increase is 1.05 (= 1 + 0.05)
26% decrease is 0.74 (= 1 – 0.26)

3 Examples to show you how **EASY** it is:

Compound interest is a popular context for these questions — it means the interest is added on each time, and the next lot of interest is calculated using the new total rather than the original amount.

> **EXAMPLE:** **Daniel invests \$1000 in a savings account which pays 8% compound interest each year. How much will there be after 6 years?**
>
> Use the formula: Amount = $1000(1.08)^6$ = \$1586.87
>
> initial amount ⌐ 8% increase ⌐ 6 years

Depreciation questions are about things (e.g. cars) which decrease in value over time.

> **EXAMPLE:** **Susan has just bought a car for \$6500.**
>
> a) **If the car depreciates by 9% each year, how much will it be worth in 3 years' time?**
>
> Use the formula: Value = $6500(0.91)^3$ = \$4898.21
>
> b) **How many complete years will it be before the car is worth less than \$3000?**
>
> Use the formula again but this time you know don't know n.
>
> Use trial and error to find how many years it will be before the value drops below \$3000.
>
> Value = $6500(0.91)^n$
>
> If n = 8, $6500(0.91)^8$ = 3056.6414....
> n = 9, $6500(0.91)^9$ = 2781.5437...
>
> It will be **9 years** before the car is worth less than \$3000.

The compound growth and decay formula can be about population and disease too.

> **EXAMPLE:** **The number of bacteria in a sample increases at a rate of 30% each day. After 6 days the number of bacteria is 7500. How many bacteria were there in the original sample?**
>
> Put the numbers you know into the formula, then rearrange to find the initial amount, N_0.
>
> $7500 = N_0(1.3)^6$
> $N_0 = 7500 \div (1.3)^6 = 1553.82...$
>
> So there were 1554 bacteria originally.

Compound growth and decay — percentages applied again and again

This method takes the original value, increases it by the percentage amount, then increases the result by the percentage, then increases that result by the percentage, then increases that result by the percentage, then...

Warm-Up and Worked Exam Questions

Have a go at these warm-up questions and see how you get on — the exam questions will be a bit more tricky, so it's important that you can do these first.

Warm-up Questions

1) Calculate 34% of $50.

2) What is 37 out of 50 as a percentage?

3) Find 15% of 60 (without using a calculator).

4) A suit costs $120 during a sale. Once the sale is over, the price of the suit rises by 15%. What is the new price of the suit?

5) You pay $200 into a bank account that pays 2.5% simple interest each year. How much money will be in the account after one year?

6) What is the percentage decrease when 1200 g is decreased to 900 g?

7) A shop is having a sale with 20% off everything. A statue is $488 in the sale. How much was the statue before the sale?

8) $3000 is invested at 3% compound interest (each year). Work out how much money is in the account at the end of 4 years, to the nearest cent.

Worked Exam Question

Study this worked exam question well — then have a go at some for yourself on the next page.

1   Oli and Ben each have a bank account that pays 8% simple interest each year.
They each deposit an amount of money and don't pay in or take out any other money.

a) Oli deposits $2000 in the account.
Work out how much will be in the account after 3 years.

8% = 0.08

Each year he gets $2000 × 0.08 = $160 interest

After 3 years he'll have $2000 + (3 × $160) = $2480

$ ....2480..........

[3 marks]

b) After the first year, Ben had $702 in his account.
Work out how much money he originally put in the account.

÷108 ($702 = 108%) ÷108
        $6.50 = 1%
×100 ($650 = 100%) ×100

$ ....650..........

[3 marks]

Exam Questions

2   Jane owns a fashion shop.

Jane sells a pair of jeans for $33.25 plus 20% tax.

Calculate how much she sells the pair of jeans for.

$ ....
[2 marks]

3   Franz always spends $2.40 a week on packs of stickers based on his favourite TV show.
The stickers normally cost $0.40 per pack but this week they are 40% cheaper.

Work out how many more packs of stickers he can get this week than in a normal week.

....
[4 marks]

4   Mrs Burdock borrows $750 to buy a sofa.
She is charged 6% compound interest each year.

Work out how much Mrs Burdock will owe if she doesn't pay back
any of the money for 3 years. Give your answer to the nearest cent.

$ ....
[3 marks]

5   The value of a football player depreciates at a rate of 25% each year
after the age of 30. At the age of 35, a player was valued at $2 000 000.

Find the player's value when he was 31 years old.
Give your answer to the nearest $100 000.

$ ....
[3 marks]

Extended

Ratios

Ratios are a pretty important topic — they can come up in all sorts of questions, so you need to be prepared. If you understand the examples on the next three pages, you'll find the questions in the exams much easier.

Reducing **Ratios** to Their **Simplest Form**

To reduce a ratio to a simpler form, divide all the numbers in the ratio by the same thing (a bit like simplifying a fraction — see p.14). It's in its simplest form when there's nothing left you can divide by.

> **EXAMPLE:** **Write the ratio 15:18 in its simplest form.**
>
> For the ratio 15:18, both numbers have a factor of 3, so divide them by 3.
>
> $\div 3 \left(\begin{array}{c} 15:18 \\ 5:6 \end{array} \right) \div 3$
>
> We can't reduce this any further. So the simplest form of 15:18 is **5:6**.

> **A handy method — use the fraction button on your calculator**
> If you enter a fraction with the ▦ or a^b/c button, the calculator automatically cancels it down when you press ▪. So for the ratio 8:12, just enter $\frac{8}{12}$ as a fraction, and you'll get the reduced fraction $\frac{2}{3}$. Now you just change it back to ratio form, i.e. 2 : 3.

The More **Awkward Cases**:

1) If the ratio contains decimals or fractions — multiply

For fractions, multiply by a number that gets rid of both denominators.

> **EXAMPLE:** **Simplify the ratio 2.4:3.6 as far as possible.**
> 1) Multiply both sides by 10 to get rid of the decimal parts.
> 2) Now divide to reduce the ratio to its simplest form.
>
> $= \times 10 \left(\begin{array}{c} 2.4:3.6 \\ 24:36 \end{array} \right) \times 10$
> $= \div 12 \left(\begin{array}{c} 24:36 \\ 2:3 \end{array} \right) \div 12$

2) If the ratio has mixed units — convert to the smaller unit

> **EXAMPLE:** **Reduce the ratio 24 mm:7.2 cm to its simplest form.**
> 1) Convert 7.2 cm to millimetres.
> 2) Simplify the resulting ratio. Once the units on both sides are the same, get rid of them for the final answer.
>
> $24 \text{ mm}:7.2 \text{ cm}$
> $= 24 \text{ mm}:72 \text{ mm}$
> $= \div 24 \searrow 1:3 \swarrow \div 24$

3) To get to the form 1 : n or n : 1 — just divide

> **EXAMPLE:** **Reduce 5:54 to the form 1:n.**
> Divide both sides by 5:
>
> $\div 5 \left(\begin{array}{c} 5:54 \\ 1:\frac{54}{5} \end{array} \right) \div 5$ or 1:10.8

Simplifying ratios is a lot like simplifying fractions

You have to divide both sides of the ratio by the same number (just like you'd divide the top and bottom of a fraction by the same number) — remember this and you'll be fine in the exam.

Ratios

Here's another page on ratios — it's more interesting than the first but not as exciting as the next one...

Scaling Up Ratios

If you know the ratio between parts and the actual size of one part,
you can scale the ratio up to find the other parts.

 **Mortar is made from mixing sand and cement in the ratio 7:2. How many buckets of mortar will be made if 21 buckets of sand are used in the mixture?**

You need to **multiply by 3** to go from 7 to 21 on the
left-hand side (LHS) — so do that to **both sides**:

sand:cement

$\times 3 \big(\begin{matrix} 7:2 \\ 21:6 \end{matrix} \big) \times 3$

So 21 buckets of sand and
6 buckets of cement are used.   Amount of mortar made = 21 + 6 = 27 buckets

The two parts of a ratio are always in **direct proportion** (see p.30). So in the example above, sand and cement are in direct proportion, e.g. if the amount of sand **doubles**, the amount of cement **doubles**.

Writing Ratios as Fractions

1) To write one part as a fraction of another part — **put one number over the other**

E.g. if apples and oranges are in the ratio 2:9 then we say there are
$\frac{2}{9}$ as many apples as oranges, or $\frac{9}{2}$ times as many oranges as apples.

2) To write one part as a fraction of the total — **add up the parts to find the total, then put the part you want over the total.**

E.g. a dough is made by mixing flour, butter and water in the ratio 3:2:1.
The total number of parts is 3 + 2 + 1 = 6.
So $\frac{3}{6} = \frac{1}{2}$ of the dough is flour, $\frac{2}{6} = \frac{1}{3}$ is butter and $\frac{1}{6}$ is water.

Increasing or Decreasing by a Ratio

To increase or decrease a quantity in the ratio a : b, you just turn the ratio into a fraction and multiply.
You can also think of this as:

"Increase" by a ratio means: $\times \dfrac{\text{big number}}{\text{small number}}$ "Decrease" by a ratio means: $\times \dfrac{\text{small number}}{\text{big number}}$

EXAMPLES:

1. Decrease 320 in the ratio 5 : 8.

The question says to decrease,
so multiply by $\dfrac{\text{small number}}{\text{big number}}$:

$320 \times \dfrac{5}{8} = 200$

2. A car is worth \$15 000. Its value increases in the ratio 13 : 12. Work out its new value.

The question says to increase,
so multiply by $\dfrac{\text{big number}}{\text{small number}}$:

$\$15\,000 \times \dfrac{13}{12} = \$16\,250$

Ratios

Finally — the last page on ratios, and maybe the most useful. It's all about how to split amounts in a ratio.

Proportional **Division**

In a proportional division question, a TOTAL AMOUNT is split into parts in a certain ratio.
The key word here is PARTS — if you think in terms of 'parts' it all becomes quite simple:

 **Jess, Mo and Greg share $9100 in the ratio 2:4:7. How much does Mo get?**

1) ADD UP THE PARTS:
   The ratio 2:4:7 means there will be a total of 13 parts: $2 + 4 + 7 = 13$ parts

2) DIVIDE TO FIND ONE "PART":
   Just divide the total amount by the number of parts: $9100 \div 13 = \$700$ (= 1 part)

3) MULTIPLY TO FIND THE AMOUNTS:
   We want to know how much Mo gets, which is 4 parts: 4 parts = $4 \times \$700 = \$2800$

Watch out for harder proportional division questions that don't give you the total amount.
You can't just follow the method above — you'll have to do a bit more work.

 **A baguette is cut into 3 pieces. The second piece is two times longer than the first, and the third piece is five times longer than the first.**

a) **Find the ratio of the lengths of the 3 pieces.**
   Give your answer in its simplest form.

   If the first piece is 1 part,
   then the second piece is $1 \times 2 = 2$ parts
   and the third piece is $1 \times 5 = 5$ parts.
   So the ratio of the lengths = 1:2:5.

b) **The first piece is 28 cm smaller than the third piece.**
   How long is the second piece?

   1) Work out how many parts 28 cm makes up.   28 cm = 3rd piece − 1st piece
                                                           = 5 parts − 1 part = 4 parts

   2) Divide to find one part.   28 cm $\div$ 4 = 7 cm

   3) Multiply to find the length of the 2nd piece.   2nd piece = 2 parts = 2×7 cm = 14 cm

---

 You need to know how to answer all kinds of ratio questions
Don't forget the useful tip from p.27 about using your calculator to simplify ratios. If you get stuck on a ratios question in the exam, it's helpful to think about what one 'part' is and take it from there...

Proportion

There can sometimes be a lot of information in proportion questions, but the method of solving them always stays the same — have a look at this page and you'll see.

Direct Proportion

Two quantities are in direct proportion (or just in proportion) if increasing one increases the other one proportionally.

1) If the quantities A and B are in direct proportion and A is doubled (or tripled, halved, etc.), so is B.

2) Remember this rule for direct proportion questions: **DIVIDE for ONE, then TIMES for ALL**

Hannah pays \$3.60 for 400 g of dried fruit.
She uses 220 g of dried fruit to make 4 fruit cakes.
How much would the dried fruit cost if she wanted to make 50 fruit cakes?

In 1 fruit cake there is: 220 g ÷ 4 = 55 g of dried fruit
So in 50 fruit cakes there is: 55 g × 50 = 2750 g of dried fruit

1 g of dried fruit would cost: \$3.60 ÷ 400 = \$0.009
So 2750 g of dried fruit would cost: 0.009 × 2750 = \$24.75

There might be lots of stages to direct proportion questions — keep track of what you've worked out at each stage.

Inverse Proportion

Two quantities are in inverse proportion if increasing one quantity causes the other quantity to decrease proportionally.

1) If the quantities C and D are in inverse proportion and C is doubled (or tripled, halved, etc.), D is halved (or divided by 3, doubled etc.).

2) The rule for finding inverse proportions is: **TIMES for ONE, then DIVIDE for ALL**

   **4 bakers can decorate 100 cakes in 5 hours.**

a)   How long would it take 10 bakers to decorate the same number of cakes?

100 cakes will take 1 baker: 5 × 4 = 20 hours

So 100 cakes will take 10 bakers: 20 ÷ 10 = 2 hours for 10 bakers

b)   How long would it take 11 bakers to decorate 220 cakes?

100 cakes will take 1 baker: 20 hours

1 cake will take 1 baker: 20 ÷ 100 = 0.2 hours
220 cakes will take 1 baker: 0.2 × 220 = 44 hours
220 cakes will take 11 bakers: 44 ÷ 11 = 4 hours

The number of bakers is inversely proportional to the number of hours — but the number of cakes is directly proportional to the number of hours.

Direct proportion means 'as one thing increases, so does the other'

With inverse proportion, as one increases, the other decreases. Don't get them confused.

Warm-Up and Worked Exam Questions

You'll have to know ratios really well for your exam — try these quick warm-up questions first and then you'll be ready to tackle those harder exam practice questions on the next page.

Warm-up Questions

1) Write these ratios in their simplest forms:
   a) 4:8   b) 12:27   c) 1.2:5.4   d) $\frac{8}{3} : \frac{7}{6}$ e) 0.5 litres:400 ml

2) Reduce 5:22 to the form 1:n.

3) A recipe uses flour and sugar in the ratio 3:2.
   How much flour do you need if you're using 300 g of sugar?

4) A nursery group has 12 girls and 6 boys.
   a) Write the ratio of girls to boys.   b) What fraction of the class are girls?

5) Increase 70 in the ratio 6:5.

6) Divide $2400 in the ratio 5:7.

7) Divide 180 in the ratio 3:4:5.

8) It costs $96 for 8 people to go on a rollercoaster 6 times.
   How much will it cost for 15 people to go on a rollercoaster 5 times?

9) It takes 2 carpenters 4 hours to make 3 bookcases.
   How long would it take 4 carpenters to make 9 bookcases?

Worked Exam Question

I'm sure you're ready to start on those exam practice questions — but before you do, here's one I answered earlier. Read through it carefully and follow the working.

1   Brian is making a fruit punch. He mixes apple juice, pineapple juice and cherryade in the ratio 4:3:7.

   a)   Write down the fraction of fruit punch that is pineapple juice.

   4 + 3 + 7 = 14 parts in total   3 of the 14 parts are pineapple juice ———— $\frac{3}{14}$

   ....
   [1 mark]

   b)   He makes 700 ml of fruit punch.
        Work out the volumes of apple juice, pineapple juice and cherryade that he uses.

   1 part = 700 ÷ (4 + 3 + 7)   First find how many ml
         = 700 ÷ 14 = 50 ml ———— 1 part is equal to.

   Multiply to find the amounts of each juice — apple juice is 4 parts, pineapple juice is 3 parts and cherryade is 7 parts.

   Apple juice: 50 ml × 4 = 200 ml
   Pineapple juice: 50 ml × 3 = 150 ml
   Cherryade: 50 ml × 7 = 350 ml

   Apple juice: ....200........ ml

   Pineapple juice: ....150........ ml

   Cherryade: ....350........ ml
   [3 marks]

Exam Questions

2   The grid on the right shows two shapes, A and B.

Give the following ratios in their simplest form.

a)   Shortest side of shape A : shortest side of shape B

....
[2 marks]

b)   Area of shape A : area of shape B

....
[3 marks]

3   Mr Appleseed's Supercompost is made by mixing soil, compost and grit in the ratio 4 : 3 : 1.
Soil costs $8 per 40 kg, compost costs $15 per 25 kg and grit costs $12 per 15 kg.
Work out the total cost of the materials for 16 kg of Mr Appleseed's Supercompost.

Start by working out how much
of each material is needed
for 16 kg of Supercompost.

$ ....
[5 marks]

4   Elijah runs a go-kart track. It takes 12 litres of petrol to
race 8 go-karts for 20 minutes. Petrol costs $1.37 per litre.

a)   16 go-karts used 12 litres of petrol. Work out how many minutes they raced for.

.... minutes
[2 marks]

b)   Calculate the cost of petrol to run 8 go-karts for 45 minutes.

$ ....
[3 marks]

Rounding Numbers

There are a few different ways of specifying where a number should be rounded. The first one is 'Decimal Places'.

Decimal Places (d.p.)

To round to a given number of decimal places:

1) Identify the position of the 'last digit' from the number of decimal places.
2) Then look at the next digit to the right — called the decider.
3) If the decider is 5 or more, then round up the last digit.
   If the decider is 4 or less, then leave the last digit as it is.
4) There must be no more digits after the last digit (not even zeros).

> 'Last digit' means the last one in the rounded version, not the one in the original number.

EXAMPLE: **What is 7.45839 to 2 decimal places?**

$$7.45839 = 7.46$$

LAST DIGIT to be written (2nd decimal place because we're rounding to 2 d.p.)

DECIDER

The LAST DIGIT rounds UP because the DECIDER is 5 or more.

Trickier Cases with Nines

1) If you have to round up a 9 (to 10), replace the 9 with 0, and carry 1 to the left.
2) Remember to keep enough zeros to fill the right number of decimal places.

EXAMPLE: **Round 45.699 to 2 d.p.**

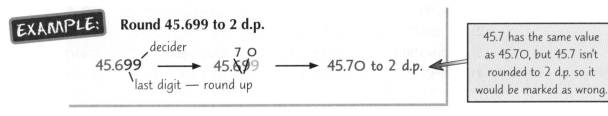

45.7 has the same value as 45.70, but 45.7 isn't rounded to 2 d.p. so it would be marked as wrong.

To the Nearest Whole Number, Ten, Hundred etc.

You might be asked to round to the nearest whole number, ten, hundred, thousand, or million:

1) Identify the last digit, e.g. for the nearest whole number it's the units position, and for the 'nearest ten' it's the tens position, etc.
2) Round the last digit and fill in with zeros up to the decimal point.

EXAMPLE: **Round 6751 to the nearest hundred.**

Last digit is in the 'hundreds' position

$$6751 = 6800$$

Fill in 2 zeros up to decimal point.

DECIDER is 5 or more ⟶ Last digit rounds UP.

 REVISION TIP

Your answer should have the right number of decimal places

If the question asks for 3 d.p., there should always be 3 digits after the decimal point — even if they're all zeros. If you can remember that, then rounding questions should be nice and easy.

Rounding Numbers

The last method of rounding is 'Significant Figures'. It's a bit trickier than decimal places, but not much.

Significant Figures (s.f.)

The method for significant figures is identical to that for decimal places, except that locating the last digit is more difficult because you have to be very careful with zeros.

> 1) **The 1st significant figure of any number is simply the first digit which isn't a zero.**

> 2) **The 2nd, 3rd, 4th, etc. significant figures follow on immediately after the 1st, regardless of whether they are zeros or not.**

$$0.002309 \qquad 2.03070$$

SIG. FIGS: 1st 2nd   3rd 4th   1st 2nd   3rd   4th

(If we're rounding to say, 3 s.f., then the LAST DIGIT is simply the 3rd sig. fig.)

> 3) **After rounding the last digit, end zeros must be filled in up to, but not beyond, the decimal point.**

No extra zeros must ever be put in after the decimal point.

EXAMPLES:

	to 3 s.f.	to 2 s.f.	to 1 s.f.
1) 54.7651	54.8	55	50
2) 17.0067	17.0	17	20
3) 0.0045902	0.00459	0.0046	0.005
4) 30895.4	30900	31000	30000

Estimating

This is very easy, as long as you follow this simple method.

> 1) Round everything to nice, easy numbers.
> 2) Then work out the answer using these numbers.

EXAMPLE: Estimate the value of $\frac{127.8 + 41.9}{56.5 \times 3.2}$, showing all your working.

1) Round all the numbers to easier ones — usually 1 or 2 s.f. is best.

$$\frac{127.8 + 41.9}{56.5 \times 3.2} \approx \frac{130 + 40}{60 \times 3}$$

2) You can round again to make later steps easier if you need to.

$$= \frac{170}{180} \approx 1$$

The first significant figure is the first non-zero digit

If you're asked to estimate something in the exam, make sure you show all your steps (including what each number is rounded to) to prove that you didn't just use a calculator.

Bounds

Finding upper and lower bounds is pretty easy, but using them in calculations is a bit trickier.

Upper and Lower Bounds

Whenever a measurement is rounded to a given UNIT, the actual measurement can be anything up to HALF A UNIT bigger or smaller.

EXAMPLE: A room is 9 m long to the nearest metre. Find upper and lower bounds for its length.

The actual length could be half a metre either side of 9 m.   lower bound = 8.5 m
upper bound = 9.5 m

Note that the actual value is greater than or equal to the lower bound but less than the upper bound. In the example above, the actual length could be exactly 8.5 m, but if it was exactly 9.5 m it would round up to 10 m instead. Or, written as an inequality (see p.3), 8.5 m ≤ actual length < 9.5 m.

EXAMPLE: The mass of a cake is given as 2.4 kg to the nearest 0.1 kg.
What are the upper and lower bounds for the actual mass of the cake?

The rounding unit here is 0.1 kg, so the actual value could be anything in the range 2.4 kg ± 0.05 kg.

lower bound = 2.4 − 0.05 = 2.35 kg
upper bound = 2.4 + 0.05 = 2.45 kg

Maximum and Minimum Values for Calculations

When a calculation is done using rounded values, there will be a difference between the CALCULATED VALUE and the ACTUAL VALUE:

EXAMPLES:

1. A floor is measured as being 5.3 m by 4.2 m, to the nearest 10 cm.
Calculate minimum and maximum possible values for the area of the floor.

1) The actual dimensions of the floor could be anything from 5.25 m to 5.35 m and 4.15 m to 4.25 m.

minimum possible floor area = 5.25 × 4.15
= 21.7875 m²

2) Find the minimum area by multiplying the lower bounds, and the maximum by multiplying the upper bounds.

maximum possible floor area = 5.35 × 4.25
= 22.7375 m²

2. To 1 d.p., $a = 5.3$ and $b = 4.2$. What are the maximum and minimum possible values of $a \div b$?

1) First find the bounds for a and b. ⟶ $5.25 \le a < 5.35$, $4.15 \le b < 4.25$

2) Now the tricky bit... The bigger the number you divide by, the smaller the answer, so:

$\max(a \div b) = \max(a) \div \min(b)$
$\min(a \div b) = \min(a) \div \max(b)$

max. value of $a \div b$ = 5.35 ÷ 4.15
= 1.29 (to 3 s.f.)

min. value of $a \div b$ = 5.25 ÷ 4.25
= 1.24 (to 3 s.f.)

Extended

Bounds tell you the possible values of something that's been rounded

When you want to find the maximum or minimum value of a calculation, working out which bound to use for each bit can be pretty confusing — so make sure you always think about it very carefully.

Standard Form

Standard form (or 'standard index form') is useful for writing VERY BIG or VERY SMALL numbers in a more convenient way, e.g. 56 000 000 000 would be 5.6×10^{10} in standard form.

0.000 000 003 45 would be 3.45×10^{-9} in standard form.

But ANY NUMBER can be written in standard form and you need to know how to do it:

What it Actually is:

A number is written in standard form if it's in the form:

$$A \times 10^n$$

This number must always be between 1 and 10.
(Or, using inequalities: $1 \leq A < 10$)

This number is just the number of places the decimal point moves.

Learn the Three Rules:

1) The front number must always be between 1 and 10.
2) The power of 10, n, is how far the decimal point moves.
3) n is positive for BIG numbers, n is negative for SMALL numbers.
   (This is much better than rules based on which way the decimal point moves.)

Four Important Examples:

1 **Express 35 600 in standard form.**

1) Move the decimal point until 35 600 becomes 3.56 ($1 \leq A < 10$).
2) The decimal point has moved 4 places so n = 4, giving: 10^4
3) 35 600 is a big number so n is +4, not –4.

35600.0
$= 3.56 \times 10^4$

2 **Express 0.0000623 in standard form.**

1) The decimal point must move 5 places to give 6.23 ($1 \leq A < 10$). So the power of 10 is 5.
2) Since 0.0000623 is a small number it must be 10^{-5} not 10^{+5}.

0.0000623
$= 6.23 \times 10^{-5}$

3 **Express 4.95×10^{-3} as an ordinary number.**

1) The power of 10 is negative, so it's a small number — the answer will be less than 1.
2) The power is –3, so the decimal point moves 3 places.

0004.95×10^{-3}
$= 0.00495$

4 **What is 146.3 million in standard form?**

Too many people get this type of question wrong. Just take your time and do it in two stages:

146.3 million
$= 146300000$
$= 1.463 \times 10^8$

The two favourite wrong answers for this are:
146.3×10^6 — which is kind of right, but it's not in standard form because 146.3 is not between 1 and 10.
1.463×10^6 — this one is in standard form, but it's not big enough.

Standard Form

Calculations with Standard Form

These are really popular exam questions — you might be asked to add, subtract, multiply or divide using numbers written in standard form.

Multiplying and Dividing

> 1) Rearrange to put the front numbers and the powers of 10 together.
> 2) Multiply or divide the front numbers, and use the power rules (see p.49) to multiply or divide the powers of 10.
> 3) Make sure your answer is still in standard form.

EXAMPLES:

1. Find $(2.24 \times 10^3) \times (6.75 \times 10^5)$.
Give your answer in standard form.

Multiply front numbers and powers separately

$(2.24 \times 10^3) \times (6.75 \times 10^5)$
$= (2.24 \times 6.75) \times (10^3 \times 10^5)$
$= 15.12 \times 10^{3+5}$ — Add the powers
$= 15.12 \times 10^8$ (see p.49)

Not in standard form — convert it
$= 1.512 \times 10 \times 10^8$
$= 1.512 \times 10^9$

2. Calculate $189\ 000 \div (5.4 \times 10^{10})$.
Give your answer in standard form.

Convert 189 000 to standard form

$189\ 000 \div (5.4 \times 10^{10})$
$= \dfrac{1.89 \times 10^5}{5.4 \times 10^{10}} = \dfrac{1.89}{5.4} \times \dfrac{10^5}{10^{10}}$

Divide front numbers and powers separately
$= 0.35 \times 10^{5-10}$ — Subtract the powers
$= 0.35 \times 10^{-5}$ (see p.49)

Not in standard form — convert it
$= 3.5 \times 10^{-1} \times 10^{-5}$
$= 3.5 \times 10^{-6}$

Adding and Subtracting

> 1) Make sure the powers of 10 are the same — you'll probably need to rewrite one of them.
> 2) Add or subtract the front numbers.
> 3) Convert the answer to standard form if necessary.

EXAMPLE: Calculate $(9.8 \times 10^4) + (6.6 \times 10^3)$. Give your answer in standard form.

$(9.8 \times 10^4) + (6.6 \times 10^3)$

1) Rewrite one number so both powers of 10 are equal: $= (9.8 \times 10^4) + (0.66 \times 10^4)$

2) Now add the front numbers: $= (9.8 + 0.66) \times 10^4$

3) 10.46×10^4 isn't in standard form, so convert it: $= 10.46 \times 10^4 = 1.046 \times 10^5$

To put standard form numbers into your calculator, use the **EXP** or the **×10ˣ** button.
E.g. enter 2.67×10^{15} by pressing **2.67** **EXP** **15** **=** or **2.67** **×10ˣ** **15** **=** .

Your calculator might display an answer such as 7.986×10^{15} as .
If so, don't forget to add in the "×10" bit when you write it down.
Some calculators do display a little "×10" or "E", so check what yours does.

Remember, n tells you how far the decimal point moves

You can also add and subtract numbers in standard form by writing them as ordinary numbers, adding or subtracting as usual, then converting the answer back to standard form at the end.

Warm-Up and Worked Exam Questions

Without a good warm-up you're likely to struggle with the harder questions. So take the time to work through these simple questions and get the basics learned before getting into the exam questions.

Warm-Up Questions

1) Round these numbers to the level of accuracy indicated:
   a) 40.218 to 2 d.p.   b) 1074 to the nearest 10   c) 39.888 to 3 s.f.   d) 27.91 to 2 s.f.

2) By rounding to 1 significant figure, estimate the answer to $\dfrac{94 \times 1.9}{0.328 + 0.201}$.

3) A distance is given as 14 km, to the nearest km.
   Find the upper and lower bounds for the distance.

4) $r = 6.3$ and $s = 2.9$, both to 1 d.p. Find the maximum and minimum possible values for:
   a) $r + s$ b) $r - s$ c) $r \times s$ d) $r \div s$

5) The half-life of a chemical isotope is 0.0000027 seconds. Write this number in standard form.

6) Find each of the following. Give your answers in standard form.
   a) $(3 \times 10^6) \times (8 \times 10^4)$ b) $(8.4 \times 10^8) \div (4.2 \times 10^4)$ c) $(7.65 \times 10^6) + (1.47 \times 10^5)$

Worked Exam Questions

With the answers written in, it's very easy to skim these worked examples and think you've understood. But that's not going to help you, so take the time to make sure you've really understood them.

1   The width of a rectangular piece of paper is 23.6 centimetres, correct to 1 decimal place.
     The length of the paper is 54.1 centimetres, correct to 1 decimal place.

   a)   Write down the lower bound for the length of the paper.

         Lower bound for length = 54.1 cm − 0.05 cm
                                = 54.05 cm

         ....**54.05**........ cm
         [1 mark]

   b)   Calculate the lower bound for the perimeter of the piece of paper.

         Lower bound for width = 23.6 cm − 0.05 cm
                               = 23.55 cm

         Lower bound for perimeter = (2 × 54.05 cm) + (2 × 23.55 cm)
                                   = 108.1 cm + 47.1 cm = 155.2 cm

         ....**155.2**........ cm
         [2 marks]

2    $A = 2.7 \times 10^5$ and $B = 5.81 \times 10^3$. Work out $A \times B$. Give your answer in standard form.

         A × B = (2.7 × 10⁵) × (5.81 × 10³)

Multiply the   = (2.7 × 5.81) × (10⁵ × 10³)
numbers and
powers separately. = 15.687   × 10⁸

         = 1.5687   × 10⁹ ←——

Alternatively you could do the whole calculation on your calculator and then put your answer in standard form.

Make sure the final answer is in standard form.

         ....**1.5687 × 10⁹**........
         [2 marks]

Extended

Exam Questions

3   Look at the following calculation: $\frac{215.7 \times 44.8}{460}$

   a)   By rounding each of the numbers to 1 s.f., give an estimate for $\frac{215.7 \times 44.8}{460}$.

....
[2 marks]

   b)   Without using your calculator, explain how you know your answer
        to part a) will be smaller than the exact number.

        ....

        ....
[1 mark]

4   A cruise ship weighs approximately 7.59×10^7 kg.
    Its passengers weigh a total of 2.1×10^5 kg.

    You need matching powers to
    be able to add together two
    numbers in standard form.

   a)   Find the total weight of the ship and passengers,
        giving your answer in standard form. Show all your working.

.... kg
[2 marks]

   b)   Express the weight of the passengers as a percentage of the total combined
        weight of the ship and passengers. Give your answer to 2 decimal places.

.... %
[2 marks]

5   Here is a rectangle.
    x = 55 mm to the nearest 5 mm.
    y = 30 mm to the nearest 5 mm.
    Calculate the upper bound for the area of this rectangle.

y

x

Not to scale

Extended

.... mm^2
[3 marks]

Sets

Sets come with some pretty weird notation, but a set is just a maths word for a collection of things.

Learn How to Use **Set Notation**

1) You can describe a set by listing everything in it, e.g. {2, 4, 6}, or by giving a rule, e.g. {things that are red} or {odd numbers}. 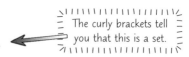 *The curly brackets tell you that this is a set.*

2) You can use a capital letter to stand for a set, e.g. A = {numbers that are multiples of four}, and a lower case letter to stand for a member or an element of a set, e.g. x is an element in A. Then you could describe this set as A = {$x : x$ is a multiple of four}.
 *The colon means 'such that'.*

3) The universal set is the group of things that the elements of a set are selected from.

ξ **THE UNIVERSAL SET**

EXAMPLES:

1. ξ = {5, 6, 7, 8, 9, 10, 11, 12, 13, 14, 15, 16, 17}

A = {Even numbers}

Write down all the elements of set A.

The elements of A are the even numbers within the universal set.

Elements of set A:
6, 8, 10, 12, 14, 16

2. ξ = {Natural numbers}

B = {Prime numbers}

Is 6 an element of set B?

6 is not a prime number, so 6 is not an element of B.

You Can Describe Sets Using **Numbers** and **Symbols**

1) If a set is described using numbers and symbols, work out what the description means in words before you start working with the set.

See p.3 for more on the inequality symbols > and <.

{$x : x < 0$} —— This is the set of numbers, x, such that x is less than 0, i.e. the set of negative numbers.

{$(x, y) : y = 2x + 2$} —— This is the set of all the points (x, y) such that $y = 2x + 2$, i.e. the set of coordinates that lie on the line $y = 2x + 2$.

EXAMPLE:
ξ = {Negative integers}, P = {$x : x > –6$}. **List all the elements of set P.**

1) Check what the universal set is.   The universal set is the negative integers.

2) Combine this with the definition of set P to find the elements of P.
So, P is the set of integers that are bigger than –6 but less than 0.
The elements of P are –5, –4, –3, –2 and –1.

2) There's some special notation for showing whether something is an element of a set or not:

$\in$ **...IS AN ELEMENT OF...** $\notin$ **...IS NOT AN ELEMENT OF...**

E.g.   strawberry $\in$ {things that are red}, 2 $\notin$ {odd numbers}

3) If a set has no elements at all, it's called the empty set. E.g. if set B = {negative numbers between 1 and 10} then set B = $\varnothing$.

{} or $\varnothing$ **THE EMPTY SET**

Extended (left margin)   *Extended* (right margin)

Sets can contain more than just numbers

For example, you are an element of the set {People who have read this sentence}. Sets can contain anything, e.g. coordinates, shapes or colours — and in the topic of probability you get sets of outcomes (see p.174).

Sets

When there's more than one set, things get more interesting — we're talking UNIONS and INTERSECTIONS.

The **Union** of Two Sets

KEY TERM: The union of two sets is a set containing all the elements that are in either set. You write "the union of set A and set B" as A ∪ B.

EXAMPLES:

1. **F = {2, 5, 6} and G = {1, 5, 7}. List all the elements of F ∪ G.**

   List everything that appears in either F or G.

   The elements of F ∪ G are 1, 2, 5, 6 and 7.

   5 appears in both sets but you must only list it once.

2. **P = {4, 7, 8} and P ∪ Q = {4, 5, 7, 8, 9}. Set Q has 2 elements. Find set Q.**

   Anything that's an element of P ∪ Q but not an element of P must be an element of Q.

   5 and 9 are elements of P ∪ Q but not elements of P.

   So 5 and 9 must be elements of Q.

   Q has 2 elements, so 5 and 9 must be its only elements.

   So Q = {5, 9}

The **Intersection** of Two Sets

KEY TERM: The intersection of two sets is a set that only contains objects that are elements of both sets. You write "the intersection of set A and set B" as A ∩ B.

EXAMPLE: ξ = {9, 10, 11, 12, 13, 14, 15, 16, 17, 18}, J = {Odd numbers}, K = {Multiples of 3}
List all the elements of J ∩ K.

1) Find the elements of J and K:

   Elements of J: 9, 11, 13, 15, 17
   Elements of K: 9, 12, 15, 18

2) Elements of J ∩ K are elements of both J and K.

   Elements of J ∩ K: 9, 15

n(A) — the **Number of Elements**

n(A) is shorthand for the number of elements of set A. n(A) = 12 means "Set A has 12 elements".

EXAMPLE: ξ = {Positive integers}, L = {x : x is less than 8}. What is n(L)?

1) Find the elements of L:

   Elements of L: 1, 2, 3, 4, 5, 6, 7

2) Count the number of elements:

   n(L) = 7

Make sure you know what all these symbols mean

REVISION TIP: It's important that you don't get ∪ and ∩ mixed up. If in doubt, say them out loud — the one that looks like a 'u' is the *union* symbol, and the one that looks like an 'n' is the *intersection* symbol.

Sets

Don't worry, there are only a few more sets definitions and symbols left to learn now.

The **Complement** of a Set

KEY TERM: The complement of a set is all the elements of the universal set that aren't in the set. The complement of set A is written as A'.

 **1.** ξ = {1, 2, 3, 4, 5, 6, 7, 8, 9, 10}, F = {Multiples of 3}
List the elements of F'.

1) First find the elements of F. | The elements of F are 3, 6 and 9.

2) The elements of F' are the elements of the universal set that aren't elements of F: | So the elements of F' are 1, 2, 4, 5, 7, 8 and 10.

2. ξ = {1, 2, 3, 4, 5, 6, 7, 8}, G = {x : $2 \leq x \leq 7$}, H = {Factors of 12}

a) Find G ∩ H'.

1) Write G and H in terms of their elements. | G = {2, 3, 4, 5, 6, 7}

2) Find H'. | H = {1, 2, 3, 4, 6} so H' = {5, 7, 8}

3) Find G ∩ H' — 5 and 7 are the only elements of both G and H'. | G ∩ H' = {5, 7}

b) Find (G ∩ H)'.

First find G ∩ H, then find its complement. | G ∩ H = {2, 3, 4 6} (G ∩ H)' = {1, 5, 7, 8}

Watch out for brackets — G ∩ H' means the intersection of G and H', but (G ∩ H)' means the complement of G ∩ H.

Subsets are Sets Within Sets

KEY TERMS: A subset is a set that is entirely contained within another set. This means that all the elements of the first set are also in the second set. A proper subset is a subset that has fewer elements than the set that contains it.

There are some useful symbols for this:

⊆ ...IS A SUBSET OF...   ⊄ ...IS NOT A SUBSET OF...

⊂ ...IS A PROPER SUBSET OF...   ⊄ ...IS NOT A PROPER SUBSET OF...

E.g. if A = {5, 7} and B = {5, 7, 11}, then "A ⊆ B" but "B ⊄ A". You can also write "A ⊆ A" but "A ⊄ A".

 ξ = {Positive integers less than 10},
S = {x : $5 \leq x \leq 9$}, T = {Odd numbers}, U = {Prime numbers}

Is (S ∩ T) ⊂ U a true statement?

1) Write S, T and U in terms of their elements. | S = {5, 6, 7, 8, 9}, T = {1, 3, 5, 7, 9}, U = {2, 3, 5, 7}

2) Find S ∩ T. | S ∩ T = {5, 7, 9}

3) If S ∩ T is a subset of U, every element of S ∩ T must also be an element of U. Decide whether this is true. | 9 is an element of S ∩ T but not an element of U. So, (S ∩ T) ⊄ U and the statement is false.

There are a lot of words and symbols to learn on these pages

This might be one of the toughest bits of this book to learn. Close the book and write down all the words and symbols related to sets you can think of, then look back and see if you missed any.

Venn Diagrams

Venn diagrams look a bit odd, but they're great for showing the relationships between sets.

Venn Diagrams Use **Circles** to **Represent Sets**

1) Each set is represented by a circle — the space inside the circle represents everything in the set.
2) Each circle is labelled with a letter — this tells you which set the circle represents.
3) There might be a number inside the circle — this tells you the number of elements of the set.

   E.g. T = {People called Tammy in my class}

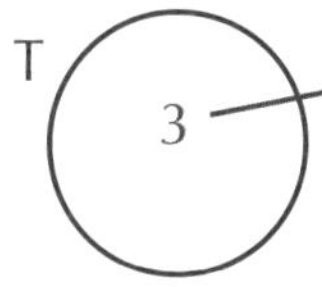

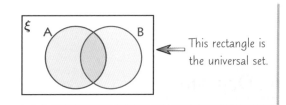

This tells you there are 3 people called Tammy in my class — so n(T) = 3.

4) The universal set is shown as a rectangle that goes around all of the circles, like this:

This rectangle is the universal set.

> Venn diagrams can also show the actual elements of the sets, not just the numbers of elements.

Venn Diagrams Show **Intersections** and **Unions**

The intersection of sets is where the circles overlap. If two sets have no shared elements then their circles won't overlap at all.

There are 12 objects that are only elements of A.

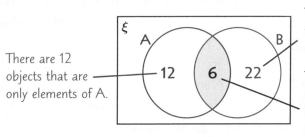

There are 22 objects that are only elements of B.

The shaded area is A ∩ B. 6 objects are elements of both A and B, so n(A ∩ B) = 6

The union of sets is all the space covered by the circles representing those sets.

You can find n(A ∪ B) by adding the number of elements in each part of A ∪ B. So here: n(A ∪ B) = 12 + 6 + 22 = 40

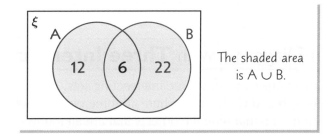

The shaded area is A ∪ B.

Using the **Numbers**

 **EXAMPLE:** P and Q are sets. n(ξ) = 40 and n(P ∪ Q) = 32.
Some other numbers of elements have been filled in on the Venn diagram below.

a) **What is n(P ∩ Q)?**

P ∩ Q is the set of objects that are elements of both P and Q — this is the region where the circles overlap: n(P ∩ Q) = 7

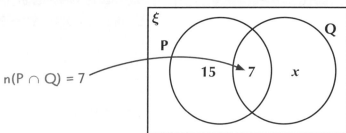

b) **Find x.** $n(P \cup Q) = 15 + 7 + x$

So, $32 = 15 + 7 + x$

$x = 32 - 15 - 7 = 10$

Venn Diagrams

Venn Diagrams Can Also Show **Subsets** and **Complements**

On a Venn diagram, the complement of a set is everything outside the circle representing that set.

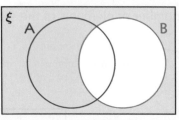

The shaded area is B′.

If set A is a proper subset of set B then on a Venn diagram the circle representing set A lies completely inside the circle representing set B.

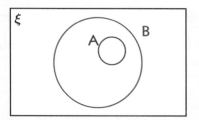

The Venn diagram shows that A ⊂ B.

Drawing a Venn Diagram

To draw a Venn diagram you need to work out whether the intersections of each pair of sets have any elements — this will tell you if the circles should overlap. Look out for any subsets too.

EXAMPLE: ξ = {Positive integers less than 20},
A = {Odd numbers}, B = {Multiples of 3}, C = {Multiples of 6}
Draw a Venn Diagram representing the relationships between A, B and C.

A = {1, 3, 5, 7, 9, 11, 13, 15, 17, 19},
B = {3, 6, 9, 12, 15, 18}, C = {6, 12, 18}
A ∩ B = {3, 9, 15}, so circles A and B overlap.
C is a subset of B, so circle C is completely inside circle B.
A ∩ C = ∅, so circles A and C do not overlap.

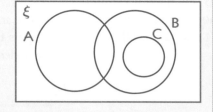

Venn Diagrams with **Three Intersecting Sets**

Venn diagrams can show three intersecting sets.
For sets A, B and C, the area where all three circles overlap represents A ∩ B ∩ C.
This is the set containing the objects that are elements of all three sets.

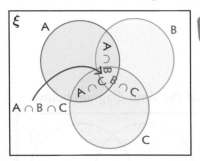

EXAMPLE: **Using set notation, describe the shaded area of the Venn diagram below.**

Everything in the shaded area is an element of Z, but not an element of X and not an element of Y.
So, they're elements of Z and X′ and Y′.
So the set is X′ ∩ Y′ ∩ Z. —— (X ∪ Y)′ ∩ Z would also be correct here.

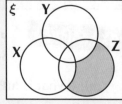

Work out the intersections and unions one by one

 You need to know how to describe each section of a Venn diagram using set notation. Draw out Venn diagrams with 2 sets and 3 sets, then describe every section of them using set notation.

Warm-Up and Worked Exam Questions

Hopefully, you now know everything you need from Section One. Just to make sure, have a go at these warm-ups. Once you're happy with those, move on to the exam questions.

Warm-Up Questions

1) ξ = {Members of a sports club}, K = {People who play badminton}.
   Peter is in the universal set, but is not in set K. What does this tell you about Peter?
2) C = {Trees}, D = {Things over 3 m tall}. Describe the elements of C ∩ D.
3) ξ = {2, 3, 4, 5, 6, 7, 8, 9, 10, 11, 12}
   J = {Odd numbers}, K = {Factors of 24}, L = {Prime numbers}
   a) Find K ∩ L. b) What is n(K ∩ L)?
   c) Is L ⊂ (J ∪ K) a true statement?
   d) Draw a Venn diagram showing all the elements in these sets.

Worked Exam Questions

Have a read through these worked exam questions before having a go at some yourself.

1 ξ = {3, 5, 6, 8, 9, 11, 12, 14, 15}, *A* = {Even numbers}, *B* = {Multiples of 3}
   Write down the elements of the following sets:

a) *A* ∪ *B*

A ∪ B is all the numbers that are either even or multiples of 3:

3, 6, 8, 9, 12, 14, 15

[1 mark]

b) *A* ∩ *B*

A ∩ B is all the numbers that are both even and multiples of 3:

6, 12

[1 mark]

2 The Venn diagram below shows the sets *A, B, C* and the universal set ξ.
   Each number on the diagram represents the **number** of elements. Find:

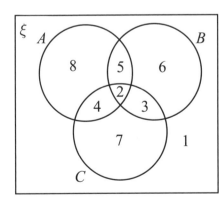

a) n(*A* ∪ *C*)

A ∪ C is everything that is in A or C:
8 + 5 + 4 + 2 + 7 + 3 = 29

29

[1 mark]

b) n(*B* ∩ *C'*)

B ∩ C' is everything that is in B but not in C:
5 + 6 = 11

11

[1 mark]

c) n(*A'* ∪ *B* ∪ *C*)

A' ∪ B ∪ C is anything that is either outside of A, inside B or inside C
— this will be everything except those that are only in A.
5 + 6 + 4 + 2 + 3 + 7 + 1 = 28

28

[1 mark]

Exam Questions

3   ξ = {Students at Hilltop College}

B = {Students in basketball club}

C = {Students in cycling club}

F = {Students in football club}

Write a statement to interpret each of the following pieces of information.

a)   n(B ∩ F) = 0

....

[1 mark]

b)   n(C ∪ F) = 25

....

[1 mark]

4   *L, M* and *N* are three sets. *L* and *M* are shown on the diagram below.

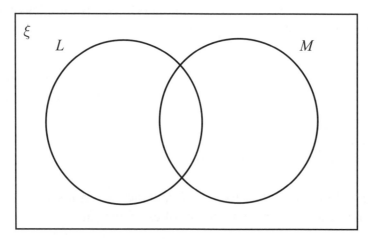

a) Shade the region represented by *L* ∩ *M*.

[1 mark]

b) Given that *L* ∩ *N* = ∅ and *N* ⊂ *M*, draw the set *N* on the diagram.

[1 mark]

5   ξ = {Odd numbers}, *R* = {3, 5, 7, 9, 11, 13, 15}

Set *S* is a subset of *R* such that *R* ∩ *S'* = {5, 7, 11, 13} and n(*S*) = 3.

Write down the elements of set *S*.

....

[2 marks]

Revision Questions for Section One

Well, that wraps up Section One — time to put yourself to the test and find out how much you really know.
- Try these questions and tick off each one when you get it right.
- When you've done all the questions for a topic and are completely happy with it, tick off the topic.

Numbers, Roots, Factors and Multiples (p.1-11) ☐

1) Work out the value of: a) $4 + 8 \div 2 \times 3$ b) $\dfrac{3 \times 6}{(2+1)^2}$

2) Put these numbers in order of size: 23   493   87   1029   3004   345   9

3) Find: a) $-10 - 6$ b) $-35 \div -5$ c) $-4 + -5 + 22 - -7$

4) What are: a) integers?   b) rational numbers?   c) prime numbers?

5) Complete the following: a) $13^2 =$ __   b) $\sqrt{49} =$ __   c) $\sqrt[3]{27} =$ __   d) $5^3 =$ __

6) Express each of these as a product of powers of prime factors: a) 1050   b) 360

7) Find: a) the LCM of 6 and 14   b) the HCF of 32 and 88

Fractions, Decimals and Percentages (p.14-24) ☐

8) a) Write $\dfrac{74}{9}$ as a mixed number   b) Write $4\frac{5}{7}$ as an improper fraction

9) Calculate: a) $\dfrac{2}{11} \times \dfrac{7}{9}$ b) $5\frac{1}{2} \div 1\frac{3}{4}$ c) $\dfrac{5}{8} - \dfrac{1}{6}$ d) $3\frac{3}{10} + 4\frac{1}{4}$

10) How do you convert: a) a fraction to a decimal?   b) a terminating decimal to a fraction?

11) Write: a) 0.04 as: (i) a fraction (ii) a percentage   b) 65% as: (i) a fraction (ii) a decimal

12) Show that $0.\dot{5}\dot{1} = \dfrac{17}{33}$.

13) What's the method for finding one amount as a percentage of another?

14) A tree's height has increased by 15% in the last year to 20.24 m. What was its height a year ago?

15) I have $850 to invest for 4 years. I can choose between two accounts:
an account that pays 6% simple interest, or an account that pays 4% compound interest.
Which account will pay more interest, and how much more?

Ratios and Proportion (p.27-30) ☐

16) Sarah is in charge of ordering stock for a clothes shop. The shop orders red scarves and blue scarves in the ratio $5:8$. Sarah orders 150 red scarves. How many blue scarves should she order?

17) What are the three steps of the method of proportional division?

18) Divide 3000 in the ratio $5:8:12$.

19) Rick bought 5 litres of milk for $2.35. How much would 3 litres cost?

Rounding, Bounds and Standard Form (p.33-37) ☐

20) Round 427.963 to: a) 2 d.p.   b) 1 d.p.   c) 2 s.f.   d) 4 s.f.

21) Estimate the value of $(124.6 + 87.1) \div 9.7$

22) A rectangle measures 15.6 m by 8.4 m, to the nearest 0.1 m. Find its maximum possible area.

23) What are the three rules for writing numbers in standard form?

24) Write these numbers in standard form: a) 970 000   b) 3 560 000 000   c) 0.00000275

25) Calculate: a) $(2.54 \times 10^6) \div (1.6 \times 10^3)$ b) $(1.75 \times 10^{12}) + (9.89 \times 10^{11})$
Give your answers in standard form.

Sets and Venn Diagrams (p.40-44) ☐

26) ξ = {Positive integers less than 16},   A = {Multiples of 5},   B = {$x : x$ is less than or equal to 10}

   a) List the elements of $A \cap B$.

   b) Fill in the boxes in the Venn diagram on the right to show the number of elements in each part of the diagram.

   c) Find $n(A \cup B')$.

Algebra Basics

Before you can really start algebra, there are some basics you need to learn.

Letters **Multiplied** Together

Watch out for these combinations of letters in algebra that regularly catch people out:

1) abc means $a \times b \times c$. The $\times$'s are often left out to make it clearer.

2) gn^2 means $g \times n \times n$. Note that only the n is squared, not the g as well — e.g. πr^2 means $\pi \times r \times r$.

3) $(gn)^2$ means $g \times g \times n \times n$. The brackets mean that BOTH letters are squared.

4) $p(q - r)^3$ means $p \times (q - r) \times (q - r) \times (q - r)$. Only the brackets get cubed.

5) Avoid writing things like -3^2. It should either be $(-3)^2 = 9$, or $-(3^2) = -9$ (you'd usually take -3^2 to be -9).

Terms

Before you can do anything else with algebra, you must understand what a term is:

 KEY TERM　A term is a collection of numbers and letters, all multiplied/divided together.

Terms are separated by $+$ and $-$ signs. Every term has a $+$ or $-$ attached to the front of it.

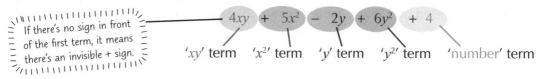

If there's no sign in front of the first term, it means there's an invisible $+$ sign.

$4xy \quad + \quad 5x^2 \quad - \quad 2y \quad + \quad 6y^2 \quad + \quad 4$

'xy' term　　'x^2' term　　'y' term　　'y^2' term　　'number' term

Simplifying or '**Collecting Like Terms**'

To simplify an algebraic expression, you combine 'like terms' — terms that have the same combination of letters (e.g. all the x terms, all the y terms, all the number terms etc.).

EXAMPLE: **Simplify $2x - 4 + 5x + 6$**

number terms

Invisible $+$ sign ——　$2x \quad -4 \quad +5x \quad +6 \quad = \quad +2x \quad +5x \quad -4 \quad +6$

x-terms

$= \qquad 7x \qquad +2 \quad = 7x + 2$

1) Put circles round each term — be sure you include the $+/-$ sign in front of each.

2) Then you can move the circles into the best order so that like terms are together.

3) Combine like terms.

 REVISION TIP

These are the basics of everything in algebra

Algebra isn't easy, so if you don't get these basics learned now, you'll be really confused later on. Always remember — every term has a $+$ or $-$ stuck to the front (even if it's invisible).

Powers

You've already seen powers on page 6 — have a look back at that page if you need a reminder. There are some special rules for powers that you need to learn — starting with the eight on this page.

Learn these **Eight** Rules

1) When MULTIPLYING, you ADD THE POWERS.

   e.g. $3^4 \times 3^6 = 3^{4+6} = 3^{10}$, $a^2 \times a^7 = a^{2+7} = a^9$

> Warning: Rules 1 & 2 don't work for things like $2^3 \times 3^7$, only for powers of the same number.

2) When DIVIDING, you SUBTRACT THE POWERS.

   e.g. $5^4 \div 5^2 = 5^{4-2} = 5^2$, $b^8 \div b^5 = b^{8-5} = b^3$

> Simple algebraic fractions can be simplified using these power rules.
>
> E.g. $\dfrac{p^3 q^6}{p^2 q^3} = p^3 q^6 \div p^2 q^3$
> $= p^{3-2} q^{6-3}$
> $= pq^3$

3) When RAISING one power to another, you MULTIPLY THEM.

   e.g. $(3^2)^4 = 3^{2\times4} = 3^8$, $(c^3)^6 = c^{3\times6} = c^{18}$

4) $x^1 = x$, ANYTHING to the POWER 1 is just ITSELF.

   e.g. $3^1 = 3$, $d \times d^3 = d^1 \times d^3 = d^{1+3} = d^4$

5) $x^0 = 1$, ANYTHING to the POWER 0 is just 1.

   e.g. $5^0 = 1$, $67^0 = 1$, $e^0 = 1$

6) $1^x = 1$, 1 TO ANY POWER is STILL JUST 1.

   e.g. $1^{23} = 1$, $1^{89} = 1$, $1^2 = 1$

> Powers can also be called 'indices' (or 'index' if it's just one).

7) FRACTIONS — Apply the power to both TOP and BOTTOM.

   e.g. $\left(1\dfrac{3}{5}\right)^3 = \left(\dfrac{8}{5}\right)^3 = \dfrac{8^3}{5^3} = \dfrac{512}{125}$, $\left(\dfrac{u}{v}\right)^5 = \dfrac{u^5}{v^5}$

8) NEGATIVE Powers — Turn it Upside Down.

People find it difficult to remember this one — whenever you see a negative power you need to think: "That means turn it the other way up and make the power positive".

   e.g. $7^{-2} = \dfrac{1}{7^2} = \dfrac{1}{49}$, $a^{-4} = \dfrac{1}{a^4}$, $\left(\dfrac{3}{5}\right)^{-2} = \left(\dfrac{5}{3}\right)^{+2} = \dfrac{5^2}{3^2} = \dfrac{25}{9}$

Rules 1 & 2 only work for powers of the same number

If you can add, subtract and multiply, there's nothing on this page you can't do — as long as you learn the rules. Try copying them over and over until you can do it with your eyes closed.

Powers

These **Two** Rules are a bit more **Tricky**

9) FRACTIONAL POWERS

The power $\frac{1}{2}$ means Square Root.

The power $\frac{1}{3}$ means Cube Root.

The power $\frac{1}{4}$ means Fourth Root etc.

e.g. $25^{\frac{1}{2}} = \sqrt{25} = 5$

$64^{\frac{1}{3}} = \sqrt[3]{64} = 4$

$81^{\frac{1}{4}} = \sqrt[4]{81} = 3$

See page 6 for more on roots. You'll be able to use your calculator in the exam if you get a root that's really hard to evaluate.

The one to really watch is when you get a negative fraction like $49^{-\frac{1}{2}}$ — people get mixed up and think that the minus is the square root, and forget to turn it upside down as well.

e.g. $49^{-\frac{1}{2}} = \frac{1}{\sqrt{49}} = \frac{1}{7}$

10) TWO-STAGE FRACTIONAL POWERS

With fractional powers like $64^{\frac{5}{6}}$, always split the fraction into a root and a power, and do them in that order: root first, then power: $(64)^{\frac{1}{6} \times 5} = \left(64^{\frac{1}{6}}\right)^5 = (2)^5 = 32$.

You can use **Fractional Powers** with **Algebra** too

EXAMPLE: Simplify $2xy^{\frac{3}{2}} \times 3x^{-\frac{5}{6}}y^{-\frac{3}{2}}$

Just deal with each bit separately:

$2xy^{\frac{3}{2}} \times 3x^{-\frac{5}{6}}y^{-\frac{3}{2}} = (2 \times 3)(x \times x^{-\frac{5}{6}})(y^{\frac{3}{2}} \times y^{-\frac{3}{2}})$

$= (2 \times 3)x^{1+\left(-\frac{5}{6}\right)}y^{\frac{3}{2}+\left(-\frac{3}{2}\right)} = 6x^{1-\frac{5}{6}}y^{\frac{3}{2}-\frac{3}{2}} = 6x^{\frac{1}{6}}$

$y^{\frac{3}{2}-\frac{3}{2}} = y^0 = 1$

EXAMPLE: Evaluate $\left(\frac{x^6}{27}\right)^{\frac{2}{3}}$

1) Break down the two-stage fractional power into a root and a power. Remember to do everything to both the top and the bottom.

$\left(\frac{x^6}{27}\right)^{\frac{2}{3}} = \left(\left(\frac{x^6}{27}\right)^{\frac{1}{3}}\right)^2 = \left(\frac{(x^6)^{\frac{1}{3}}}{27^{\frac{1}{3}}}\right)^2 = \left(\frac{x^{\left(6 \times \frac{1}{3}\right)}}{\sqrt[3]{27}}\right)^2$

This uses power rule 3 — when you raise one power to another, you multiply them together.

2) Work out the root and deal with the powers that are left.

$= \left(\frac{x^2}{3}\right)^2 = \frac{(x^2)^2}{3^2} = \frac{x^4}{9}$

These power rules might be a bit trickier — but they are essential

People often get fractional powers wrong, so you should write down these rules and make sure you learn them. Then, if they come up in the exam, you won't have anything to worry about.

Expanding Brackets

You often find brackets in algebraic expressions. The first thing you need to be able to do is to expand them (multiply them out).

Single Brackets

The main thing to remember when multiplying out brackets is that the thing outside the bracket multiplies each separate term inside the bracket.

EXAMPLE: Expand the following:

a) $4a(3b - 2c)$

$= (4a \times 3b) + (4a \times -2c)$

$= 12ab - 8ac$

b) $-4(3p^2 - 7q^3)$

$= (-4 \times 3p^2) + (-4 \times -7q^3)$

$= -12p^2 + 28q^3$

Note: both signs have been reversed.

Double Brackets

Double brackets are trickier than single brackets — you have to multiply everything in the first bracket by everything in the second bracket. You'll get 4 terms, and usually 2 of them will combine to leave 3 terms. There's a handy way to multiply out double brackets — it's called the FOIL method:

First — multiply the first term in each bracket together

Outside — multiply the outside terms (i.e. the first term in the first bracket by the second term in the second bracket)

Inside — multiply the inside terms (i.e. the second term in the first bracket by the first term in the second bracket)

Last — multiply the second term in each bracket together

EXAMPLE: Expand and simplify $(2p - 4)(3p + 1)$.

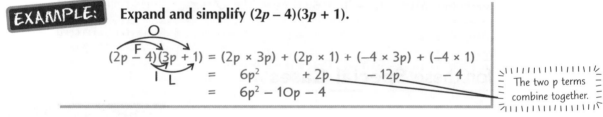

$(2p - 4)(3p + 1) = (2p \times 3p) + (2p \times 1) + (-4 \times 3p) + (-4 \times 1)$

$= 6p^2 + 2p - 12p - 4$

$= 6p^2 - 10p - 4$

The two p terms combine together.

Always write out SQUARED BRACKETS as TWO BRACKETS (to avoid mistakes), then multiply out as above.

So $(3x + 5)^2 = (3x + 5)(3x + 5) = 9x^2 + 15x + 15x + 25 = 9x^2 + 30x + 25$.

(DON'T make the mistake of thinking that $(3x + 5)^2 = 9x^2 + 25$ — this is wrong.)

Triple Brackets

1) For three brackets, just multiply two together as above, then multiply the result by the remaining bracket.

It doesn't matter which pair of brackets you multiply together first.

2) If you end up with three terms in one bracket, you won't be able to use FOIL. Instead, you can reduce it to a series of single bracket multiplications — like in the example below.

EXAMPLE: Expand and simplify $(x + 2)(x + 3)(2x - 1)$.

$(x + 2)(x + 3)(2x - 1) = (x + 2)(2x^2 + 5x - 3) = x(2x^2 + 5x - 3) + 2(2x^2 + 5x - 3)$

$= (2x^3 + 5x^2 - 3x) + (4x^2 + 10x - 6)$

$= 2x^3 + 9x^2 + 7x - 6$

Extended

Use the FOIL method so you don't miss out any terms

When multiplying squared brackets, write them as two brackets — you should get four terms (and two of them will combine). For cubed brackets, write them as three brackets like above.

Factorising

Now that you know how to expand brackets, it's time to put them back in. This is known as factorising.

Factorising — Putting Brackets In

This is the reverse of multiplying out brackets. Here's the method to follow:

> 1) Take out the biggest number that goes into all the terms.
> 2) For each letter in turn, take out the highest power (e.g. x, x^2 etc.) that will go into EVERY term.
> 3) Open the brackets and fill in all the bits needed to reproduce each term.
> 4) Check your answer by multiplying out the brackets to make sure it matches the original expression.

 **EXAMPLES:**

1. **Factorise** $3x^2 + 6x$

Biggest number that'll divide into 3 and 6

Highest power of x that will go into both terms

$$3x(x + 2)$$

Check: $3x(x + 2) = 3x^2 + 6x$ ✓

2. **Factorise** $8x^2y + 2xy^2$

Biggest number that'll divide into 8 and 2

Highest powers of x and y that will go into both terms

$$2xy(4x + y)$$

Check: $2xy(4x + y) = 8x^2y + 2xy^2$ ✓

3. **Factorise** $3x + 6y - kx - 2ky$

Factorise the x and y terms separately.

The $(3 - k)$ bracket appears in both terms, so you can factorise again.

$$3x - kx + 6y - 2ky = x(3 - k) + 2y(3 - k) = (3 - k)(x + 2y)$$

Check: $(3 - k)(x + 2y) = 3x + 6y - kx - 2ky$ ✓ ← Use FOIL to expand the brackets out and check your answer.

Look Out for these Special Cases

You need to be able to recognise and factorise a squared bracket that has been expanded — the general form of these is: → $a^2 + 2ab + b^2 = (a + b)^2$

 **EXAMPLE:**

Factorise: a) $x^2 + 6x + 9$ **Answer:** $x^2 + 6x + 9 = (x + 3)^2$

$3^2 = 9$, and $2 \times x \times 3 = 6x$, so this is a squared bracket.

b) $4c^2 + 4cd + d^2$ **Answer:** $4c^2 + 4cd + d^2 = (2c + d)^2$

Watch out: $4c^2 = (2c)^2$, so $2 \times 2c \times d = 4cd$.

The 'difference of two squares' (D.O.T.S. for short) is where you have 'one thing squared' take away 'another thing squared'. There's a quick and easy way to factorise it — just use this rule: → $a^2 - b^2 = (a + b)(a - b)$

 **EXAMPLE:**

Factorise: a) $x^2 - 1$ **Answer:** $x^2 - 1 = (x + 1)(x - 1)$

Don't forget that 1 is a square number (it's 1^2).

b) $3x^2 - 75y^2$ **Answer:** $3x^2 - 75y^2 = 3(x^2 - 25y^2) = 3(x + 5y)(x - 5y)$

This time, you had to take out a factor of 3 first.

Extended (left margin)   *Extended* (right margin)

 EXAM TIP

Factorising is the opposite of multiplying out brackets

There's no excuse for making mistakes when factorising — in the exam you can check your answer by multiplying the brackets out. Do it right, and you'll get back to the original expression.

Warm-Up and Worked Exam Questions

Take a deep breath and go through these warm-up questions one by one. Then you'll be ready
for the really exciting bit (well, slightly more exciting anyway) — the exam questions.

Warm-Up Questions

1) Simplify: a) $4a + c - 2a - 6c$ b) $3r^2 - 2r + 4r^2 - 1 - 3r$ c) $5r \times -2s \times 6$

2) Evaluate: a) $4^5 \times 4^{-2}$ b) $\left(1\frac{2}{7}\right)^2$ c) $27^{\frac{2}{3}}$ d) $\left(\frac{2}{3}\right)^{-2}$

3) Simplify: a) $3x^3 \times x^2$ b) $8y^5 \div 4y^2$ c) $5a^7 \times 2a^4$ d) $(x^3)^4$

E 4) Simplify fully $a^7 \times (25a^6b^{10}c^5)^{\frac{1}{2}}$.

5) Multiply out: a) $4(2p + 7)$ b) $(4x - 2)(2x + 1)$ c) $a(5a - 3)$

6) Expand: a) $(x - 3)^2$ b) $(4y + 5)^2$

7) Factorise: a) $6p - 12q + 4$ b) $4cd^2 - 2cd + 10c^2d^3$

E 8) Factorise: a) $2m + 5n + 2pm + 5pn$ b) $z^2 + 8z + 16$ c) $x^2 - 4y^2$

Worked Exam Questions

Don't skip over these worked exam questions just because they already have the answers written in.
Work through them yourself so you know what's going on, then have a go at the next page.

1 Expand and simplify where possible.

Multiply out the brackets first, then collect like terms.

a) $3(x - 1) + 5(x + 2)$

$(3 \times x) + (3 \times -1) + (5 \times x) + (5 \times 2) = 3x - 3 + 5x + 10$
$= 8x + 7$

...... $8x + 7$ ......

[2 marks]

b) $9 - 3(x + 2)$

$9 + (-3 \times x) + (-3 \times 2) = 9 - 3x - 6$
$= 3 - 3x$

Careful with the minus signs here.

...... $3 - 3x$ ......

[2 marks]

2 Factorise the following expressions fully.

a) $x^2 - 16$

This is a difference of two squares:
$x^2 - 16 = x^2 - 4^2$
$= (x + 4)(x - 4)$

...... $(x + 4)(x - 4)$ ......

[1 mark]

Here you have to spot that 9 and 4 are square numbers.

b) $9n^2 - 4m^2$

$9n^2 - 4m^2 = (3n)^2 - (2m)^2$

$= (3n + 2m)(3n - 2m)$

...... $(3n + 2m)(3n - 2m)$ ......

[2 marks]

Extended

Exam Questions

3 Expand and simplify the following:

a) $(y + 3)(y - 3)$

....
[2 marks]

b) $(2z - 1)(z - 5)$

....
[2 marks]

4 Fully factorise $2v^3w + 8v^2w^2$

....
[2 marks]

5 Completely simplify the expression $(9a^4)^{\frac{1}{2}} \times \dfrac{2ab^2}{6a^3b}$

....
[3 marks]

6 Factorise the following expressions.

a) $9x^2 - 100$

....
[2 marks]

b) $12m + 3ml - 4n - ln$

....
[2 marks]

7 Expand and simplify $(x - 1)(2x + 3)(2x - 3)$.

$-4x^2 - 6x + 6x - 9$

$(x - 1)(4x^2 - 9)$

$4x^3 - 9x - 4x^2 + 9$

.....$4x^3 - 9x - 4x^2 + 9$..........
[3 marks]

Solving Equations

The basic idea of solving equations is very simple — keep rearranging until you end up with x = number. The two most common methods for rearranging equations are: 1) 'same to both sides' and 2) do the opposite when you cross the '='. I'll use the 'same to both sides' method on these pages.

Rearrange Until You Have x = Number

The easiest ones to solve are where you just have a mixture of x's and numbers.

1) First, rearrange the equation so that all the x's are on one side and the numbers are on the other. Combine terms where you can.

2) Then divide both sides by the number multiplying x to find the value of x.

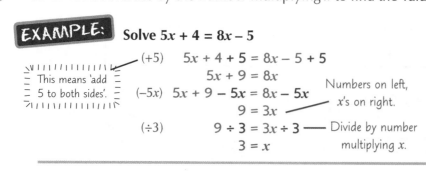

EXAMPLE: Solve $5x + 4 = 8x - 5$

This means 'add 5 to both sides'.

(+5) $5x + 4 + 5 = 8x - 5 + 5$
$5x + 9 = 8x$
(−5x) $5x + 9 - 5x = 8x - 5x$ Numbers on left, x's on right.
$9 = 3x$
(÷3) $9 \div 3 = 3x \div 3$ —— Divide by number multiplying x.
$3 = x$

Once you're happy with the method, you don't have to write everything out in full — your working might be:
$5x + 9 = 8x$
$9 = 3x$
$3 = x$

Multiply Out Brackets First

If your equation has brackets in it...

1) Multiply them out before rearranging.

2) Solve it in the same way as above.

EXAMPLE: Solve $3(3x - 2) = 5x + 10$

$9x - 6 = 5x + 10$
(−5x) $9x - 6 - 5x = 5x + 10 - 5x$
$4x - 6 = 10$
(+6) $4x - 6 + 6 = 10 + 6$
$4x = 16$
(÷4) $4x \div 4 = 16 \div 4$
$x = 4$

Get Rid of Fractions

1) Fractions make everything more complicated — so you need to get rid of them before doing anything else (such as multiplying out brackets).

2) To get rid of fractions, multiply every term of the equation by whatever's on the bottom of the fraction. If there are two fractions, multiply by both denominators (or by a common multiple of them).

EXAMPLES:

1. Solve $\dfrac{x+2}{4} = 4x - 7$

(×4) $\dfrac{4(x+2)}{4} = 4(4x) - 4(7)$

$x + 2 = 16x - 28$

Multiply every term by 4 to get rid of the fraction.

$30 = 15x$ —— And solve.
$2 = x$

2. Solve $\dfrac{3x+5}{2} = \dfrac{4x+10}{3}$

Multiply everything by 2 then by 3.

(×2), (×3) $\dfrac{2 \times 3 \times (3x+5)}{2} = \dfrac{2 \times 3 \times (4x+10)}{3}$

$3(3x+5) = 2(4x+10)$

And solve. —— $9x + 15 = 8x + 20$

$x = 5$

EXAM TIP

Remember that you're trying to get x on its own

You can check your answer by putting your value of x back into both sides of the original equation — you should get the same number on each side. If you don't, you've made a mistake somewhere.

Solving Equations

Now you know the basics of solving equations, it's time to put it all together into a handy step-by-step method.

Solving Equations Using the 6-Step Method

Here's the method to follow (just ignore any steps that don't apply to your equation):

1) Get rid of any fractions.
2) Multiply out any brackets.
3) Collect all the x-terms on one side and all number terms on the other.
4) Reduce it to the form '$Ax = B$' (by combining like terms).
5) Finally divide both sides by A to give '$x = $ ', and that's your answer.
6) If you had '$x^2 = $ ' instead, square root both sides to end up with '$x = \pm$ '.

EXAMPLE: Solve $\dfrac{3x + 4}{5} + \dfrac{4x - 1}{3} = 14$

Multiply everything by 5 then by 3.

1) Get rid of any fractions.   (×5), (×3) $\dfrac{5 \times 3 \times (3x + 4)}{5} + \dfrac{5 \times 3 \times (4x - 1)}{3} = 5 \times 3 \times 14$

$3(3x + 4) + 5(4x - 1) = 210$

2) Multiply out any brackets. $9x + 12 + 20x - 5 = 210$

3) Collect all the x-terms on one side and all number terms on the other.

(−12), (+5) $9x + 20x = 210 - 12 + 5$

4) Reduce it to the form '$Ax = B$' (by combining like terms).

$29x = 203$

5) Finally divide both sides by A to give '$x = $ ', and that's your answer.

(÷29) $x = 7$ (You're left with '$x = $ ' so you can ignore step 6.)

Dealing with Squares

You might get an x^2 in an equation. If this happens, you'll end up with '$x^2 = ...$' at step 5, and then step 6 is to take square roots. There's one very important thing to remember: whenever you take the square root of a number, the answer can be positive or negative, which is shown using the symbol '$\pm$'.

EXAMPLE: Solve $3x^2 = 75$.

(÷3) $x^2 = 25$

($\sqrt{\ }$) $x = \pm 5$

You always get a positive and negative version of the same number (your calculator only gives the positive answer), because $5^2 = 5 \times 5 = 25$ but $(-5)^2 = (-5) \times (-5) = 25$ as well.

Learn the 6-step method for solving equations

Write down all 6 steps without looking to make sure you've learned them all. You might not need to use all 6 to solve your equation — ignore any that you don't need and move on to the next step.

Making Formulas from Words

Before we go any further, there are a few definitions you need to know:

KEY TERMS

An expression is a collection of terms (see p.48). Expressions don't have an = sign in them.
An equation is an expression with an = sign in it (so you can solve it).
A formula is a rule that helps you work something out (it will also have an = sign in it).

Making a **Formula** from **Given Information**

Making formulas from words can be a bit confusing as you're given a lot of information.
You just have to go through it slowly and carefully and extract the maths from it.

EXAMPLES:

1. Tiana is x years old. Leah is 5 years younger than Tiana. Martin is 4 times as old as Tiana.

    a) Write an expression for Leah's age in terms of x.

Tiana's age is x
So Leah's age is $x - 5$ — Leah is 5 years younger, so subtract 5

    b) Write an expression for Martin's age in terms of x.

Tiana's age is x
So Martin's age is $4 \times x = 4x$ — 4 times older

2. Windsurfing lessons cost \$15 per hour, plus a fixed fee of \$20 for equipment hire. h hours of lessons cost \$$W$. Write a formula for W in terms of h.

One hour costs 15, so h hours will cost $15 \times h$ — $W = 15h + 20$ — Don't forget to add on the fixed fee (20)

Because you're asked for a formula, you must include the 'W =' bit to get full marks (i.e. don't just put 15h + 20).

3. In rugby union, tries score 5 points and conversions score 2 points. In a game, Morgan scores a total of M points, made up of t tries and c conversions. Write a formula for M in terms of t and c.

Tries score 5 points — t tries will score $5 \times t = 5t$ points
Conversions score 2 points — c conversions will score $2 \times c = 2c$ points
So total points scored are $M = 5t + 2c$

Using Your **Formula** to **Solve Equations**

Sometimes, you might be asked to use a formula to solve an equation.

EXAMPLE: A decorator uses the formula $C = 200r + 150$, where C is the cost in \$ and r is the number of rooms. Gabrielle spends \$950. How many rooms does she have decorated?

$C = 200r + 150$ ——— Write down the formula first.

$950 = 200r + 150$ ——— Replace C with the value given in the question (\$950).

(-150) $950 - 150 = 200r + 150 - 150$ — Now solve the equation.

$800 = 200r$

$(\div 200)$ $800 \div 200 = 200r \div 200$

$4 = r$ So Gabrielle has 4 rooms decorated.

EXAM TIP

All the information you need will be given in the question

Don't get confused by wordy questions — read each sentence slowly and then write down the maths that you can extract from it. Then, if you're asked to, solve it just like any other equation.

Rearranging Formulas

Rearranging formulas means making one letter the subject, e.g. getting '$y = $' from '$2x + z = 3(y + 2p)$' — you have to get the subject on its own.

Use the **Solving Equations** Method to **Rearrange Formulas**

Rearranging formulas is similar to solving equations. The method below is the same as the method for solving equations, except that there's an extra step at the start.

1) Get rid of any square root signs by squaring both sides.

2) Get rid of any fractions.

3) Multiply out any brackets.

4) Collect all the subject terms on one side and all non-subject terms on the other.

5) Reduce it to the form '$Ax = B$' (by combining like terms). You might have to do some factorising here too.

6) Divide both sides by A to give '$x = $ '.

7) If you're left with '$x^2 = $ ', square root both sides to get '$x = \pm$ ' (don't forget the $\pm$).

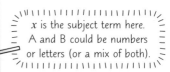

x is the subject term here. A and B could be numbers or letters (or a mix of both).

Don't worry if you have some other root/power, e.g. cubes (see p.6). Steps 1) and 7) still work in the same sort of way.

What to Do If...

...the **Subject** Appears in a **Fraction**

You won't always need to use all 7 steps in the method above — just ignore the ones that don't apply.

EXAMPLE: **Make b the subject of the formula $a = \dfrac{5b + 3}{4}$.**

There aren't any square roots, so ignore step 1.

2) Get rid of any fractions.	(by multiplying every term by 4, the denominator)	$(\times 4)$ $\quad 4a = \dfrac{4(5b + 3)}{4}$

$$4a = 5b + 3$$

There aren't any brackets, so ignore step 3.

4) Collect all the subject terms on one side and all non-subject terms on the other.

(remember that you're trying to make b the subject) $\quad (-3)$ $\quad 5b = 4a - 3$

5) It's now in the form $Ax = B$.	(where A = 5 and B = 4a − 3)

6) Divide both sides by 5 to give '$b = $ '.	$(\div 5)$ $\quad b = \dfrac{4a - 3}{5}$

b isn't squared, so you don't need step 7.

The subject is the letter on its own

Remember that rearranging formulas is exactly the same as solving equations, except that instead of ending up with 'x = number' (e.g. $x = 3$), you'll end up with 'x = expression' (e.g. $x = 2y + 4$).

Rearranging Formulas

Carrying straight on from the previous page, now it's time for what to do if...

...there's a **Square** or **Square Root** Involved

If the subject appears as a square or in a square root, you'll have to use steps 1 and 7 (not necessarily both).

EXAMPLE: **Make v the subject of the formula $u = 4v^2 + 5w$.**

There aren't any square roots, fractions or brackets so ignore steps 1-3 (this is pretty easy so far).

4) Collect all the subject terms on one side and all non-subject terms on the other.

$(-5w)$ $\quad 4v^2 = u - 5w$

5) It's now in the form $Ax^2 = B$ (where $A = 4$ and $B = u - 5w$)

6) Divide both sides by 4 to give '$v^2 = \quad$'. $\quad (\div 4) \quad v^2 = \dfrac{u - 5w}{4}$

7) Square root both sides to get '$v = \pm \quad$'. $\quad (\sqrt{}) \quad v = \pm\sqrt{\dfrac{u - 5w}{4}} \quad$ Don't forget the $\pm$

EXAMPLE: **Make n the subject of the formula $m = \dfrac{\sqrt{n + 5}}{k}$.**

1) Get rid of any square roots by squaring both sides. $\quad m^2 = \dfrac{n + 5}{k^2}$

> $\sqrt{a}$ means the positive square root, so you don't need a $\pm$.

2) Get rid of any fractions. $\quad k^2 m^2 = n + 5$

There aren't any brackets, so ignore step 3.

4) Collect all the subject terms on one side and all non-subject terms on the other.

(-5) $\quad n = k^2 m^2 - 5 \quad$ This is in the form '$n = \quad$' so you don't need to do steps 5-7.

Extended

...the Subject Appears **Twice**

You'll just have to do some factorising, usually in step 5.

EXAMPLE: **Make p the subject of the formula $p = \dfrac{p + 1}{q - 1}$.**

There aren't any square roots, so ignore step 1.

2) Get rid of any fractions. $\quad p(q - 1) = p + 1 \qquad$ 3) Multiply out any brackets. $\quad pq - p = p + 1$

4) Collect all the subject terms on one side and all non-subject terms on the other.

$pq - 2p = 1$

> This is where you factorise — p was in both terms on the LHS, so it comes out as a common factor.

5) Combine like terms on each side of the equation. $\quad p(q - 2) = 1$

6) Divide both sides by $(q - 2)$ to give '$p = \quad$'. $\quad p = \dfrac{1}{q - 2} \quad$ (p isn't squared, so you don't need step 7.)

Extended

Remember — you square first and square root last

Rearranging formulas is a bit harder if the subject appears twice. But if this happens, don't panic — just follow the 7-step method and be prepared to do some factorising (see page 52 if you need a reminder).

Algebraic Fractions

Unfortunately, fractions aren't just for numbers — you can get algebraic fractions too.
Fortunately, everything you learned about fractions on p.14-16 can be applied to algebraic fractions as well.

Simplifying Algebraic Fractions

You can simplify algebraic fractions by cancelling terms on the top and bottom — deal with each letter individually and cancel as much as you can. You might have to factorise first (see pages 52 and 63-64).

EXAMPLES:

1. Simplify $\dfrac{21x^3y^2}{14xy^3}$

÷7 on the top and bottom

÷x on the top and bottom to leave x^2 on the top

÷y^2 on the top and bottom to leave y on the bottom

$$\dfrac{\overset{3}{\cancel{21}}\overset{x^2}{\cancel{x^3}}\cancel{y^2}}{\underset{2}{\cancel{14}}\cancel{x}\underset{y}{\cancel{y^3}}} = \dfrac{3x^2}{2y}$$

2. Simplify $\dfrac{x^2-16}{x^2+2x-8}$

Factorise the top using D.O.T.S.

$$\dfrac{(x+4)(x-4)}{(x-2)(x+4)} = \dfrac{x-4}{x-2}$$

Factorise the quadratic on the bottom (see p.63)

Then cancel the common factor of $(x+4)$

Multiplying/Dividing Algebraic Fractions

1) To multiply two fractions, just multiply tops and bottoms separately.

2) To divide, turn the second fraction upside down then multiply.

EXAMPLE: Simplify $\dfrac{x^2}{4} \times \dfrac{2}{x+1}$

Cancel the number terms first...

$$\dfrac{x^2}{\underset{2}{\cancel{4}}} \times \dfrac{\cancel{2}}{x+1} = \dfrac{x^2}{2(x+1)}$$

EXAMPLE: Simplify $\dfrac{2}{x} \div \dfrac{x^3}{5}$

$$\dfrac{2}{x} \div \dfrac{x^3}{5} = \dfrac{2}{x} \times \dfrac{5}{x^3} = \dfrac{10}{x^4}$$

Adding/Subtracting Algebraic Fractions

Adding or subtracting is a bit more difficult:

1) Work out the common denominator (see p.15).
2) Multiply top and bottom of each fraction by whatever gives you the common denominator.
3) Add or subtract the numerators only.

For the common denominator, find something both denominators divide into.

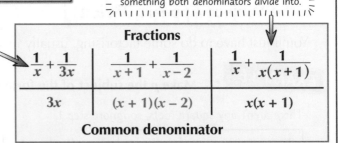

Fractions		
$\dfrac{1}{x} + \dfrac{1}{3x}$	$\dfrac{1}{x+1} + \dfrac{1}{x-2}$	$\dfrac{1}{x} + \dfrac{1}{x(x+1)}$
$3x$	$(x+1)(x-2)$	$x(x+1)$

Common denominator

EXAMPLE: Write $\dfrac{3x}{(x+3)} + \dfrac{x-3}{(x-2)}$ as a single fraction.

1st fraction: × top & bottom by $(x-2)$
2nd fraction: × top & bottom by $(x+3)$

$$\dfrac{3x}{(x+3)} + \dfrac{x-3}{(x-2)} = \dfrac{3x(x-2)}{(x+3)(x-2)} + \dfrac{(x+3)(x-3)}{(x+3)(x-2)}$$

Common denominator will be $(x+3)(x-2)$

Add the numerators

$$= \dfrac{3x^2-6x}{(x+3)(x-2)} + \dfrac{x^2-9}{(x+3)(x-2)} = \dfrac{4x^2-6x-9}{(x+3)(x-2)}$$

EXAM TIP

Put fractions over a common denominator

One more thing — never do this: $\dfrac{\cancel{x}}{\cancel{x}+y} = \dfrac{1}{y}$ ✗ It's WRONG and will lose you marks.

Extended

Warm-Up and Worked Exam Questions

It's easy to think you've learned everything in the section until you try the warm-up questions. Don't panic if there are bits you've forgotten — just go back over them until you can answer all of the questions.

Warm-Up Questions

1) Solve these equations to find the value of x:
   a) $8x - 5 = 19$ b) $3(2x + 7) = 3$ c) $4x - 9 = x + 6$

2) The cost of hiring a bicycle is \$12 per day, plus a deposit of \$18.
   If the cost for hiring it for d days is \$$C$, find a formula for C in terms of d.

3) Make q the subject of the formula $p = \dfrac{q}{7} + 2r$

4) Make z the subject of the formula $x = \dfrac{y + 2z}{3}$

5) Simplify: a) $\dfrac{16ab^2c^2 + 8bc}{4bc^4}$ b) $\dfrac{x^4 - 4y^2}{x^3 - 2xy}$

Worked Exam Questions

Here are a couple of exam questions that I've done for you. You won't get any help for the questions on the next page though — so make the most of it while you can.

1 Solve the equation $\dfrac{5}{4}(2c - 1) = 3c - 2$

$$\frac{5}{4}(2c - 1) = 3c - 2$$

Get rid of the fraction...   (×4) $5(2c - 1) = 4(3c - 2)$

...multiply out the brackets... $10c - 5 = 12c - 8$

...and solve.   (−10c) $-5 = 2c - 8$

(+8) $3 = 2c$

(÷2) $1.5 = c$

$c = \underline{\ \ 1.5\ \ }$

[3 marks]

2 Write $\dfrac{2}{3} + \dfrac{m - 2n}{m + 3n}$ as a single fraction.

$$\frac{2}{3} + \frac{m - 2n}{m + 3n} = \frac{2 \times (m + 3n)}{3 \times (m + 3n)} + \frac{3 \times (m - 2n)}{3 \times (m + 3n)}$$

$$= \frac{2m + 6n + 3m - 6n}{3(m + 3n)}$$

$$= \frac{5m}{3(m + 3n)}$$

Finding the common denominator is the tricky bit — you often just need to multiply the denominators together.

$\dfrac{5m}{3(m + 3n)}$

[3 marks]

Exam Questions

3 Rearrange the formula $\dfrac{a+2}{3} = b - 1$ to make a the subject.

$\times 3 \quad \times 3$

$a + 2 = 3b - 3$
$\quad -2 \qquad -2$

$a = 3b + 5$

.$a = 3b \pm 5$.......................

[2 marks]

4 Solve the following equations.

a) $40 - 3x = 17x$
$\quad + 3x \quad + 3x \qquad x = 2$

$\dfrac{20x}{20} = \dfrac{40}{20}$

$x = $ .2.............................

[2 marks]

b) $2y - 5 = 3y - 12$
$\quad -3y + 5 \quad -3y + 5 \qquad y = 7$

$2y - 3y = -7$

$\dfrac{-1y}{-1} = \dfrac{-7}{-1}$

$y = $ ..7.............................

[2 marks]

5 Write an expression for the area of the triangle below.
Give your answer in the form $ax^2 + bx + c$.

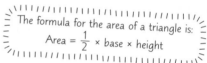

The formula for the area of a triangle is:
Area $= \frac{1}{2} \times$ base $\times$ height

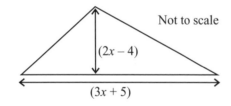

Not to scale

$(2x - 4)$

$(3x + 5)$

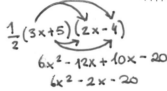

$\frac{1}{2}(3x + 5)(2x - 4)$

$6x^2 - 12x + 10x - 20$

$6x^2 - 2x - 20$

....

[3 marks]

6 Write $\dfrac{1}{x-5} + \dfrac{2}{x-2}$ as a single fraction.

....

[3 marks]

7 Rearrange this formula to make n the subject: $x = \sqrt{\dfrac{(1+n)}{(1-n)}}$

....

[5 marks]

Extended

Factorising Quadratics

There are several ways of solving a quadratic equation, as detailed on the following pages.
You need to know all the methods as they sometimes ask for specific ones in the exam.

Factorising a Quadratic

1) 'Factorising a quadratic' means 'putting it into 2 brackets'.
2) The standard format for quadratic equations is: $ax^2 + bx + c = 0$.
3) Some questions have $a = 1$, making them much easier. E.g. $x^2 + 3x + 2 = 0$
4) As well as factorising a quadratic, you might be asked to solve it.
   This just means finding the values of x that make each bracket 0 (see example below).

See the next page for when 'a' is not 1.

Factorising Method when a = 1

1) ALWAYS rearrange into the STANDARD FORMAT: $x^2 + bx + c = 0$.
2) Write down the TWO BRACKETS with the x's in: $(x \quad)(x \quad) = 0$.
3) Then find 2 numbers that MULTIPLY to give c (the end number) but also ADD/SUBTRACT to give b (the coefficient of x).
4) Fill in the +/– signs and make sure they work out properly.
5) As an ESSENTIAL CHECK, expand the brackets to make sure they give the original equation.
6) Finally, SOLVE THE EQUATION by setting each bracket equal to 0.

Ignore any minus signs at this stage.

You only need to do step 6) if the question asks you to solve the quadratic
— if it just tells you to factorise, you can stop at step 5).

EXAMPLE: Solve $x^2 – x = 12$.

1) $x^2 – x – 12 = 0$ 1) Rearrange into the standard format.

2) $(x \quad)(x \quad) = 0$ 2) Write down the initial brackets.

3)
	Add/subtract to give:	
1×12	Add/subtract to give:	13 or 11
2×6	Add/subtract to give:	8 or 4
3×4	Add/subtract to give:	7 or ①

3) Find the right pairs of numbers that multiply to give c (= 12), and add or subtract to give b (= 1) (remember, we're ignoring the +/– signs for now).

$(x \quad 3)(x \quad 4) = 0$ This is what we want.

4) $(x + 3)(x – 4) = 0$

4) Now fill in the +/– signs so that 3 and 4 add/subtract to give –1 (= b).

5) Check:
$(x + 3)(x – 4) = x^2 – 4x + 3x – 12$
$= x^2 – x – 12$ ✓

5) ESSENTIAL check — EXPAND the brackets to make sure they give the original equation.

But we're not finished yet — we've only factorised it, we still need to...

6) $(x + 3) = 0 \Rightarrow x = –3$
$(x – 4) = 0 \Rightarrow x = 4$

6) SOLVE THE EQUATION by setting each bracket equal to 0.

Factorising quadratics is not easy — but it is important

REVISION TIP

To work out which signs you need, look at c. If c is positive, the signs will be the same (both positive or both negative), but if c is negative they will be different (one positive and one negative).

Extended

Factorising Quadratics

It gets a bit more complicated when a isn't 1, but don't panic — just follow the method on this page.

When 'a' is **Not 1**

The basic method is still the same, but it's a bit trickier — the initial brackets are different as the first terms in each bracket have to multiply to give a. Finding the other numbers to go in the brackets is harder as there are more combinations to try. The best way to get to grips with it is to have a look at an example.

EXAMPLE: Solve $3x^2 + 7x - 6 = 0$.

1) $3x^2 + 7x - 6 = 0$

2) $(3x\quad)(x\quad) = 0$

3) Number pairs: 1×6 and 2×3

> $(3x\quad 1)(x\quad 6)$ multiplies to give $18x$ and $1x$ which add/subtract to give $17x$ or $19x$
>
> $(3x\quad 6)(x\quad 1)$ multiplies to give $3x$ and $6x$ which add/subtract to give $9x$ or $3x$
>
> $(3x\quad 3)(x\quad 2)$ multiplies to give $6x$ and $3x$ which add/subtract to give $9x$ or $3x$
>
> $(3x\quad 2)(x\quad 3)$ multiplies to give $9x$ and $2x$ which add/subtract to give $11x$ or $\boxed{7x}$ ✓

   $(3x\quad 2)(x\quad 3)$

4) $(3x - 2)(x + 3)$

5) $(3x - 2)(x + 3) = 3x^2 + 9x - 2x - 6$
    $= 3x^2 + 7x - 6$ ✓

6) $(3x - 2) = 0 \Rightarrow x = \frac{2}{3}$
    $(x + 3) = 0 \Rightarrow x = -3$

1) Rearrange into the standard format.

2) Write down the initial brackets — this time, one of the brackets will have a $3x$ in it.

3) The tricky part: first, find pairs of numbers that multiply to give c ($= 6$), ignoring the minus sign for now.

   Then, try out the number pairs you just found in the brackets until you find one that gives $7x$. But remember, each pair of numbers has to be tried in 2 positions (as the brackets are different — one has $3x$ in it).

4) Now fill in the +/– signs so that 9 and 2 add/subtract to give $+7$ ($= b$).

5) ESSENTIAL check — EXPAND the brackets.

6) SOLVE THE EQUATION by setting each bracket equal to 0 (if a isn't 1, one of your answers will be a fraction).

EXAMPLE: Solve $2x^2 - 9x = 5$.

1) Put in the standard format: $2x^2 - 9x - 5 = 0$

2) Initial brackets: $(2x\quad)(x\quad) = 0$

3) Number pairs: 1×5

> $(2x\quad 5)(x\quad 1)$ multiplies to give $2x$ and $5x$ which add/subtract to give $3x$ or $7x$
>
> $(2x\quad 1)(x\quad 5)$ multiplies to give $1x$ and $10x$ which add/subtract to give $\boxed{9x}$ or $11x$ ✓

   $(2x\quad 1)(x\quad 5)$

4) Put in the signs: $(2x + 1)(x - 5)$

5) Check:
    $(2x + 1)(x - 5) = 2x^2 - 10x + x - 5$
    $= 2x^2 - 9x - 5$ ✓

6) Solve:
    $(2x + 1) = 0 \Rightarrow x = -\frac{1}{2}$
    $(x - 5) = 0 \Rightarrow x = 5$

Factorising quadratics when 'a' is not 1 is quite a lot harder

The problem is that it's a lot harder to work out the right combination of numbers to go in the brackets. Don't get stressed out — just take your time and work through the possibilities one at a time.

Extended

The Quadratic Formula

The solutions to ANY quadratic equation $ax^2 + bx + c = 0$ are given by this formula:

$$x = \frac{-b \pm \sqrt{b^2 - 4ac}}{2a}$$

LEARN THIS FORMULA — and how to use it. It WON'T be given to you in the exam, so it's important that you spend time memorising it. Using it isn't that hard, but there are a few mistakes that people often make — so DON'T FORGET these important details:

Quadratic Formula — Five **Important Details**

1) Take it nice and slowly — always write it down in stages as you go.

2) **WHENEVER YOU GET A MINUS SIGN, YOU SHOULD ALWAYS BE VERY CAREFUL**

3) Remember it's $2a$ on the bottom line, not just a — and you divide ALL of the top line by $2a$.

4) The $\pm$ sign means you end up with two solutions (by replacing it in the final step with '+' and '−').

5) If you get a negative number inside your square root, go back and check your working. Some quadratics do have a negative value in the square root, but they won't come up in the exam.

If either 'a' or 'c' is negative, the −4ac effectively becomes +4ac, so watch out. Also, be careful if b is negative, as −b will be positive.

Extended

EXAMPLE: **Solve $3x^2 + 7x = 1$, giving your answers to 2 decimal places.**

$3x^2 + 7x - 1 = 0$

$a = 3, \quad b = 7, \quad c = -1$

$x = \dfrac{-b \pm \sqrt{b^2 - 4ac}}{2a}$

$= \dfrac{-7 \pm \sqrt{7^2 - 4 \times 3 \times -1}}{2 \times 3}$

$= \dfrac{-7 \pm \sqrt{49 + 12}}{6}$

$= \dfrac{-7 \pm \sqrt{61}}{6}$

$= \dfrac{-7 + 7.81...}{6}$ or $\dfrac{-7 - 7.81...}{6}$

$= 0.1350...$ or $-2.468...$

So to 2 d.p. the solutions are:
$x = 0.14$ or -2.47

1) First get it into the form $ax^2 + bx + c = 0$.

2) Then carefully identify a, b and c.

3) Put these values into the quadratic formula and write down each stage.

4) Finally, as a check put these values back into the original equation: E.g. for $x = 0.1350...$:
$3 \times 0.1350...^2 + 7 \times 0.1350... = 1$

Notice that you do two calculations at the final stage — one + and one −.

When to use the quadratic formula:
• If you have a quadratic that won't easily factorise.
• If the question mentions decimal places or significant figures.
• If the question asks you to use it.

You will usually get two solutions in these questions

REVISION TIP This formula looks difficult to learn, but after you've said "minus b plus or minus the square root of b squared minus four a c all over 2 a" a few times, you won't be able to forget it.

Completing the Square

There's just one more method to learn for solving quadratics — it's called 'completing the square'.

Solving Quadratics by 'Completing the Square'

To 'complete the square', you have to:

1) Write down a SQUARED bracket, and then   2) Stick a number on the end to 'COMPLETE' it.

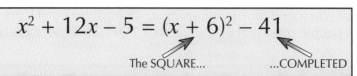

$$x^2 + 12x - 5 = (x + 6)^2 - 41$$

The SQUARE...   ...COMPLETED

It's not that bad if you learn all the steps:

1) As always, REARRANGE THE QUADRATIC INTO THE STANDARD FORMAT: $ax^2 + bx + c$ (the rest of this method is for $a = 1$).

2) WRITE OUT THE INITIAL BRACKET: $\left(x + \frac{b}{2}\right)^2$ — just divide the value of b by 2.

3) MULTIPLY OUT THE BRACKETS and COMPARE TO THE ORIGINAL to find what you need to add or subtract to complete the square.

4) Add or subtract the ADJUSTING NUMBER to make it MATCH THE ORIGINAL.

If a isn't 1, you have to divide through by a or take out a factor of a at the start — see the next page.

EXAMPLE: **a)** Express $x^2 + 8x + 5$ in the form $(x + m)^2 + n$.

1) It's in the standard format. —— $x^2 + 8x + 5$

2) Write out the initial bracket. —— $(x + 4)^2$ Original equation had +5 here...

3) Multiply out the brackets and compare to the original. —— $(x + 4)^2 = x^2 + 8x + 16$ ...so you need −11

$(x + 4)^2 - 11 = x^2 + 8x + 16 - 11$

$= x^2 + 8x + 5$ ✓ —— matches original now!

4) Subtract adjusting number (11).

So the completed square is: $(x + 4)^2 - 11$.

Now use the completed square to solve the equation. There are three more steps for this:

b) Hence solve $x^2 + 8x + 5 = 0$.

$(x + 4)^2 - 11 = 0$

5) Put the number on the other side (+11).

$(x + 4)^2 = 11$

6) Square root both sides (don't forget the ±!) ($\sqrt{\ }$).

$x + 4 = \pm\sqrt{11}$

7) Get x on its own (−4).

$x = -4 \pm \sqrt{11}$

So the two solutions are:

$x = -4 + \sqrt{11} = -0.683$ (3 s.f.) and

$x = -4 - \sqrt{11} = -7.32$ (3 s.f.)

If you really don't like steps 3-4, just remember that the value you need to add or subtract is always $c - \left(\frac{b}{2}\right)^2$.

Make a SQUARE (bracket) and COMPLETE it (add or take away)

Completing the square basically means working out a squared bracket which is almost the same as your quadratic and then working out what has to be added or subtracted to make it the same as the original.

Completing the Square

Completing the square can still be done when a isn't 1 — it just takes an extra step.

Completing the Square When 'a' Isn't 1

If a isn't 1, completing the square is a bit trickier. You follow the same method as on the previous page, but you have to take out a factor of a from the x^2 and x-terms before you start (which often means you get some fractions). This time, the number in the brackets is $\frac{b}{2a}$.

EXAMPLE: Write $2x^2 + 5x + 9$ in the form $a(x + m)^2 + n$.

1) It's in the standard format. —— $2x^2 + 5x + 9$

2) Take out a factor of 2. —— $2\left(x^2 + \frac{5}{2}x\right) + 9$

3) Write out the initial bracket. —— $2\left(x + \frac{5}{4}\right)^2$

4) Multiply out the bracket and compare to the original. —— $2\left(x + \frac{5}{4}\right)^2 = 2x^2 + 5x + \frac{25}{8}$

5) Add on adjusting number $\left(\frac{47}{8}\right)$. —— $2\left(x + \frac{5}{4}\right)^2 + \frac{47}{8} = 2x^2 + 5x + \frac{25}{8} + \frac{47}{8}$

$= 2x^2 + 5x + 9$ ✓ —— matches original

Original equation had +9 here...

...so you need $9 - \frac{25}{8} = \frac{47}{8}$

So the completed square is: $2\left(x + \frac{5}{4}\right)^2 + \frac{47}{8}$

The Completed Square Helps You Sketch the Graph

You can use the completed square to work out important details about the graph — like the turning point (maximum or minimum) and whether it crosses the x-axis.

1) For a positive quadratic (where the x^2 coefficient is positive), the adjusting number tells you the minimum y-value of the graph. If the completed square is $a(x + m)^2 + n$, this minimum y-value will occur when the brackets are equal to 0 (because the bit in brackets is squared, so is never negative) — i.e. when $x = -m$.

2) The solutions to the equation tell you where the graph crosses the x-axis. If the adjusting number is positive, the graph will never cross the x-axis as it will always be greater than 0 (this means that the quadratic has no solutions that are real numbers).

EXAMPLE: Sketch the graph of $y = 2x^2 + 5x + 9$.

1) From above, completed square form is $2\left(x + \frac{5}{4}\right)^2 + \frac{47}{8}$.

2) The minimum point occurs when the bracket is equal to 0 — this will happen when $x = -\frac{5}{4}$.

3) At this point, the graph takes its minimum value, which is the adjusting number $\left(\frac{47}{8}\right)$.

4) The adjusting number is positive, so the graph will never cross the x-axis.

5) Find where the curve crosses the y-axis by substituting $x = 0$ into the equation and mark this on your graph. $y = 0 + 0 + 9 = 9$

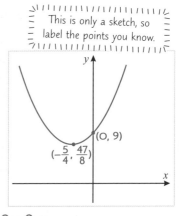

This is only a sketch, so label the points you know.

(graph labels: $(0, 9)$ and $\left(-\frac{5}{4}, \frac{47}{8}\right)$)

Take out a factor of 'a' from the x² and x-terms

REVISION TIP

After you've done that, you can complete the square like usual. When you multiply out the brackets, remember to multiply by the number in front of them. Doing lots of practice will help.

Extended

Warm-Up and Worked Exam Questions

Quadratics probably aren't your favourite topic ever. But once you get used to them, through lots of practice, you'll find a lot of the questions are really similar.

Warm-Up Questions

1) Factorise: a) $x^2 + 11x + 28$ b) $x^2 + 16x + 28$ c) $x^2 + 12x - 28$
2) Solve by factorisation: a) $x^2 + 8x + 15 = 0$ b) $x^2 + 5x - 14 = 0$ c) $x^2 - 7x + 7 = -5$
3) Factorise $3x^2 + 32x + 20$.
4) Solve $3x^2 - 3x = 2$, giving your answers to 2 decimal places.
5) Express $x^2 - 10x + 9$ as a completed square, and hence solve $x^2 - 10x + 9 = 0$.
6) Complete the square for the expression $2x^2 + 16x + 39$.

Worked Exam Questions

If you've got the hang of the warm-up questions, you'll find the exam questions are pretty much the same.

1   The expression $5x^2 - 19x + 18$ is an example of a quadratic expression.

a)   Fully factorise the expression $5x^2 - 19x + 18$.

Number pairs are 1×18, 2×9, 3×6.
$(5x \quad 9)(x \quad 2)$ multiplies to give $9x$ and $10x$ which add to give $19x$.

$$5x^2 - 19x + 18 = (5x - 9)(x - 2)$$

Be careful, you want $-19x$, so the signs are both $-$.

$(5x - 9)(x - 2)$
....
[2 marks]

b)   Use your answer to part a) to solve the equation $5x^2 - 19x + 18 = (x - 2)^2$.

Replace the left-hand side with ————— $(5x - 9)(x - 2) = (x - 2)^2$
the factorisation from part a).

$(5x - 9)(x - 2) - (x - 2)^2 = 0$ ——— Get one side equal to 0.

$(x - 2)((5x - 9) - (x - 2)) = 0$

Factorise — you can take
out a factor of $(x - 2)$ here.

$(x - 2)(4x - 7) = 0$ ——— Tidy up what's inside the brackets.

$x - 2 = 0$ or $4x - 7 = 0$

Set each bracket
equal to 0 and solve.

$x = 2$ or $x = \dfrac{7}{4}$

$x = \underline{\quad 2 \quad}$ or $x = \underline{\dfrac{7}{4}}$
[4 marks]

2   Solve the quadratic equation $x^2 + 5x + 3 = 0$, giving your answers to 2 decimal places.

The question asks for answers 'to 2 decimal places' so it's best to use the quadratic formula.

$a = 1$, $b = 5$ and $c = 3$

$$x = \frac{-b \pm \sqrt{b^2 - 4ac}}{2a} = \frac{-5 \pm \sqrt{5^2 - 4 \times 1 \times 3}}{2 \times 1} = \frac{-5 \pm \sqrt{13}}{2} = -0.697... \text{ or } -4.302...$$

The answers are to 2 d.p. so you ————— $x = \underline{\quad -0.70 \quad}$ or $x = \underline{\quad -4.30 \quad}$
need to include the 0s on the end.
[3 marks]

Exam Questions

3   Solve the equation $3x^2 + 18x + 24 = 0$.

Start by dividing everything by 3.

$x =$ .... or $x =$ ....

[3 marks]

4   The shape on the right is made from a square and a triangle.

The sides of the square are $(x + 3)$ cm long and the height of the triangle is $(2x + 2)$ cm. The area of the whole shape is 60 cm².

Don't forget, a length can't have a negative value.

Find the value of x.

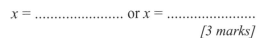
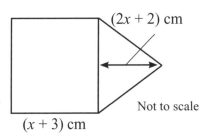

$(2x + 2)$ cm

Not to scale

$(x + 3)$ cm

$x =$ ....

[7 marks]

5   A curve has equation $y = 2x^2 - 8x + 19$.

a)   Write the expression $2x^2 - 8x + 19$ in the form $a(x + b)^2 + c$.

....

[3 marks]

b)   Find the coordinates of the minimum point of the graph of $y = 2x^2 - 8x + 19$.

....

[1 mark]

c)   Does the graph of the equation cross the x-axis? Explain your answer.

Think about the minimum value of the graph.

....

....

[1 mark]

Simultaneous Equations

Simultaneous equations are when you have two equations that you have to solve at the same time. You have to find values of x and y that work in both equations. The rules are quite simple, but you must follow ALL the steps, in the right order, and treat them as a strict method.

There are two types of simultaneous equations:

Where both equations are linear.

1 $2x = 6 - 4y$ and $-3 - 3y = 4x$

Where one is quadratic.

2 $7x + y = 1$ and $2x^2 - y = 3$

1 Six Steps for **Linear Simultaneous Equations**

Solve the simultaneous equations $2x = 6 - 4y$ and $-3 - 3y = 4x$.

1) Rearrange both equations into the form $ax + by = c$, and label the two equations ① and ②.

a, b and c are numbers (which can be negative)

$2x + 4y = 6$ — ①

$-4x - 3y = 3$ — ②

2) Match up the numbers in front (the 'coefficients') of either the x's or y's in both equations. You may need to multiply one or both equations by a suitable number. Relabel them ③ and ④.

① × 2: $4x + 8y = 12$ — ③

$-4x - 3y = 3$ — ④

3) Add or subtract the two equations to eliminate the terms with the same coefficient.

③ + ④ $0x + 5y = 15$

4) Solve the resulting equation.

$5y = 15 \Rightarrow y = 3$

If the coefficients have the same sign (both +ve or both –ve) then subtract. If the coefficients have opposite signs (one +ve and one –ve) then add.

5) Substitute the value you've found back into equation ① and solve it.

Sub $y = 3$ into ①: $2x + (4 × 3) = 6 \Rightarrow 2x + 12 = 6 \Rightarrow 2x = -6 \Rightarrow x = -3$

6) Substitute both these values into equation ② to make sure it works. If it doesn't then you've done something wrong and you'll have to do it all again.

Sub x and y into ②: $(-4 × -3) - (3 × 3) = 12 - 9 = 3$, which is right, so it's worked.
So the solutions are: $x = -3$, $y = 3$

Make sure to check that your answers work

In the exam, always put your values of x and y into the other equation to make sure they work — it's the best way to spot if you've made a mistake and could save you some valuable marks.

Simultaneous Equations

2 Seven Steps for **TRICKY** Simultaneous Equations

EXAMPLE: Solve these two equations simultaneously:

$$7x + y = 1 \quad \text{and} \quad 2x^2 - y = 3$$

1) Rearrange the quadratic equation so that you have the non-quadratic unknown on its own. Label the two equations ① and ②.

$$7x + y = 1 \quad — \quad ①$$
$$y = 2x^2 - 3 \quad — \quad ②$$

2) Substitute the quadratic expression into the other equation. You'll get another equation — label it ③.

$$7x + y = 1 \quad — \quad ①$$
$$y = \boxed{2x^2 - 3} \quad — \quad ②$$

$$\Rightarrow 7x + (2x^2 - 3) = 1 \quad — \quad ③$$

In this example, put the expression for y into equation ① in place of y.

3) Rearrange to get a quadratic equation. And guess what... You've got to solve it.

$$2x^2 + 7x - 4 = 0$$
$$(2x - 1)(x + 4) = 0$$
So $2x - 1 = 0$ OR $x + 4 = 0$
$\quad x = 0.5$ OR $x = -4$

Remember — if it won't factorise, you can use the formula. Have a look at p.65 for more details.

4) Put the first value back in one of the original equations (pick the easy one).

① $7x + y = 1$

Substitute in $x = 0.5$: $3.5 + y = 1$, so $y = 1 - 3.5 = -2.5$

5) Put the second value back in the same original equation (the easy one again).

① $7x + y = 1$

Substitute in $x = -4$: $-28 + y = 1$, so $y = 1 + 28 = 29$

6) Substitute both pairs of answers back into the other original equation to check they work.

② $y = 2x^2 - 3$

Substitute in $x = 0.5$: $y = (2 \times 0.25) - 3 = -2.5$
Substitute in $x = -4$: $y = (2 \times 16) - 3 = 29$

7) Write the pairs of answers out again, clearly, at the bottom of your working.

The two pairs of solutions are: $x = 0.5, y = -2.5$ and $x = -4, y = 29$

Extended

Remember to write out the two pairs clearly

You're basically combining the two equations to make one quadratic equation, so you need to make sure you can also solve quadratic equations before attempting these questions.

Solving Equations Using Graphs

You can also use graphs to solve simultaneous equations — just plot the graph of each equation, and the solutions are the points where the graphs cross (you can usually just read off the coordinates from the graph).

Plot **Both Graphs** and See Where They **Cross**

 **EXAMPLE:** Draw the graphs of $y = 2x + 3$ and $y = 6 - 4x$ and use the diagram to solve the equations simultaneously.

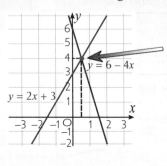

1) DRAW BOTH GRAPHS.

 There's more on drawing straight-line graphs on p.86.

2) LOOK FOR WHERE THE GRAPHS CROSS.

The straight lines cross at one point.
Reading the x- and y- values of this point
gives the solution $x = \frac{1}{2}$ and $y = 4$.

If you were asked for the point where the graphs cross, give your answer in coordinate form — i.e. (x, y).

The point at which the two graphs cross is actually the solution you'd find if you set the two equations equal to each other (so in the first example, you're actually solving $2x + 3 = 6 - 4x$).
This fact comes in handy for the next (trickier) example.

EXAMPLE: The equation $y = x^2 - 4x + 3$ is shown on the graph below.
By drawing a suitable straight line, solve the equation $x^2 - 5x + 3 = 0$.

1) WORK OUT WHICH STRAIGHT LINE YOU NEED.

This is a bit tricky — you need to rearrange
the given equation $x^2 - 5x + 3 = 0$ so that
you have $x^2 - 4x + 3$ (the graph) on one side.

$x^2 - 5x + 3 = 0$

Adding x to both sides:

The sides of this equation represent the two graphs $y = x^2 - 4x + 3$ and $y = x$.

$x^2 - 4x + 3 = x$

So the line needed is $y = x$.

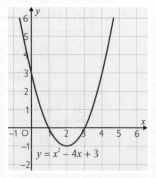

2) DRAW IN THE LINE AND READ OFF THE SOLUTIONS.

Once you have two graphs, read off
the x-values where they cross.

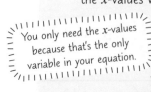 You only need the x-values because that's the only variable in your equation.

The graphs cross at two points.
Reading the x-values of these points
gives the solutions $x = 0.7$ and $x = 4.3$.

The actual solutions are $0.69722...$ and $4.30277...$
You won't be expected to read the graph to that level of
accuracy, so you'll get the marks if you're near enough.

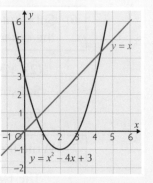

Extended

The solutions are where the graphs intersect

EXAM TIP Try to be as accurate as possible with your drawings. If either of your graphs are wrong,
then the intersections will be in the wrong place and you'll end up with the wrong solutions.

Inequalities

Inequalities aren't as difficult as they look. Once you've learned how they work, most of the algebra for them is identical to ordinary equations (have a look back at p.55-56 if you need a reminder).

Algebra with Inequalities

The key thing about inequalities is to solve them just like regular equations but WITH ONE EXCEPTION:

> **Whenever you MULTIPLY OR DIVIDE by a NEGATIVE NUMBER, you must FLIP THE INEQUALITY SIGN.**

EXAMPLES:

1. x **is an integer such that** $-4 < x \leq 3$.
Write down all the possible values of x.

1) Work out what each bit of the inequality is telling you:

$-4 < x$ means 'x is greater than -4',
$x \leq 3$ means 'x is less than or equal to 3'.

2) Now just write down all the values that x can take.
(Remember, integers are just positive or negative whole numbers.)

$$-3, -2, -1, 0, 1, 2, 3$$

−4 isn't included because of the <, but 3 is included because of the ≤.

2. **Solve** $2x + 7 > x + 11$.

Just solve it like an equation:

$(-7) \quad 2x + 7 - 7 > x + 11 - 7$
$\qquad\quad 2x > x + 4$
$(-x) \quad 2x - x > x + 4 - x$
$\qquad\qquad x > 4$

3. **Solve** $9 - 2x > 15$.

Again, solve it like an equation:

$(-9) \quad 9 - 2x - 9 > 15 - 9$
$\qquad\qquad -2x > 6$
$(\div -2) \quad -2x \div (-2) < 6 \div (-2)$
$\qquad\qquad\quad x < -3$

The > has turned into a <, because we divided by a negative number.

4. **Solve** $-2 \leq \dfrac{x+4}{4} \leq 5$.

1) First multiply everything by 4:

$$4 \times -2 \leq \frac{4 \times (x+4)}{4} \leq 4 \times 5$$
$$-8 \leq x + 4 \leq 20$$

Don't be put off because there are two inequality signs — just do the same thing to each bit of the inequality.

2) Then subtract 4 to finish it off:

$$-8 - 4 \leq x + 4 - 4 \leq 20 - 4$$
$$-12 \leq x \leq 16$$

You Can Show Inequalities on Number Lines

Drawing inequalities on a number line is easy — all you have to remember is that you use an open circle (O) for > or < and a coloured-in circle (●) for ≥ or ≤.

EXAMPLE: Show the inequality $-4 < x \leq 3$ on a number line.

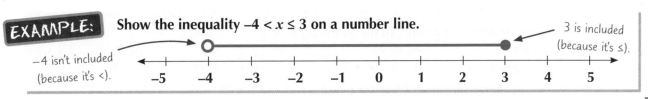

−4 isn't included (because it's <).
3 is included (because it's ≤).

Treat inequalities like equations — but remember the exception

The good news is, if you know how to solve equations, you also know how to solve inequalities. The bad news is, if you forget to flip the inequality sign when dividing by a negative number, you'll lose marks.

Extended

Graphical Inequalities

These questions always involve drawing straight-line graphs and then shading regions on a graph.

Showing **Inequalities** on a **Graph**

There are four steps for finding the region that satisfies some inequalities:

EXAMPLE: a) **Find the region that satisfies all three of the following inequalities:**
$$x + y < 5 \qquad y \leq x + 2 \qquad y > 1$$

1) CONVERT EACH INEQUALITY TO AN EQUATION
   by simply putting an '=' in place of the inequality sign. $x + y = 5$, $y = x + 2$ and $y = 1$

2) DRAW THE GRAPH FOR EACH EQUATION (see p.86) — if the
   inequality sign is < or > draw a dashed line, but if it's ≥ or ≤ draw a solid line.

   You need dotted lines for $x + y = 5$ and $y = 1$ and a solid line for $y = x + 2$.

3) WORK OUT WHICH SIDE OF EACH LINE YOU WANT — put a point (usually
   the origin, (0, 0)) into the inequality to see if it's on the correct side of the line.

   $x + y < 5$: $x = 0$, $y = 0$ gives $0 < 5$, which is **true**.
   This means the origin is on the **correct** side of the line.

   $y \leq x + 2$: $x = 0$, $y = 0$ gives $0 \leq 2$, which is **true**.
   So the origin is on the **correct** side of this line.

   $y > 1$: $x = 0$, $y = 0$ gives $0 > 1$, which is **false**.
   So the origin is on the **wrong** side of this line.

   Dashed lines mean the region doesn't include the points on the line.   A solid line means the region does include the points on the line.

   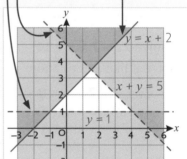

4) SHADE THE UNWANTED REGIONS — then
   the bit that isn't shaded is the region you want.

   Shade the regions that **don't** satisfy the inequalities:
   • above $x + y = 5$ (because the origin **isn't** on this side),
   • above $y = x + 2$ (because the origin **isn't** on this side),
   • below $y = 1$ (because the origin **is** on this side).

Extended (left margin)   *Extended* (right margin)

Finding the **Optimum Point** in your region

You might have to find the maximum or minimum value of a quantity within the region you've found.
The maximum or minimum value will always be at one of the corners of your region, unless:

• you have < or > inequalities — any points on a dashed line are not included in the region.
• the variables (usually x and y) are integers and the corners do not have integer values.

In these cases you will have to test other values in the region, not just the corners (see below).

EXAMPLE: b) **Given that x and y are integers, find the maximum value of**
$$S = 3x + 2y, \text{ where } x + y < 5, \, y \leq x + 2 \text{ and } y > 1.$$

1) Write down all the points in the region that you need to check.

   The points satisfying all conditions are (0, 2), (1, 2) (2, 2) and (1, 3).

   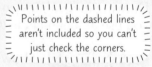
   Points on the dashed lines aren't included so you can't just check the corners.

2) Test these values of x and y in the formula for S:

   At (0, 2):   At (1, 2):   At (2, 2):   At (1, 3):
   $S = 0 + 4 = 4$ $S = 3 + 4 = 7$ $S = 6 + 4 = 10$ $S = 3 + 6 = 9$

   So the maximum value of S is 10 (when $x = 2$ and $y = 2$).

EXAM TIP

Remember to shade the regions you <u>don't</u> want

Testing the inequalities using (0, 0) makes the calculations easy. However, if (0, 0) is on one of
the lines, you might have to use a different point — just pick one that's easy to use, e.g. (1, 1).

Warm-Up and Worked Exam Questions

Have a go at these warm-up questions and check that you're comfortable with them before moving on to the exam questions. If you find anything a bit tricky, go back and read over it until you understand it.

Warm-Up Questions

1) Solve these simultaneous equations:
   a) $y = x$
   $y = 9 - 2x$
   b) $y = 2x$
   $y = x + 1$
   c) $x + y = 5$
   $x - y = 1$

2) Solve the simultaneous equations $2x + 3y = 19$ and $2x + y = 9$.

3) Find x and y, given that $2x - 10 = 4y$ and $3y = 5x - 18$.

4) Solve the simultaneous equations $y = 2 - 3x$ and $y + 2 = x^2$.

5) By sketching the graphs, find the solutions of the simultaneous equations $y = 4x - 4$ and $y = 6 - x$.

6) Solve these inequalities: a) $2q + 2 \leq 12$ b) $4p + 12 > 30$

7) a) On the same axis, draw the graphs of $y = 0$, $y = 2x$, $y = 6 - x$.
   b) R is the region defined by the inequalities $y \leq 2x$, $y \leq 6 - x$, $y \geq 0$. Label this region R.

Worked Exam Questions

To ease you into the exam questions on the next page, I've done two for you (aren't I kind?). Have a look at these worked exam questions, and make sure you understand each step.

1   Solve this pair of simultaneous equations.

$4x + 3y = 16$ ①
$4x + 2y = 12$ ②

①－②: $4x + 3y = 16$
         $- 4x + 2y = 12$
              $y = 4$

Eliminate the x term by subtracting the equations

Substitute $y = 4$ into equation ① $4x + (3 \times 4) = 16$
$4x = 4$ so $x = 1$

Check your answer by putting $x = 1$ and $y = 4$ into ① $(4 \times 1) + (3 \times 4) = 16$ ✓

$x = \underline{\quad 1 \quad}$ $y = \underline{\quad 4 \quad}$

[2 marks]

2   Clare wants to use the graph of $4x^2 - 3x + 2$ to solve the equation $4x^2 - 4x - 1 = 0$. Find the equation of the straight line she should draw on the graph.

Rearrange the equation that Clare wants to solve so that it has $4x^2 - 3x + 2$ on one side.

$4x^2 - 4x - 1 = 0$
$4x^2 - 4x - 1 + (x + 3) = 0 + (x + 3)$
$4x^2 - 3x + 2 = x + 3$

The expression on the other side is the line that she needs to draw.

$y = x + 3$

[2 marks]

Extended

Exam Questions

3   Solve this pair of simultaneous equations.

        $2x + 3y = 12$
        $5x + 4y = 9$

                            $x = ... , \quad y = ...$
                                      [4 marks]

4   By drawing two straight lines on the grid
    provided, solve these simultaneous equations:

        $y = x + 1$
        $y = \frac{1}{3}x + 3$

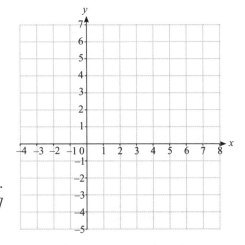

            $x = ... , \quad y = ...$
                    [3 marks]

5   Look at the grid on the right.

    a)   On the grid, draw the region
           that satisfies these inequalities:

           $x < 4$

           $y \geq 3$

           $y - x \leq 1$

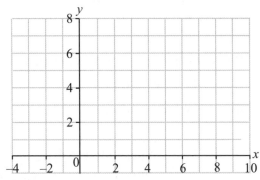

                        [4 marks]

    b)   Find the integer values of x and y that minimise the value of
           $D = 3y - 4x$, where $x < 4$, $y \geq 3$ and $y - x \leq 1$.

                        Points on a dashed line are
                        not included in the region.

                            $x = ... , \quad y = ...$
                                      [3 marks]

6   Solve the following pair of simultaneous equations.

        $2x^2 + y = 51$
        $y = (x + 6)^2$

                          $x = ... , \quad y = ...$

        and $x = ... , \quad y = ...$
                                      [6 marks]

Extended

Extended

Sequences

Sequences are lists of numbers or shapes that follow a rule. You need to be able to spot what the rule is.

Finding **the Rule** for **Number Sequences**

The trick to finding the rule for number sequences is to write down what you have to do to get from one number to the next in the gaps between the numbers. There are 2 main types to look out for:

1) Add or subtract the same number   These are known as linear sequences.

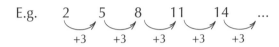   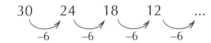

The RULE: 'Add 3 to the previous term'   'Subtract 6 from the previous term'

2) Multiply or divide by the same number each time   These are known as exponential sequences.

The RULE: 'Multiply the previous term by 3'   'Divide the previous term by 10'

Sometimes you might get sequences that follow a different rule — e.g. you might have to add or subtract a changing number each time, or add together the two previous terms (see the examples below).

EXAMPLE: **Find the next two terms in each of the following sequences.**

a) 1, 3, 6, 10, 15, ...

'The number you add on increases by one each time' (i.e. +2, +3, +4, …) so the next two terms are:

15 + 6 = 21   This is the sequence of
21 + 7 = 28   triangular numbers.

b) 1, 1, 2, 3, 5, ...

The rule is 'add together the two previous terms', so the next two terms are:

3 + 5 = 8   This is known as the
5 + 8 = 13   Fibonacci sequence.

Finding **the Rule** for **Shape Sequences**

If you have a sequence of shape patterns, you need to be able to continue the sequence. You might also have to find the rule for the sequence to work out how many shapes there'll be in a later pattern.

EXAMPLE: **On the right, there are some patterns made of circles.**
a) Draw the next pattern in the sequence.
b) Work out how many circles there will be in the 10th pattern.

a) Just continue the sequence — the circles make a square pattern.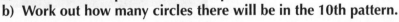

b) Find the rule for the number of circles: there's $1^2 = 1$ circle in the first pattern, $2^2 = 4$ circles in the second pattern, $3^2 = 9$ circles in the third pattern etc. The rule is 'square the number of the pattern'. So in the 10th pattern, there'll be $10^2 = 100$ circles.

Always write the change in the gaps between the numbers

It's the most straightforward way to spot the pattern. If you do this, you'll see straight away if the difference is the same, changing by a certain amount, or multiplying. Read on to learn more about sequences...

Sequences

You might be asked to "find an expression for the *n*th term of a sequence" — this is a rule with *n* in, like $5n - 3$. It gives every term in a sequence when you put in different values for *n*.

Finding the **nth Term** of a **Sequence**

This method works for linear sequences — where you add or subtract the same number each time.

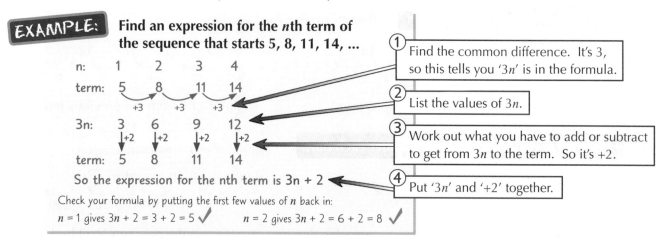

EXAMPLE: **Find an expression for the *n*th term of the sequence that starts 5, 8, 11, 14, ...**

① Find the common difference. It's 3, so this tells you '3*n*' is in the formula.

② List the values of 3*n*.

③ Work out what you have to add or subtract to get from 3*n* to the term. So it's +2.

④ Put '3*n*' and '+2' together.

So the expression for the nth term is 3n + 2

Check your formula by putting the first few values of *n* back in:
$n = 1$ gives $3n + 2 = 3 + 2 = 5$ ✓ $n = 2$ gives $3n + 2 = 6 + 2 = 8$ ✓

Deciding if a Term is in a Sequence

You might be given the *n*th term and asked if a certain value is in the sequence. The trick here is to set the expression equal to that value and solve to find *n*. If *n* is a whole number, the value is in the sequence.

EXAMPLE: **The *n*th term of a sequence is given by $n^2 - 2$.**

Have a look at p.56 for more on solving equations.

a) **Find the 6th term in the sequence.**

This is dead easy — just put $n = 6$ into the expression:
$6^2 - 2 = 36 - 2$
$= 34$

b) **Is 45 a term in this sequence?**

Set it equal to 45... $n^2 - 2 = 45$
$n^2 = 47$ ...and solve for n.
$n = \sqrt{47} = 6.8556...$

n is not a whole number, so 45 is **not** in the sequence.

Some Questions use **Special Notation**

Extended

You might see a question use subscript notation to describe a sequence. This isn't too complicated — you just need to recognise it:

 x_n means "the *n*th term in the sequence". E.g. x_1 is the first term, x_{20} is the 20th term, etc.

EXAMPLE: **A sequence is defined by $x_n = 5n - 3$. Find:**

a) x_{10}
This is just asking for the 10th term, so set $n = 10$:
$x_{10} = 5(10) - 3 = 50 - 3 = 47$

b) $x_6 - x_4$
Find the 6th term... $x_6 = 5(6) - 3 = 30 - 3 = 27$
...and the 4th term... $x_4 = 5(4) - 3 = 20 - 3 = 17$
...and subtract. $x_6 - x_4 = 27 - 17 = 10$

Follow the steps above to find the nth term of a linear sequence

Once you've found the *n*th term rule, you can use it to easily find the 500th term, or even the 500 000th term — if you tried to work these out without it, you'd need lots of extra sheets of paper and a spare pen.

Sequences

Now you know how to find the *n*th term of a linear sequence, let's look at some trickier types of sequence.

Quadratic and Cubic Sequences

Quadratic means the nth term will contain an n^2 term. Cubic means the nth term will contain an n^3 term.

If the terms in a sequence are increasing by a different amount each time, it might be a quadratic or cubic sequence. There are two methods you can use for these.

Easy Ones — Compare to the Square or Cube Numbers

The easy method is to compare the sequence to the list of square or cube numbers and add/subtract what you need.

Square numbers: 1, 4, 9, 16, 25, ... $\longrightarrow$ *n*th term = n^2

Cube numbers: 1, 8, 27, 64, 125, ... $\longrightarrow$ *n*th term = n^3

EXAMPLE: **Find an expression for the nth term of the sequence 2, 5, 10, 17, ...**

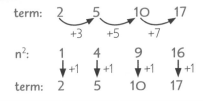

term: 2   5   10   17
        +3 +5 +7

n^2:   1   4   9   16
        +1 +1 +1 +1

term: 2   5   10   17

The sequence increases by a different amount each time. Try comparing the sequence to n^2.

To get from n^2 to each term you add 1.

So the expression for the nth term is $n^2 + 1$

Hard Ones — Find the Second or Third Difference

For harder sequences, you need to work out the differences between the differences, called the second differences, and sometimes the third differences as well. These can tell you what kind of sequence it is:

Constant second difference k:
Quadratic sequence with $\frac{k}{2}n^2$ term

Constant third difference k:
Cubic sequence with $\frac{k}{6}n^3$ term

Be careful — you divide by 6 for cubic sequences, not 3.

EXAMPLE: **Find the *n*th term of the sequence that starts 4, 11, 22, 37...**

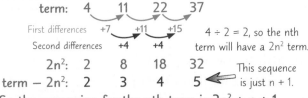

term: 4   11   22   37

First differences   +7   +11   +15

Second differences   +4   +4

$2n^2$:   2   8   18   32

term − $2n^2$:   2   3   4   5

$4 \div 2 = 2$, so the nth term will have a $2n^2$ term.

This sequence is just $n + 1$.

So the expression for the nth term is $2n^2 + n + 1$

1) Find the differences (first, second, third) until you get the same number each time.
2) Use the rules above to find the quadratic or cubic term.
3) Subtract this term from each term in the sequence. This will give you a simpler sequence that you can work with.

Exponential Sequences

The rule for sequences where you multiply by the same number each time is actually quite easy, as long as you remember the rule:

*n*th term = $a \times r^{(n-1)}$
where a is the first term and r is what you multiply by each time.

EXAMPLE: **An exponential sequence x_n starts 6, 12, 24, 48, 96...**
a) Find the *n*th term of the sequence.

The first term is 6, and you multiply by 2 each time.
So the nth term is $6 \times 2^{(n-1)}$

b) Find x_{10}.

Put n = 10 into the formula:
$x_{10} = 6 \times 2^9 = 6 \times 512 = 3072$

REVISION TIP

Make sure you know the square and cube numbers

Quadratic and cubic sequences are harder if you don't know them — see p.5 for a reminder.

Algebraic Proportion

Proportion questions involve two variables (often x and y) which are linked in some way. You'll have to figure out the relationship between them, and use this to find values of x or y, given one value.

Simple Proportions

∝ means 'is proportional to'.

The easiest types of proportions you can get are direct proportion ($y \propto x$) and inverse proportion ($y \propto \frac{1}{x}$).

Direct Proportion — BOTH INCREASE TOGETHER

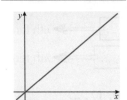

The graph is a straight line through the origin: $y = kx$

If it doesn't go through the origin, it's not a direct proportion.

Inverse Proportion — One INCREASES, one DECREASES

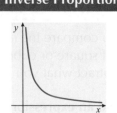

The graph is $y = \frac{k}{x}$.

See p.93 for more on these graphs.

Trickier Proportions

Harder proportions involve y varying proportionally or inversely to some function of x, e.g. x^2, x^3, $\sqrt{x}$.
You can always turn a proportion statement into an equation by replacing '∝' with '$= k$' like this:

	Proportion	Equation
'y is proportional to the square of x'	$y \propto x^2$	$y = kx^2$
't is proportional to the square root of h'	$t \propto \sqrt{h}$	$t = k\sqrt{h}$
'D varies with the cube of t'	$D \propto t^3$	$D = kt^3$
'V is inversely proportional to r cubed'	$V \propto \dfrac{1}{r^3}$	$V = \dfrac{k}{r^3}$

k is just a constant (unknown number).

Handling Questions on Proportion

1) Use the information in the question to write down a proportion statement.

2) Replace '∝' with '$= k$' to make an equation (as above).

Once you've got it in the form of an equation with k, the rest is easy.

3) Find a pair of values of x and y somewhere in the question, and substitute them into the equation so that you can find k.

4) Put the value of k into the equation and it's now ready to use, e.g. $y = 3x^2$.

5) They might then ask you to find y, giving you a value for x (or find x from y).

> **EXAMPLE:** **G is inversely proportional to the square root of H. When $G = 2$, $H = 16$.**
> **Find an equation for G in terms of H, and use it to find the value of G when $H = 36$.**
>
> 1) Write as a proportion. $G \propto \dfrac{1}{\sqrt{H}}$
>
> 2) Replace ∝ with '$= k$' to form an equation. $G = \dfrac{k}{\sqrt{H}}$
>
> 3) Use the values of G and H (2 and 16) to find k. $2 = \dfrac{k}{\sqrt{16}} = \dfrac{k}{4} \Rightarrow k = 8$
>
> 4) Put the value of k back into the equation. $G = \dfrac{8}{\sqrt{H}}$ — This is the equation for G in terms of H.
>
> 5) Use your equation to find the value of G. $G = \dfrac{8}{\sqrt{H}} = \dfrac{8}{\sqrt{36}}$
> $= \dfrac{8}{6}$
> $= \dfrac{4}{3}$

Don't let proportion questions confuse you

EXAM TIP As soon as you see the word "proportional" in an exam question, write the information down as a proportion statement. Then just convert it into an equation, and you've done the hard part.

Warm-Up and Worked Exam Questions

OK, the topics in this section look a bit nasty — but for all of them, it's just a case of learning the symbols and methods and practising lots of questions...

Warm-Up Questions

1) Write down the next two terms in each of these sequences:
   a) 2, 6, 10, 14...   b) 1, 3, 9, 27...   c) 2, 3, 5, 8, 12...

2) Find an expression for the nth term of these sequences:
   a) 2, 3, 4, 5...   b) 2, 8, 18, 32, 50...

3) Find an expression for the nth term of the sequence: 2, 6, 18, 54...

4) Write each of the following as an equation:
   a) A is proportional to the square of r b) $D \propto \dfrac{1}{R}$

   c) H is inversely proportional to the cube of D d) $V \propto S^3$

Worked Exam Questions

I'll show you how to do these exam questions, then you're on your own for the questions on the next page. Enjoy.

1   A sequence starts 2, 9, 16, 23, ... The expression for the nth term of this sequence is $7n - 5$.

   a)   What is the 30th term of the sequence?

   30th term = (7 × 30) − 5 = 205

   ....205.........
   [1 mark]

   b)   Is 55 a term in this sequence? Explain your answer.

   If 55 is a term in the sequence, then 7n − 5 = 55, 7n = 60 so n = 8.571...

   n is not a whole number, so 55 is not a term in the sequence.

   [2 marks]

2   The gravitational force, f, between two objects is inversely proportional to the square of the distance, d, between them. When $d = 100$, $f = 20$. Write an equation connecting f and d and use it to find the value of f when $d = 800$.

   $f \propto \dfrac{1}{d^2}$, so $f = \dfrac{k}{d^2}$

   When d = 100 and f = 20, $20 = \dfrac{k}{100^2}$, so k = 20 × 100² = 200 000

   So the equation is $f = \dfrac{200\,000}{d^2}$

   When d = 800, $f = \dfrac{200\,000}{800^2}$ = 0.3125

   $f =$ ....0.3125..........
   [3 marks]

Exam Questions

3   The patterns in the sequence below represent the first three triangle numbers.

a)   Draw the next pattern in the sequence.

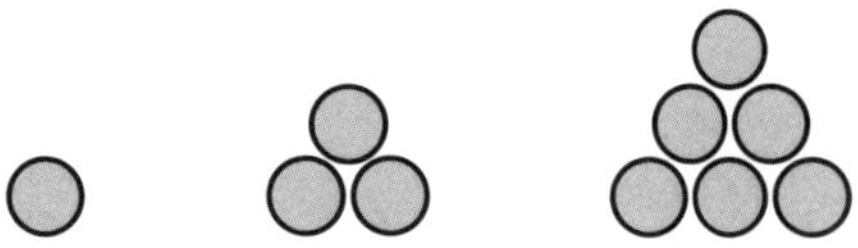

[1 mark]

b)   How many circles are in the tenth pattern in the sequence? Give a reason for your answer.

....

....

[2 marks]

4   A quadratic sequence starts 2, 6, 12, 20, …
Find the next term in the sequence.

Find the pattern in the differences between each pair of terms and use this to find the next term.

....
[2 marks]

5   Habib is playing an online game. The score he gets, S, in the game
is inversely proportional to the time taken, t seconds, to complete the game.

a)   Habib completes the game in 15 seconds and gets a score of 6000 points.
Express S in terms of d.

....
[3 marks]

b)   On the axes to the right,
sketch the graph of S against d.

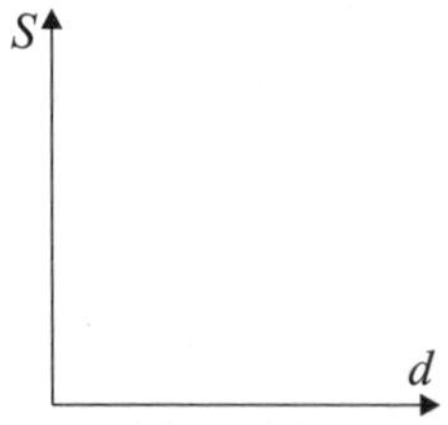

[1 mark]

6   The nth terms of two sequences are given by $x_n = n^3 - 3n + 2$ and $y_n = x_{n+1} - x_n$.
Find a formula for the nth term for y_n in terms of n.

....
[5 marks]

Section Two — Algebra

Revision Questions for Section Two

There's no denying, Section Two has some really nasty maths — so check now how much you've learned.
- Try these questions and tick off each one when you get it right.
- When you've done all the questions for a topic and are completely happy with it, tick off the topic.

Algebra (p.48-60) ☐

1) Simplify by collecting like terms: $3x + 2y - 5 - 6y + 2x$

2) Simplify the following: a) $x^3 \times x^6$ b) $y^7 \div y^5$ c) $(z^3)^{-4}$ d) $t^{\frac{1}{5}} \times t^{-\frac{3}{5}}$

3) Expand these brackets: a) $3(2x + 1)$ b) $(x + 2)(x - 3)$ c) $(x - 1)(x + 3)(x + 5)$

4) Factorise: a) $10xy + 4x^2$ b) $7x^2y + 21xz^2$

5) Factorise: a) $49 - 81p^2q^2$ b) $x^2 + 8xy + 16y^2$

6) Solve these equations: a) $5(x + 2) = 8 + 4(5 - x)$ b) $x^2 - 21 = 3(5 - x^2)$

7) Imran buys d DVDs and c CDs. DVDs cost \$7 each and CDs cost \$5 each. He spends \$$P$ in total. Write a formula for P in terms of d and c.

8) Make p the subject of these: a) $\dfrac{1}{p} + 3q = r$ b) $\dfrac{p}{p + y} = 4$

9) Write $\dfrac{2}{x + 3} + \dfrac{1}{x - 1}$ as a single fraction.

Quadratics (p.63-67) ☐

10) Solve the following by factorising them first: a) $x^2 + 9x + 18 = 0$ b) $5x^2 - 17x - 12 = 0$

11) Find the solutions of these equations (to 2 d.p.) using the quadratic formula:
     a) $x^2 + x - 4 = 0$ b) $5x^2 + 6x = 2$ c) $(2x + 3)^2 = 15$

12) Find the solutions of these equations by completing the square:
     a) $x^2 + 12x + 15 = 0$ b) $2x^2 - 5x = 3$

Simultaneous Equations (p.70-72) ☐

13) Solve the following pair of simultaneous equations: $4x + 5y = 23$ and $3y - x = 7$

14) Solve these simultaneous equations: $y = 3x + 4$ and $x^2 + 2y = 0$

Inequalities (p.73-74) ☐

15) Solve these inequalities: a) $4x + 3 \leq 6x + 7$ b) $-9 \leq 3 - 2x < 5$

16) Show on a graph the region described by these conditions: $x + y \leq 6$, $y > 0.5$, $y \leq 2x - 2$

Sequences (p.77-79) ☐

17) For each of the following sequences, find the next term and write down the rule you used.
     a) 3, 10, 17, 24, ...   b) 1, 4, 16, 64, ...   c) 2, 5, 7, 12, ...

18) Find the expression for the nth term in the following sequences:
     a) 5, 9, 13, 17, ...   b) 11, 8, 5, 2, ...

19) Is 34 a term in the sequence given by the expression $7n - 1$?

20) Find the expression for the nth term in the sequence: 0, 3, 8, 15, 24, ...

21) Find the expression for the nth term in the following sequences:
     a) 7, 70, 700, 7000, ...   b) 3, 12, 33, 72, 135, ...

Algebraic Proportion (p.80) ☐

22) Write the following statement as an equation: "y is proportional to the square of x".

23) p is proportional to the cube of q. When $p = 9$, $q = 3$. Find the value of p when $q = 6$.

Coordinates

To start off with, here's some basic stuff about coordinates which will be really useful for the rest of this section.

The Four **Quadrants**

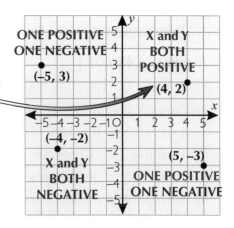

1) A graph has four different quadrants (regions). The top-right region is the easiest because here all the coordinates in it are positive.

2) You have to be careful in the other regions though, because the x- and y-coordinates could be negative, and that makes them much more difficult.

3) Coordinates are always written in brackets like this: (x, y)
    — remember x is across, and y is up.

Finding Coordinates Using **Geometrical Information**

EXAMPLE: **A parallelogram has vertices (3, 1), (5, 4) and (9, 1).**
The x and y coordinates of its fourth vertex are both positive. What are their values?

Do a quick sketch and it's very easy — just mark in the 4th vertex by eye.

Check: to get from (3, 1) to (5, 4) you go along 2 and up 3 — the missing point needs to be the same distance from (9, 1).

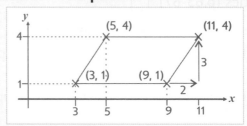

Finding the **Midpoint** of a Line Segment

Finding the coordinates of a midpoint is pretty easy...

> Find the average of the two x-coordinates, then do the same for the y-coordinates.
> These will be the coordinates of the midpoint.

A line segment is part of a line. Lines continue forever in both directions, but line segments have two end points. Things that are actually line segments are often referred to as lines though.

EXAMPLE: **Point P has coordinates (8, 3) and point Q has coordinates (−4, 8).**
Find the midpoint of the line PQ.

See p.152 for finding the length of a line segment.

1) Average of x-coordinates $= \dfrac{8 + (-4)}{2} = 2$

2) Average of y-coordinates $= \dfrac{3 + 8}{2} = 5.5$

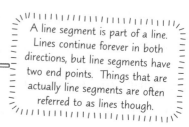

So, coordinates of midpoint = (2, 5.5)

Extended

Midpoints — add the x's together and halve, then do the same for the y's

Don't forget the basics otherwise you'll lose marks needlessly — x comes before y in (x, y), and x goes aCROSS while y goes up and down. Finding a line's midpoint is as simple as finding the average of the x's and y's.

Straight-Line Graphs

There are some straight lines you should be able to immediately recognise from their equation.

Horizontal and Vertical lines: 'x = a' and 'y = a'

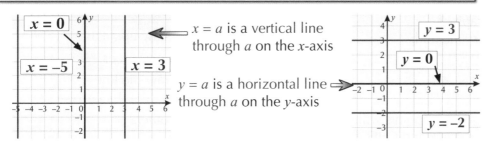

$x = a$ is a vertical line through a on the x-axis

$y = a$ is a horizontal line through a on the y-axis

A common error is to mix up $x = 3$ and $y = 3$, etc. Remember — all the points on $x = 3$ have an x-coordinate of 3, and all the points on $y = 3$ have a y-coordinate of 3.

The Main Diagonals: 'y = x' and 'y = −x'

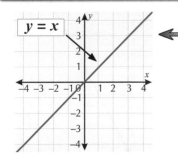

$y = x$ is the main diagonal that goes UPHILL from left to right.

The x- and y-coordinates of each point are the same.

$y = -x$ is the main diagonal that goes DOWNHILL from left to right.

The x- and y-coordinates of each point are negatives of each other, e.g. $(-4, 4)$.

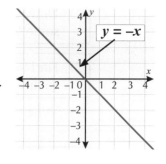

Other Sloping Lines Through the Origin: 'y = ax' and 'y = −ax'

$y = ax$ and $y = -ax$ are the equations for A SLOPING LINE THROUGH THE ORIGIN

The value of a (known as the gradient) tells you the steepness of the line. The bigger a is, the steeper the slope. A MINUS SIGN tells you it slopes DOWNHILL.

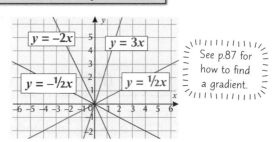

See p.87 for how to find a gradient.

Learn to Recognise Straight Lines from Their Equations

All other straight-line equations just contain 'something x, something y and a number'.

EXAMPLE:

Decide whether each of the following are equations of straight lines.

$$2y - 4x = 7 \qquad y = x^2 + 3 \qquad xy + 3 = 0 \qquad 6y - 8 = x \qquad \frac{2}{y} - \frac{1}{x} = 7$$

Straight lines: $2y - 4x = 7$
                  $6y - 8 = x$

These equations only have something x, something y and a number. These 'terms' can be added or subtracted in any order.

Not straight lines: $y = x^2 + 3$
                      $xy + 3 = 0$
                      $\frac{2}{y} - \frac{1}{x} = 7$

x^2, xy, $\frac{2}{y}$ and $\frac{1}{x}$ mean that these aren't straight-line equations.

REVISION TIP

Simple lines you have to learn

Vertical line: $x = a$, horizontal line: $y = a$, main diagonals: $y = x$ and $y = -x$. Other types of straight line are a bit harder, but drawing a sketch will help if you're stuck — see the next page for more.

Plotting Straight-Line Graphs

You could be asked to draw a straight-line graph in the exam. We'll cover two methods on this page.

The 'Table of 3 Values' Method

You can easily draw the graph of any equation using this easy method:

Don't forget to use a ruler to draw your line — you can lose exam marks if you don't.

1) Choose 3 values of x and draw up a table.
2) Work out the corresponding y-values.
3) Plot the coordinates and draw the line.

If it's a straight-line equation, the 3 points will be in a straight line with each other. If they aren't, you need to go back and CHECK YOUR WORKING.

EXAMPLE: Draw the graph of $y = 2x - 3$ for values of x from –1 to 4.

1) Draw up a table with some suitable values of x.

x	O	2	4
y			

2) Find the y-values by putting each x-value into the equation:

x	O	2	4
y	–3	1	5

When $x = 4$, $y = 2x - 3$
$= 2 \times 4 - 3 = 5$

3) Plot the points and draw the line.

The table gives the points (O, –3), (2, 1) and (4, 5)

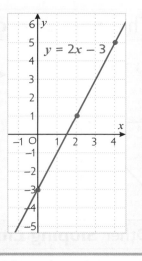

The 'x = 0, y = 0' Method

1) Set $x = 0$ in the equation, and find y — this is where it crosses the y-axis.
2) Set $y = 0$ in the equation and find x — this is where it crosses the x-axis.
3) Plot these two points and join them up with a straight line.

Make sure it's definitely a straight line before using this method — have a look at the previous page to see how you can check.

EXAMPLE: Draw the graph of $3x + 5y = 15$ between $x = -1$ and $x = 6$.

Putting $x = O$ gives "$5y = 15$" $\Rightarrow$ $y = 3$

Putting $y = O$ gives "$3x = 15$" $\Rightarrow$ $x = 5$

So plot (0, 3) and (5, 0) on the graph and join them up with a straight line.

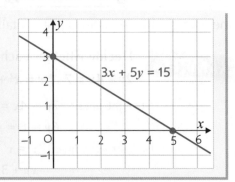

Drawing straight-line graphs isn't as scary with these simple methods

This page gives you two simple methods for drawing straight-line graphs. Usually, you'll be able to use whichever you find easier — but learn them both, just in case you're told to use a specific one in the exam.

Finding the Gradient

There's one more method for drawing straight-line graphs, but first you need to know about gradients.

Finding the **Gradient**

 KEY TERM — The gradient of a line is a measure of its slope. The bigger the number, the steeper the line.

EXAMPLE: Find the gradient of the straight line shown.

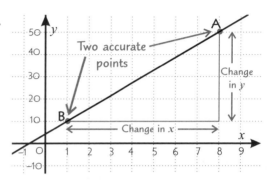

1) Find two accurate points and complete the triangle.

   Choose easy points with positive coordinates.
   Two points that can be read accurately are:
   Point A: (8, 50)   Point B: (1, 10)

2) Find the change in y and the change in x.

   Change in $y = 50 - 10 = 40$
   Change in $x = 8 - 1 = 7$

   Make sure you subtract the x-coordinates the SAME WAY ROUND as you do the y-coordinates.

3) LEARN this formula, and use it:

   $$\text{GRADIENT} = \frac{\text{CHANGE IN Y}}{\text{CHANGE IN X}}$$

   $\text{Gradient} = \frac{40}{7} = 5.71$ (to 3 s.f.)

   Make sure you get the formula the right way up.
   Remember it's VERy HOt — VERtical over HOrizontal.

4) Check the sign is right.

   If it slopes uphill left → right (⟋) then it's positive.
   If it slopes downhill left → right (⟍) then it's negative.

   As the graph goes uphill, the gradient is positive. So the gradient is 5.71 (not –5.71).

You can also use the formula if you're just given the coordinates of two points.

EXAMPLE: Find the gradient of the straight line that goes through (5, 1) and (3, 7).

1) Find the change in y and the change in x.

   Change in $y = 1 - 7 = -6$
   Change in $x = 5 - 3 = 2$

   Here we've done 'coordinates of first point – coordinates of second point'.

2) Use the formula:

   $\text{Gradient} = \dfrac{\text{change in } y}{\text{change in } x} = \dfrac{-6}{2} = -3$

Extended (left margin)   *Extended* (right margin)

 REVISION TASK

Gradient = change in y over change in x

It's really important you feel comfortable with this method for finding gradients — practise by drawing straight lines on a grid and finding their gradient. They come up in lots of graph questions, such as when you're asked to find the equation of a straight line (see the next page).

"y = mx + c"

Using 'y = mx + c' is the simplest way of dealing with straight-line equations, and it's very useful in exams. The first thing you have to do is rearrange the equation into the standard format like this:

Straight line:		Rearranged into 'y = mx + c'	
$y = 2 + 3x$	→	$y = 3x + 2$	(m = 3, c = 2)
$x - y = 0$	→	$y = x + 0$	(m = 1, c = 0)
$4x - 3 = 5y$	→	$y = \frac{4}{5}x - \frac{3}{5}$	(m = $\frac{4}{5}$, c = $-\frac{3}{5}$)

where:
'm' = gradient of the line.
'c' = 'y-intercept' (where it hits the y-axis)

WATCH OUT: people mix up 'm' and 'c' when they get something like $y = 5 + 2x$.
Remember, 'm' is the number in front of the 'x' and 'c' is the number on its own.

Finding the **Equation** of a Straight-Line **Graph**

When you're given the graph itself, it's quick and easy to find the equation of the straight line.

EXAMPLE: **Find the equation of the line on the graph in the form y = mx + c.**

1) Find 'm' (gradient) and 'c' (y-intercept).

$$'m' = \frac{\text{change in } y}{\text{change in } x} = \frac{15}{30} = \frac{1}{2}$$

$$'c' = 15$$

2) Use these to write the equation in the form y = mx + c.

$$y = \frac{1}{2}x + 15$$

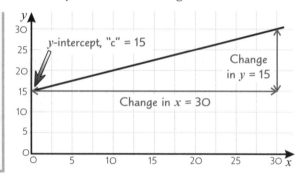

y-intercept, "c" = 15
Change in y = 15
Change in x = 30

Finding the **Equation** of a Line **Through Two Points**

If you're given two points on a line you can find the gradient (see p.87). Then you can use the gradient and one of the points to find the equation of the line.

EXAMPLE: **Find the equation of the straight line that passes through (–2, 9) and (3, –1). Give your answer in the form y = mx + c.**

1) Use the two points to find 'm' (gradient).

$$m = \frac{\text{change in } y}{\text{change in } x} = \frac{-1 - 9}{3 - (-2)} = \frac{-10}{5} = -2$$

So $y = -2x + c$

2) Substitute one of the points into the equation you've just found.

Substitute (–2, 9) into eqn:
$$9 = -2(-2) + c$$
$$9 = 4 + c$$

3) Rearrange the equation to find 'c'.

$$c = 9 - 4$$
$$c = 5$$

4) Substitute back into y = mx + c:

$$y = -2x + 5$$

Sometimes you'll be asked to give your equation in other forms such as $ax + by + c = 0$. Just rearrange your $y = mx + c$ equation to get it in this form.

Extended

m is the gradient and c is the y-intercept

The key thing to remember is that m is the number in front of the *x*, and c is the number on its own. If you remember that, then $y = mx + c$ is a very easy way of identifying straight lines.

Parallel and Perpendicular Lines

On the previous page, you saw how to write the equation of a straight line. You also have to be able to write the equation of a line that's parallel or perpendicular to the straight line you're given.

Parallel Lines

KEY TERM

Parallel lines all have the same gradient.

This means their $y = mx + c$ equations all have the same value of m.
So the lines: $y = 2x + 3$, $y = 2x$ and $y = 2x - 4$ are all parallel.

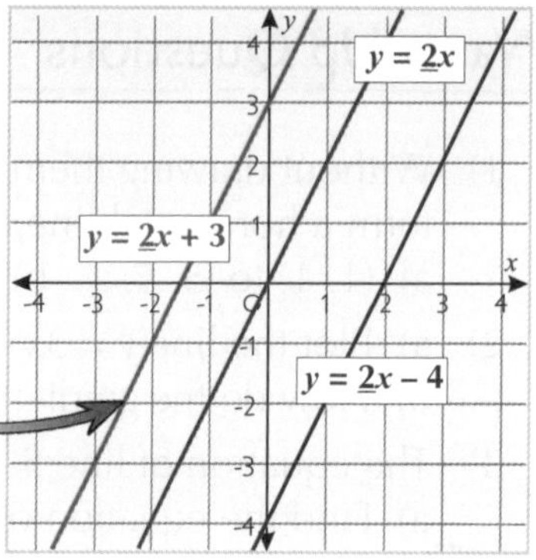

EXAMPLE: **Line J has a gradient of –2. Find the equation of Line K, which is parallel to Line J and passes through the point (3, 4).**

Lines J and K are parallel so their gradients are the same $\Rightarrow$ $m = -2$ ← 1) First find the m value for Line K.

$y = -2x + c$ ← 2) Substitute the value for m into $y = mx + c$ to give you the 'equation so far'.

When $x = 3$, $y = 4$: $4 = (-2 \times 3) + c$ $\Rightarrow 4 = -6 + c \Rightarrow c = 10$ ← 3) Substitute the x and y values for the given point on Line K and solve for c.

$y = -2x + 10$ ← 4) Write out the full equation.

Extended

Perpendicular Lines

KEY TERM

Perpendicular lines cross at a right angle. If you multiply their gradients together you get –1.

So if the gradient of the first line is m, the gradient of the perpendicular line will be $-\frac{1}{m}$, because $m \times -\frac{1}{m} = -1$.

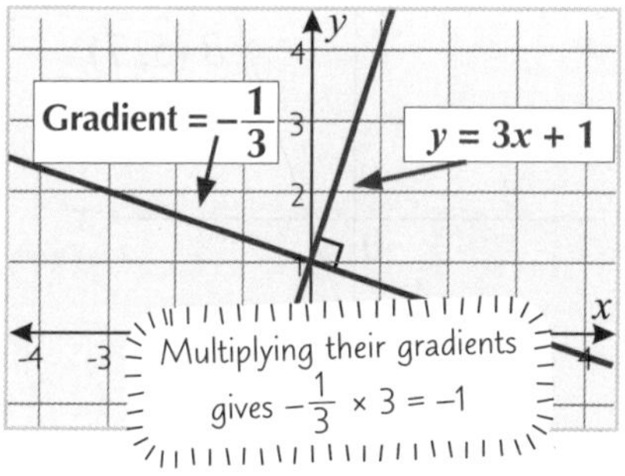

EXAMPLE: **Lines A and B are perpendicular and intersect at (3, 3). If Line A has the equation $3y - x = 6$, what is the equation of Line B?**

Find m (the gradient) for Line A.	$3y - x = 6 \Rightarrow 3y = x + 6$ $\Rightarrow y = \frac{1}{3}x + 2$, so $m_A = \frac{1}{3}$
Find the m value for the perpendicular line (Line B).	$m_B = -\frac{1}{m_A} = -1 \div \frac{1}{3} = -3$
Put this into $y = mx + c$ to give the 'equation so far'.	$y = -3x + c$
Put in the x and y values of the point and solve for c.	$x = 3$, $y = 3$ gives: $3 = (-3 \times 3) + c$ $\Rightarrow 3 = -9 + c \Rightarrow c = 12$
Write out the full equation.	$y = -3x + 12$

Extended

Parallel lines have the same gradient

Perpendicular lines can be a little more tricky, so it's important that you remember that their gradients multiply together to give –1. Make sure the equation of your first line is in the form $y = mx + c$ before you try to find $-\frac{1}{m}$. You should practise finding c using m and a point on the line too.

Warm-Up and Worked Exam Questions

On the day of the exam, you should be confident with straight-line graphs. If you struggle with any of the warm-up questions, go back over the section again before you go any further.

Warm-Up Questions

1) Without drawing them, state whether the lines passing through the following points form a horizontal line, a vertical line, the line $y = x$ or the line $y = -x$.
   a) (1, 1) to (5, 5)   b) (0, 4) to (–3, 4)   c) (–1, 3) to (–1, 7)   d) (4, –4) to (–3, 3).

2) a) Plot the line $y = 3x - 4$.
   b) How do the gradient and y-intercept of $y = 3x + 2$ compare with those of $y = 3x - 4$?

3) The equation of line S is $y = -5x + 1$.
   a) Find the equation of the line which is parallel to line S and passes through the point (0, 4).
   b) Find the gradient of a line which is perpendicular to S.

Worked Exam Question

You know what to do — work carefully through this example and make sure you understand it. Then you can do some exam questions for yourself.

1   Line **L** passes through the points A (0, –3) and B (5, 7), as shown below.

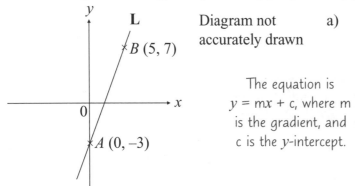

Diagram not accurately drawn

a)   Find the equation of line **L**.

$$m = \frac{\text{change in } y}{\text{change in } x} = \frac{(7 - (-3))}{(5 - 0)}$$

$$m = 2$$

The line passes through (0, –3), so c = –3.

The equation is $y = mx + c$, where m is the gradient, and c is the y-intercept.

$$\underline{y = 2x - 3}$$

[3 marks]

b)   Find the equation of the line which is parallel to line **L** and passes through the point (2, 10).

m = 2, so $y = 2x + c$ ← A line which is parallel to line L will have the same gradient.

10 = (2 × 2) + c ← Substitute in the x and y values of the point to find c.

c = 10 – 4 = 6

So $y = 2x + 6$

$$\underline{y = 2x + 6}$$

[2 marks]

c)   Find the equation of the line which is perpendicular to line **L** and passes through the point (–2, 3).

The gradient of a line which is perpendicular to line L will be $-\frac{1}{m}$.

$$\text{Gradient} = -\frac{1}{2}$$

Use $y = mx + c$ to find c.   When $x = -2$, $y = 3$ so: $3 = -\frac{1}{2} \times -2 + c$

$$c = 2$$

$$\underline{y = -\frac{1}{2}x + 2}$$

[3 marks]

Extended

Exam Questions

2 The lines **K** and **L** are drawn on the axes on the right.

a) Find the equation of **K** in the form $y = mx + c$.

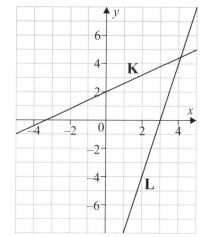

....

[3 marks]

b) A third line, **N**, has the equation $y = 4x + 2$.
Draw **N** on the axes.

[2 marks]

c) Find the coordinates of the point where **L** intersects the y-axis.

(................ , ...)
[2 marks]

3 Point P has coordinates $(6, 2)$ and point Q has coordinates $(-4, 1)$.

a) Find the coordinates of the midpoint of PQ.

(................ , ...)
[2 marks]

b) Point R has coordinates (a, b). The midpoint of PR is $(3, 5)$.
Find the values of a and b.

$a =$ ....

$b =$ ....
[3 marks]

4 James plots the points A $(5, 7)$, B $(1, -1)$, C $(13, 4)$ and D $(3, -2)$. He claims he can draw a line perpendicular to AB that passes through the midpoint of both AB and CD.

Is he correct? Explain your answer.

[4 marks]

Extended

Quadratic Graphs

KEY TERM

Quadratic graphs have the form $y = ax^2 + bx + c$ (where a, b and c are numbers). They always have an x^2 term (but no higher powers of x or fractions like $\frac{1}{x}$).

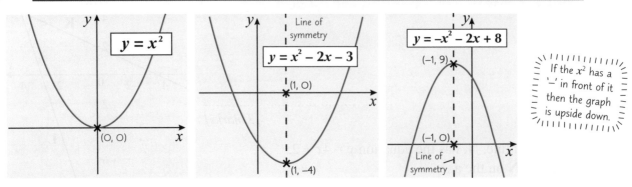

$y = x^2$

$(0, 0)$

Line of symmetry

$y = x^2 - 2x - 3$

$(1, 0)$

$(1, -4)$

$y = -x^2 - 2x + 8$

$(-1, 9)$

$(-1, 0)$

Line of symmetry

If the x^2 has a '–' in front of it then the graph is upside down.

Plotting Quadratics

EXAMPLE:

Complete the table of values for the equation $y = x^2 + 2x - 3$ and then draw the graph.

x	–5	–4	–3	–2	–1	0	1	2	3
y	12	5	0	–3	–4	–3	0	5	12

1) Work out each y-value by substituting the corresponding x-value into the equation.

$y = (-5)^2 + (2 \times -5) - 3$
$= 25 - 10 - 3 = 12$

$y = (2)^2 + (2 \times 2) - 3$
$= 4 + 4 - 3 = 5$

> To check you're doing it right, make sure you can get the y-values they've already given you.

2) Plot the points and join them with a smooth curve. Definitely DON'T use a ruler.

> DON'T let one point move your line off in the wrong direction. When you plot a quadratic graph, you never get spikes or bumps.

This point is obviously wrong.

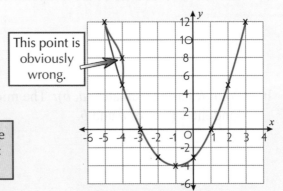

Solving Quadratic Equations

EXAMPLE:

Use the graph of $y = x^2 + 2x - 3$ to solve the equation $x^2 + 2x - 3 = 0$.

The equation $x^2 + 2x - 3 = 0$ is what you get when you put $y = 0$ into the graph's equation, $y = x^2 + 2x - 3$.

So to solve the equation, all you do is read the x-values where $y = 0$, i.e. where it crosses the x-axis.

So the solutions are $x = -3$ and $x = 1$.

Quadratic equations usually have 2 solutions.

EXAM TIP

Graph-plotting questions are easy marks if you're accurate

Filling in tables of values and plotting graphs are easy questions, but don't rush them and make silly mistakes. Take your time — if your curve isn't smooth, check the points in your table.

Harder Graphs

You also need to be able to recognise these trickier graphs by their general shapes.

1/x (Reciprocal) Graphs: y = A/x or y = Ax⁻¹

 Reciprocal graphs have the form $y = \dfrac{A}{x}$ (or Ax^{-1}) where A is a number.

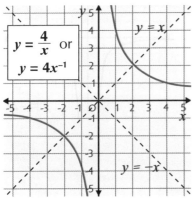

These are all the same basic shape, except the negative ones are in opposite quadrants to the positive ones (as shown). The two halves of the graph don't touch.

The graphs don't exist for $x = 0$.

They're all symmetrical about the lines $y = x$ and $y = -x$.

You get this type of graph with inverse proportion — see p.80.

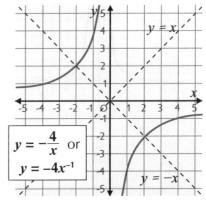

Reciprocal graphs always have asymptotes — these are lines that the graphs get closer and closer to, but never touch. For these graphs, the asymptotes are always $x = 0$ and $y = 0$ (the axes).

x³ (Cubic) Graphs

 Cubic graphs have an x^3 term (but no higher powers of x).

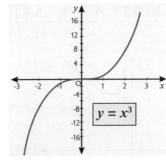
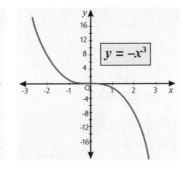
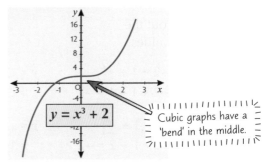

Cubic graphs have a 'bend' in the middle.

EXAMPLE: Draw the graph of $y = -x^3 - 10$ for values of x between -3 and $+2$.

Start by making a table of values.

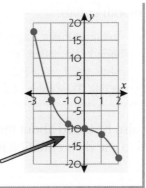

E.g. $y = -(-2)^3 - 10$
$= -2$

Plot the points and join them with a smooth curve — don't use your ruler.

 ## Knowing the general shape will help you plot the graph

It's much easier to notice if your graph plot has gone wrong if you know what the shape of the graph is supposed to be. Close the book and sketch the graphs of $\frac{1}{x}$, $-\frac{1}{x}$, x^3 and $-x^3$.

Harder Graphs

You might be getting a bit tired of graphs right now — this might be a good moment to get a glass of juice...
Are you back? Good, then let's take a look at the next tricky graph you need to know: $1/x^2$.

1/x² Graphs: $y = A/x^2$ or $y = Ax^{-2}$

These are a bit like reciprocal graphs (see previous page) — except the two bits are next to each other.

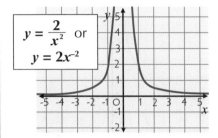

$y = \dfrac{2}{x^2}$ or
$y = 2x^{-2}$

The positive ones are above the
x-axis and the negative ones are
below the x-axis. They're all
symmetrical about the y-axis.

These graphs also have asymptotes
at $x = 0$ and $y = 0$

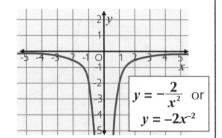

$y = -\dfrac{2}{x^2}$ or
$y = -2x^{-2}$

Combination Graphs — use a Table of Values

1) If you get a question with a combination of different terms (e.g. $x^2 + \dfrac{1}{x} - 3$),
   the graph might not look like the standard shape.

2) For questions like these, you can still plot the graphs using a table of values.

 **EXAMPLE:**

**Complete the table of values for the equation $y = x + 1 + \dfrac{2}{x}$
and then draw the graph.**

x	-4	-2	-1	-0.5	0.5	1	2	4
y	-3.5	-2	-2	-3.5	5.5	4	4	5.5

First work out the
missing y-values.

$y = -2 + 1 + \dfrac{2}{-2}$
$\quad = -2 + 1 - 1 = -2$

$y = 0.5 + 1 + \dfrac{2}{0.5}$
$\quad = 0.5 + 1 + 4 = 5.5$

$y = -1 + 1 + \dfrac{2}{-1}$
$\quad = -1 + 1 - 2 = -2$

$y = 1 + 1 + \dfrac{2}{1}$
$\quad = 1 + 1 + 2 = 4$

Then plot the points and join
them with smooth curves.

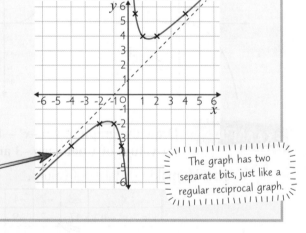

This graph has a diagonal asymptote, shown
here by the dotted line. You don't need to
show this if you are just asked to draw the
graph. There's also an asymptote at $x = 0$.

The graph has two
separate bits, just like a
regular reciprocal graph.

3) You could also be asked about the turning points of the graph —
   you'd need to use differentiation for this (see pages 107-108).

Use your calculator to complete the table of values

EXAM TIP

Using a calculator might save you time in the exam and it means you're less likely to make
a mistake. Plot the points accurately and join them up with smooth curves to get the marks.

Harder Graphs

You're nearly there — just a couple more pages of tough graphs left.

Exponential Graphs: $y = k^x$ or $y = k^{-x}$

Exponential graphs have the form $y = k^x$, where k is some positive number.

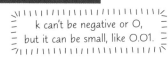
k can't be negative or O, but it can be small, like 0.01.

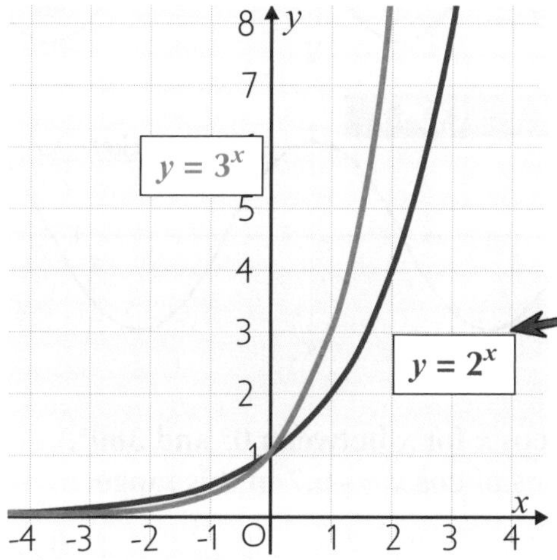

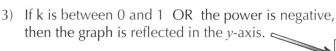
$y = 3^x$
$y = 2^x$

1) These 'exponential' graphs are always above the x-axis, and always go through the point (0, 1).

2) If k > 1 and the power is positive, the graph curves upwards.

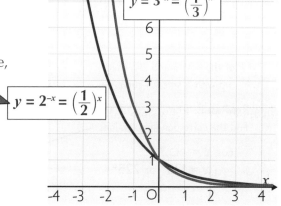
$y = 3^{-x} = \left(\frac{1}{3}\right)^x$
$y = 2^{-x} = \left(\frac{1}{2}\right)^x$

3) If k is between 0 and 1 OR the power is negative, then the graph is reflected in the y-axis.

4) All of these graphs get closer and closer to the x-axis but never touch it — so they have an asymptote at $y = 0$.

EXAMPLE: **This graph shows how the number of rabbits (N) living in a forest increases over time. The equation of the graph is $N = fg^t$, where t is the number of years since they were first counted. f and g are positive constants. Find the values of f and g.**

When $t = 0$, $N = 30$ so substitute these values into the equation:

$g^0 = 1$, so you can find f.

$30 = fg^0 \Rightarrow 30 = f \times 1 \Rightarrow f = 30$

Substitute in $t = 3$, $N = 1920$: $\quad N = 30g^t \Rightarrow 1920 = 30g^3$
$$\Rightarrow g = \sqrt[3]{64}$$
$$\Rightarrow g = 4$$

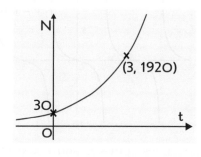
(3, 1920)
30

k^x graphs always pass through (0, 1)

For questions involving k^x, just use the information you're given. If you're given a graph, you can substitute known values into the equation to find the missing constants, like in the example above.

Trig Graphs

The graphs of sin, cos and tan all have a different pattern. Make sure you learn all three.

Sin 'Waves' and Cos 'Buckets'

1) The underlying shape of the sin and cos graphs is identical — they both bounce between y-limits of exactly +1 and –1.

2) The only difference is that the sin graph is shifted right by 90° compared to the cos graph.

3) For 0° – 360°, the shapes you get are a Sin 'Wave' (one peak, one trough) and a Cos 'Bucket' (starts at the top, dips, and finishes at the top).

4) Sin and cos repeat every 360° and they go on forever in both directions along the x-axis.

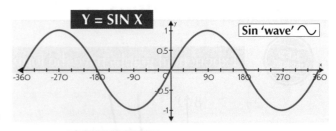

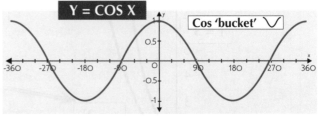

EXAMPLE: Complete the table and draw the graph of $y = \cos x$ for x between 0° and 360°, and use your graph to estimate the two solutions of $\cos x = -0.7$ in this range.

x	0°	30°	60°	90°	120°	150°	180°	210°	240°	270°	300°	330°	360°
$\cos x$	1	0.87	0.5	0	–0.5	–0.87	–1	–0.87	–0.5	0	0.5	0.87	1

Plot the points and join them up with a smooth curve.

Read across from $y = -0.7$ and find the corresponding x values.

$\cos x = -0.7$
$\Rightarrow x \approx 135°$ or $225°$

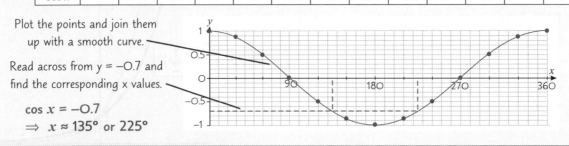

Tan x can be Any Value at all

tan x is different from sin x or cos x — it goes between $-\infty$ and $+\infty$. It also repeats every 180°.

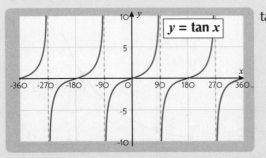

tan x goes from $-\infty$ and $+\infty$ every 180°.

So it repeats every 180° and takes every possible value in each 180° interval.

tan x is undefined at $\pm 90°$, $\pm 270°$,...

As you approach one of these undefined points from the left, tan x goes off to infinity.

As you approach from the right, it drops to minus infinity.

The graph approaches but never touches these lines — they're asymptotes.

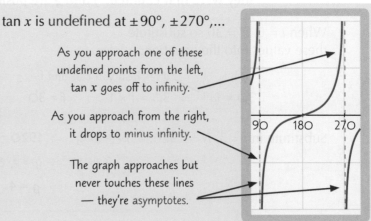

Do a quick sketch of each graph

sin$x$ and cos$x$ look pretty similar so they're easy to mix up. Remember that sin$x$ passes through (0, 0) and cos x passes through (0, 1). tan$x$ is the weird one that shoots off to $-\infty$ and $+\infty$ every 180°.

Warm-Up and Worked Exam Questions

The warm-up questions quickly cover the basic facts you'll need in the exam. The exam questions come later — but unless you've learned the facts first, you'll find the exams much harder than they should be.

Warm-Up Questions

1) a) Complete the table of values for $y = x^2 - 2x - 1$.

x	−2	−1	0	1	2	3	4	5
y								

b) Plot the x and y values from the table and join the points up to form a smooth curve.
c) Use your curve to find the value of y when $x = 3.5$.
d) Find the two values of x when $y = 5$.

2) Sketch the graph of $y = \dfrac{3}{x}$.

3) To the right is the graph of $y = \cos x$ for $0° \leq x \leq 360°$. As shown on the graph, $\cos 50° = 0.643$. Give another value of x, found on this graph, where $\cos x = 0.643$.

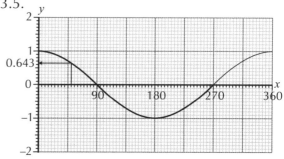

Worked Exam Question

Take a good look at this exam question — unlike the real thing, the answers are helpfully written in.

1 The temperature (T °C) of a piece of metal changes over time (t seconds) as it is rapidly heated and then cooled again. It is modelled by the equation $T = -t^2 + 8t - 7$.

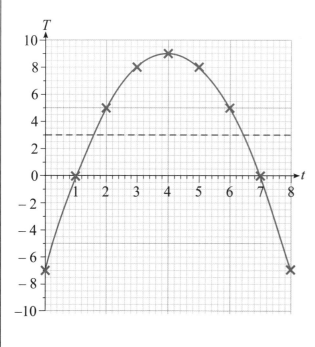

a) Fill in the two missing values in the table.

t	0	1	2	3	4	5	6	7	8
T	−7	0	5	8	9	8	5	0	−7

[2 marks]

b) Use the table to draw the graph of $T = -t^2 + 8t - 7$ on the grid.

Plot the points on the grid and draw a smooth curve through them.

[4 marks]

c) At what time did the metal reach its highest temperature?

$t = $ ....**4**............ s
[1 mark]

d) Using your graph, solve the equation $-t^2 + 8t - 7 = 3$.

Draw the line $T = 3$ and read off where it crosses the curve.

$t = $ ....**1.8**............ s and $t = $ ....**6.2**............ s
[2 marks]

Exam Questions

2   This question is about the equation $y = x^2 - 4x + 4$.

a)   Complete this table of values.

x	0	1	2	3	4	5
y	4	....	....	....	4	9

[3 marks]

b)   Draw the graph of $y = x^2 - 4x + 4$ for values of x between 0 and 5 on the axes below.

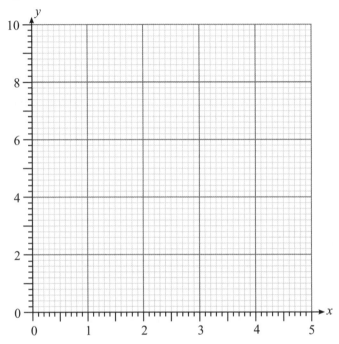

[4 marks]

c)   Use your graph to estimate the solutions to $2 = x^2 - 4x + 4$.
Give your answers to 1 decimal place.

x = ... x = ...

[2 marks]

3   Sketches of different graphs are shown below.

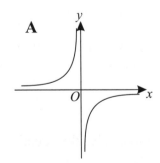

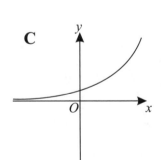

Match each equation below to one of the graphs above.

a) $y = x^3 + 1$ ....   b) $y = \left(\frac{3}{2}\right)^x$ ....   c) $y = -\frac{1}{x}$ ....

[3 marks]

Exam Questions

4   a)   Complete this table of values for the equation $y = \sin x$.

x	0°	30°	90°	150°	180°	210°	270°	330°	360°
y	0	....	....	0.5	0	–0.5	....	....	0

[4 marks]

b)   Use your table to draw the graph of $y = \sin x$ on the grid, for $0° \le x \le 360°$.

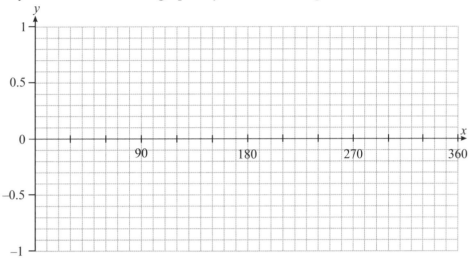

[4 marks]

c)   By drawing a straight line on the grid, estimate two values of x in the interval $0° \le x \le 360°$ that satisfy $\sin x = 0.3$. Give your answers to the nearest degree.

$x = ...°$ $x = ...°$

[2 marks]

5   a)   Complete this table of values for the equation $y = x + \dfrac{4}{x} - 3$.

x	0.2	0.5	1	2	3	4	5
y	....	5.5	2	1	1.333...	2	....

[2 marks]

b)   On the axes on the left, draw the graph of $y = x + \dfrac{4}{x} - 3$ for $0.2 \le x \le 5$.

[4 marks]

c)   Draw a suitable straight line on your graph to estimate the solution to the equation $x + \dfrac{4}{x} - 3 = 5x + 5$ in the interval $0.2 \le x \le 5$. Give your answer to 1 d.p.

$x = ...$

[3 marks]

Extended

Extended

Real-Life Graphs

Real-life graphs show how one quantity changes based on another.

Conversion Graphs

Conversion graphs can be used to convert between currencies, lengths, volumes, masses, etc.

EXAMPLES:

1. Lucas goes to Florida and spends $36 on a toy. Use the graph to find what this is in pounds.

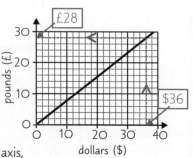

1) Draw a line from a value on one axis.   Start from $36 on the horizontal axis.

2) Keep going until you hit the LINE.

3) Then change direction and go straight to the other axis.

4) Read off the value from this axis. The two values are equivalent.   You end up at £28 on the vertical axis, so $36 is equivalent to £28.

2. Draw a graph to convert between pounds and Russian roubles, given that £1 = 83 roubles.

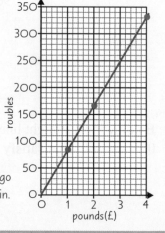

1) Work out 3 pairs of values.

   You're told £1 = 83 roubles. It's easy to work out that £2 = 166 roubles, and £4 = 332 roubles.

2) Plot these points accurately and draw a line through them.

   Your line should go through the origin.

Graphs Can Show **How Much** You'll **Pay**

Graphs are great for showing how much you'll be charged for using a service or buying multiple items.

EXAMPLE: **A business rents out computer games. The graph shows how much it charges.**

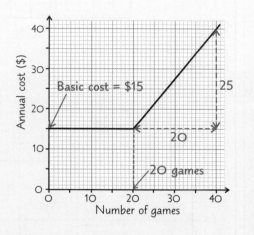

a) How many games are included in the basic annual cost?

20   The first section of the graph is horizontal. You pay $15 if you rent between 0 and 20 games. It's only if you rent more than 20 games that you pay more.

b) Estimate the cost per game for additional games.

Gradient of sloped section = cost per game

$$\frac{\text{vertical change}}{\text{horizontal change}} = \frac{25}{20} = \$1.25 \text{ per game}$$

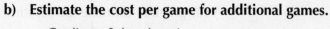

Learn how to convert graph questions into marks

EXAM TIP Real-life graphs aren't too bad as long as you follow the steps above. If you're asked to draw a graph in the exam, plot all the points clearly and accurately — they could get you a mark.

Distance-Time Graphs

Distance-time graphs just show how distance changes over time.

Distance-Time Graphs

Distance-time graphs can look a bit complicated at first, but they're not too bad as long as you remember these 4 important points:

- At any point, GRADIENT = SPEED.
- The STEEPER the graph, the FASTER it's going.
- FLAT SECTIONS are where it is STOPPED.
- If the gradient's negative, it's COMING BACK.

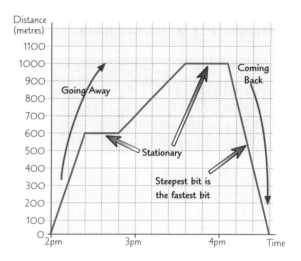

EXAMPLE: Henry went out for a ride on his bike. After a while he got a puncture and stopped to fix it. This graph shows the first part of Henry's journey.

a) **What time did Henry leave home?**

He left home at the point where the line starts. **At 8:15**

b) **How far did Henry cycle before getting a puncture?**

The horizontal part of the graph is where Henry stopped.

12 km

c) **What was Henry's speed before getting a puncture?**

Using the speed formula is the same as finding the gradient.

$$\text{speed} = \frac{\text{distance}}{\text{time}} = \frac{12 \text{ km}}{0.5 \text{ hours}}$$
$$= 24 \text{ km/h}$$

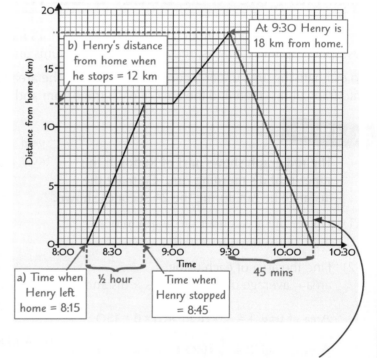

At 9:30 Henry is 18 km from home.

b) Henry's distance from home when he stops = 12 km

a) Time when Henry left home = 8:15

½ hour

Time when Henry stopped = 8:45

45 mins

d) **At 9:30 Henry turns round and cycles home at 24 km/h. Complete the graph to show this.**

You have to work out how long it will take Henry to cycle the 18 km home:

$$\text{time} = \frac{\text{distance}}{\text{speed}} = \frac{18 \text{ km}}{24 \text{ km/h}} = 0.75 \text{ hours}$$
$$0.75 \times 60 \text{ mins} = 45 \text{ mins}$$

Decimal times are confusing, so convert it to minutes.

45 minutes after 9:30 is 10:15, so that's the time Henry gets home. Now you can complete the graph.

The gradient of a distance-time graph = speed

REVISION TIP Look at the axes before starting questions like this — once you know that it's a distance-time graph, just use the 4 key points from the blue box. Practise that speed formula too — see p.135.

Speed-Time Graphs

This page looks pretty much the same as the last page — but there are some huge differences.

Speed-Time Graphs

- At any point, GRADIENT = ACCELERATION.
- NEGATIVE SLOPE is DECELERATION (slowing down).
- FLAT SECTIONS are STEADY SPEED.
- AREA UNDER GRAPH = DISTANCE TRAVELLED.

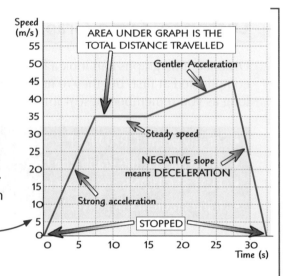

The units of acceleration equal the speed units per time units.

For speed in m/s and time in seconds the units of acceleration are m/s per s — this is written as m/s^2.

Be careful not to get speed and distance-time graphs mixed up — always check the axes.

Estimating the **Area Under a Curve**

It's easy to find the area under a speed-time graph if it's made up of straight lines — just split it up into triangles, rectangles and trapeziums and use the area formulas (see p.139).

To estimate the area under a curved graph, divide the area under the graph approximately into trapeziums, then find the area of each trapezium and add them all together.

EXAMPLE:

The red graph shows part of Rudolph the super-rabbit's morning run. Estimate the distance he ran during the 24 seconds shown.

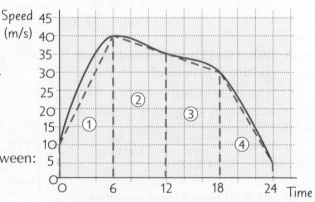

1) Divide the area under the graph into trapeziums of equal width.

2) Find the area of each using
   area = average of parallel sides × distance between:

   Area of trap. 1 = $\frac{1}{2}$ × (10 + 40) × 6 = 150

   Area of trap. 2 = $\frac{1}{2}$ × (40 + 35) × 6 = 225

   Area of trap. 3 = $\frac{1}{2}$ × (35 + 30) × 6 = 195

   Area of trap. 4 = $\frac{1}{2}$ × (30 + 5) × 6 = 105

3) Add to get the total area:

   Total area = 150 + 225 + 195 + 105 = 675

   So Rudolph ran about 675 m in total.

You could use this to estimate the average speed — just divide the total distance by the time taken.

You can find the average acceleration by finding the gradient between two points on a speed-time curve, or estimate the acceleration at a specific point by drawing a tangent to the curve (see next page).

The gradient of a speed-time graph = acceleration

It's easy to get these mixed up with distance-time graphs, so make sure you check the axes. Here the area under the graph is the distance travelled, and the gradient at any point is the acceleration.

Gradients of Real-Life Graphs

Gradients are great — you can get lots of information from them, like 'you're accelerating slowly'.

The **Gradient** of a Graph **Represents** the **Rate**

No matter what kind of graph you have,
the meaning of the gradient is always:

(y-axis UNITS) PER (x-axis UNITS)

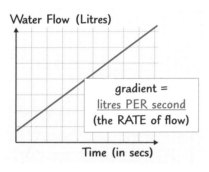

gradient =
litres PER second
(the RATE of flow)

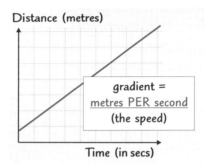

gradient =
metres PER second
(the speed)

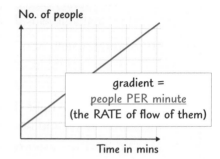

gradient =
people PER minute
(the RATE of flow of them)

Finding the **Average Gradient**

You could be asked to find the average gradient between two points on a curve.

EXAMPLE: **Vicky is growing a sunflower. She records its height each day and uses this to draw the graph shown. What is the average growth per day between days 40 and 80?**

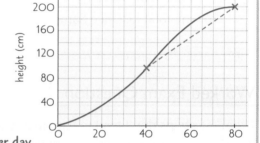

1) Draw a straight line connecting the points.
2) Find the gradient of the straight line.

$$\text{Gradient} = \frac{\text{change in } y}{\text{change in } x} = \frac{200 - 100}{80 - 40} = \frac{100}{40} = 2.5 \text{ cm per day}$$

Estimating the **Rate** at a **Given Point**

To estimate the rate at a single point on a curve, draw a tangent that touches the curve at that point. The gradient of the tangent is the same as the rate at the chosen point.

EXAMPLE: **Dan plots a graph to show the distance he travelled during a bike race. Estimate Dan's speed after 40 minutes.**

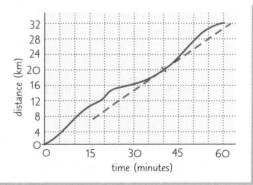

1) Draw a tangent to the curve at 40 minutes.
2) Find the gradient of the straight line.

$$\text{Gradient} = \frac{\text{change in } y}{\text{change in } x} = \frac{28 - 20}{55 - 40} = \frac{8}{15} \text{ km per minute}$$
$$= 32 \text{ km per hour}$$

Extended

The gradient is always y-axis units per x-axis units

Just remember to look at the units and keep a ruler to hand and you'll have no problem with this. Also practise finding the gradient — take a look back at page 87 if you need a reminder.

Warm-Up and Worked Exam Questions

Here's the last batch of warm-up questions on graphs — they'll get your brain working, ready for those exam practice questions.

Warm-Up Questions

1) Use the graph opposite to answer the questions below.

   a) A water tank holds 8 gallons. How many litres is this? *'Gallons' are an imperial measurement of volume.*

   b) Approximately how many gallons of water would fit into a 20 litre container?

2) The graph on the right shows Ben's car journey to the supermarket and home again.

   a) Did he drive faster on his way to the supermarket, or on his way home?

   b) How long did he spend at the supermarket?

Extended

3) The graph on the right shows the time that Sameel took to run a race. Use the graph to find:

   a) how many seconds Sameel was running at 5 m/s.

   b) the total distance Sameel ran.

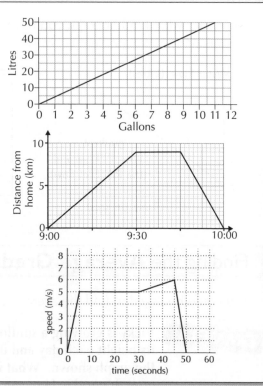

Worked Exam Question

Exam questions don't tend to vary that wildly — the basic format is often pretty similar. You'd be silly not to spend a bit of time learning how to answer a common question, wouldn't you?

1   An electricity company offers its customers two different price plans.

Plan **A**: $18 each month, plus 10 cents for each unit used.

Plan **B**: No monthly cost, just 40 cents for each unit used.

a) Use the graph to find the cost of using 70 units in a month for each plan.

Look for 70 units on the *x*-axis, go up to the line for Plan A and read across to the *y*-axis. Repeat for Plan B.

Plan **A** ....$25.... Plan **B** ....$28....

[2 marks]

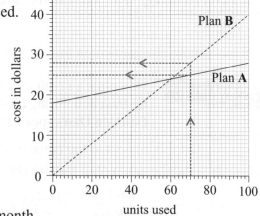

b) Mr Barker uses about 85 units of electricity each month. Which price plan would you advise him to choose? Explain your answer.

Mr Barker should use Plan A because it is cheaper. Using 85 units

with Plan A would cost $26.50. 85 units with Plan B would cost $34.

[2 marks]

Exam Questions

2   Selby and Tyrone run in a 30 km race, shown on the distance-time graph below.

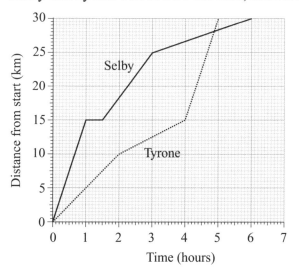

a)   During the race, Selby stops at a bench to get his breath back. After how many hours did he stop at the bench?

.... hours
[1 mark]

b)   Who won the race? How can you tell this from the graph?

....

....
[1 mark]

c)   Work out Selby's speed between 1.5 and 3 hours into the race. Give your answer to 2 d.p.

.... km/h
[2 marks]

3   James rolls a ball down a series of ramps and records its velocity.
He plots the results on the velocity-time graph shown below.

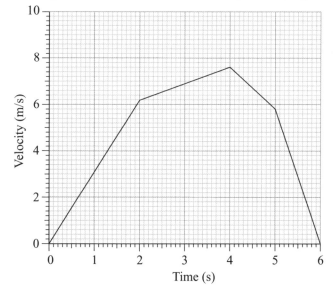

a)   Find the acceleration of the ball at 3 seconds.

The acceleration is constant between 2 and 4 seconds.

.... m/s^2
[2 marks]

b)   Calculate the total distance that the ball travelled.

.... m
[3 marks]

c)   Work out the average speed of the ball.

.... m/s
[2 marks]

Functions

A function takes an input, processes it and outputs a value. There are two main ways of writing a function: $f(x) = 5x + 2$ or $f: x \rightarrow 5x + 2$. Both of these say 'the function f takes a value for x, multiplies it by 5 and adds 2. Functions can look a bit scary, but they're just like equations but with y replaced by $f(x)$.

Evaluating Functions

This is easy — just put the numbers into the function and work out the answer.

> **EXAMPLE:** $f(x) = x^2 - x + 7$. Find a) $f(3)$ and b) $f(-2)$
>
> a) $f(3) = (3)^2 - (3) + 7 = 9 - 3 + 7 = 13$ b) $f(-2) = (-2)^2 - (-2) + 7 = 4 + 2 + 7 = 13$

Combining Functions

1) You might get a question with two functions, e.g. $f(x)$ and $g(x)$, combined into a single function (called a composite function).

2) Composite functions are written e.g. $fg(x)$, which means 'do g first, then do f' — you always do the function closest to x first.

3) To find a composite function, rewrite $fg(x)$ as $f(g(x))$, then replace $g(x)$ with the expression it represents and put this into f.

Watch out — usually $fg(x) \neq gf(x)$. Never assume that they're the same.

> **EXAMPLE:** If $f(x) = 2x - 10$ and $g(x) = -\frac{x}{2}$, find: a) $fg(x)$ and b) $gf(x)$.
>
> a) $fg(x) = f(g(x)) = f(-\frac{x}{2}) = 2(-\frac{x}{2}) - 10 = -x - 10$
>
> b) $gf(x) = g(f(x)) = g(2x - 10) = -\left(\frac{2x - 10}{2}\right) = -(x - 5) = 5 - x$

Inverse Functions

The inverse of a function $f(x)$ is another function, $f^{-1}(x)$, which reverses $f(x)$. Here's the method to find it:

1) Write out the equation $x = f(y)$. ◄ ──── $f(y)$ is just the expression $f(x)$, but with y's instead of x's.
2) Rearrange the equation to make y the subject.
3) Finally, replace y with $f^{-1}(x)$.

> **EXAMPLE:** If $f(x) = \frac{12 + x}{3}$, find $f^{-1}(x)$.
>
> So here you just rewrite the function replacing $f(x)$ with x and x with y.
>
> 1) Write out $x = f(y)$: $x = \frac{12 + y}{3}$
>
> 2) Rearrange to make y the subject: $3x = 12 + y$
> $y = 3x - 12$
>
> 3) Replace y with $f^{-1}(x)$: $f^{-1}(x) = 3x - 12$

You can check your answer by seeing if $f^{-1}(x)$ reverses $f(x)$, e.g. $f(9) = \frac{21}{3} = 7$, $f^{-1}(7) = 21 - 12 = 9$

Remember — do the function closest to x first

When you're working with composite functions, order does matter. If you learn the three-step method in the box above, you shouldn't have too much trouble finding inverse functions.

Extended (left margin) *Extended* (right margin)

Differentiation

Differentiation is really useful — if you take a function and differentiate it, it'll let you work out the gradient of its graph. The method might seem weird at first, but you'll get used to it after you've done a few questions.

Use the Formula to **Differentiate Powers of x**

This means 'the result of differentiating the thing in the brackets'.

$$\frac{d}{dx}(x^n) = nx^{n-1}$$

If $y = x^n$, then you write: $\frac{dy}{dx}$

 EXAMPLES:

1. **Differentiate y when $y = x^5$**

n is just the power of x, so here $n = 5$

$$\frac{dy}{dx} = nx^{n-1} = 5x^4$$

2. **Differentiate $6x^3$**

Ignore the 6 and just differentiate the x bit...

... then simplify.

$$\frac{dy}{dx} = 6(3x^2)$$
$$= 18x^2$$

3. **Differentiate y when $y = 24x$**

$x = x^1$, so $n = 1$:

$$\frac{dy}{dx} = 24(1 \times x^0)$$
$$= 24$$

When you've only got an x-term you just end up with the number in front of the x.

4. **Differentiate $\frac{3}{x^2}$**

If you get an x on the bottom of a fraction, move it to the top and make the power of x negative (see page 49).

$$\frac{3}{x^2} = 3 \times \frac{1}{x^2} = 3x^{-2}$$

$$\frac{dy}{dx} = 3(-2 \times x^{-3}) = -6x^{-3} \text{ or } -\frac{6}{x^3}$$

Differentiate **Each Term** in an Equation **Separately**

Even if there are loads of terms in the equation, it doesn't matter.
Differentiate each bit separately and you'll be fine.

 EXAMPLE   Find $\frac{dy}{dx}$ for $y = 4x^3 - 2x + 3$.

If you differentiate a number on its own, it always becomes 0 and disappears.

Think of this as three separate differentiations:

$$\frac{dy}{dx} = \frac{d}{dx}(4x^3) - \frac{d}{dx}(2x^1) + \frac{d}{dx}(3x^0) = 4(3x^2) - 2(1x^0) + 3(0x^{-1}) = 12x^2 - 2$$

Use **Differentiation** to Find a **Gradient**

Differentiating the equation of a curve gives you an expression for the curve's gradient.
Then you can find the gradient of the curve at any point by substituting the value for x into the expression.

EXAMPLE: **Find the gradient of the graph $y = x^2$ at $x = 1$ and $x = -2$.**

Differentiate to get the gradient expression:

$$y = x^2 \Rightarrow \frac{dy}{dx} = 2x$$

Now when $x = 1$,

$$\frac{dy}{dx} = 2 \times 1 = 2$$

So the gradient at $x = 1$ is 2.

And when $x = -2$,

$$\frac{dy}{dx} = 2 \times -2 = -4$$

So the gradient at $x = -2$ is -4.

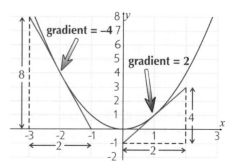

This graph shows how you'd find the gradients by drawing tangents. If your tangents were slightly off you'd get different gradients with this method though.

Differentiation

Some graphs have stationary points — places where the graph 'levels off'. You find them by differentiating.

Stationary Points are When the Gradient is Zero

A stationary point is a point on a curve where the gradient equals zero.
A turning point is a type of stationary point which can be a maximum or a minimum.

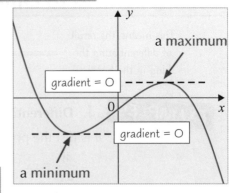

a maximum

gradient = 0

gradient = 0

a minimum

To find the stationary points of a graph, you need to find the points where: $\Longrightarrow$ $\dfrac{dy}{dx} = 0$

EXAMPLE: Find the coordinates of the two turning points of the graph of $y = x + \dfrac{4}{x}$.

1 $y = x + \dfrac{4}{x} \Rightarrow y = x + 4x^{-1}$ $\quad \dfrac{dy}{dx} = 1x^0 + 4(-1)x^{-2}$

$= 1 - \dfrac{4}{x^2}$

1) First differentiate to find $\dfrac{dy}{dx}$.

2 $0 = 1 - \dfrac{4}{x^2} \Rightarrow 1 = \dfrac{4}{x^2} \Rightarrow x^2 = 4 \Rightarrow x = 2 \text{ and } -2$

2) Now set $\dfrac{dy}{dx}$ equal to 0, and solve for x.

3 When $x = 2$, $y = 2 + \dfrac{4}{2} \Rightarrow y = 4$

When $x = -2$, $y = -2 + \dfrac{4}{-2} \Rightarrow y = -4$

So the turning points are at (2, 4) and (−2, −4).

3) Substitute the x-values into the ORIGINAL equation to find the y-values of the turning points.

Differentiate Again to see if it's a Maximum or a Minimum

1) If you differentiate $\dfrac{dy}{dx}$ you get the second derivative, $\dfrac{d^2y}{dx^2}$.

2) $\dfrac{d^2y}{dx^2}$ is the rate of change of the gradient — it's positive when the gradient is increasing and negative when the gradient is decreasing.

3) You can tell the type of turning point from the second derivative: $\Longrightarrow$

If $\dfrac{d^2y}{dx^2} > 0$ it's a minimum

If $\dfrac{d^2y}{dx^2} < 0$ it's a maximum

EXAMPLE: Determine the nature of each turning point of the graph of $y = x + \dfrac{4}{x}$.

Differentiate $\dfrac{dy}{dx}$ from above: $\dfrac{dy}{dx} = 1 - 4x^{-2} \Rightarrow \dfrac{d^2y}{dx^2} = 0 - 4(-2)x^{-3} = \dfrac{8}{x^3}$

Put in the x-values of the stationary points to find if $\dfrac{d^2y}{dx^2}$ is positive or negative.

$x = 2 \Rightarrow \dfrac{d^2y}{dx^2} = \dfrac{8}{8} = 1 > 0$, so (2, 4) is a minimum.

$x = -2 \Rightarrow \dfrac{d^2y}{dx^2} = \dfrac{8}{-8} = -1 < 0$, so (−2, −4) is a maximum.

4) Another useful way to determine the nature of a turning point is to find the gradient either side of it:
 • If the gradient goes from positive to negative, it's a maximum.
 • If the gradient goes from negative to positive, it's a minimum.

Don't get maxima and minima the wrong way round

When a question talks about maxima, minima, turning points or stationary points, you should always think "differentiation". Even if it uses letters other than x and y, you can still differentiate in exactly the same way.

Extended

Extended

Warm-Up and Worked Exam Questions

That's another section wrapped up. Here's one last bundle of warm-up questions to see how you did.

Warm-Up Questions

1) If $f(x) = 5x - 1$, $g(x) = 8 - 2x$ and $h(x) = x^2 + 3$, find:
   a) $f(4)$ b) $h(-2)$ c) $gf(x)$ d) $fh(x)$ e) $gh(-3)$ f) $f^{-1}(x)$

2) Find: a) $\dfrac{dy}{da}$ when $y = a^7$ b) $\dfrac{dy}{dt}$ when $y = 10t^5$ c) $\dfrac{dy}{ds}$ when $y = s$ d) $\dfrac{dy}{dw}$ when $y = -\dfrac{2}{3}w^6$

3) Find $\dfrac{dy}{dx}$ when $y = 9x^4 + x^3 + 4x^2$

4) Find the gradient of the graph of each of the following equations at $x = 2$.
   a) $y = -2x - 1$ b) $y = 2x^3 - 3$ c) $y = -\dfrac{1}{2}x^3 + 2$ d) $y = \dfrac{2}{x}$

5) Find the coordinates of the turning points of these graphs.
   For each, say if the turning point is a maximum or minimum.
   a) $y = 2x^2$ b) $y = -x^2 + 4x - 8$ c) $y = x^3 + 6x^2 + 1$

(margin label: Extended)

Worked Exam Questions

Two worked exam questions coming up below all about differentiation. There are loads of places differentiation can sneak into the exam so get a good feel for these before moving on to the next page.

1   $F = \dfrac{13}{x^2} + x^3$. Find $\dfrac{dF}{dx}$.

       Don't be put off by the F.
       The method is the same as when it's y.

Write the fraction as a power of x. $F = 13x^{-2} + x^3$

Differentiate each term using $\dfrac{d}{dx}(x^n) = nx^{n-1}$

$$\dfrac{dF}{dx} = 13(-2x^{-3}) + 3x^2$$
$$= -26x^{-3} + 3x^2$$

Rewrite the power of x as a fraction.

$$= -\dfrac{26}{x^3} + 3x^2$$

$$\dfrac{dF}{dx} = \dfrac{-\dfrac{26}{x^3} + 3x^2}{}$$

[2 marks]

2   The height above ground level, h metres, of part of a rollercoaster track can be modelled by the equation $h = -2x^2 + 15x + 12$ for $0 \le x \le 8$.

Find the maximum height of this part of the rollercoaster. Show your working.

Differentiate. $\dfrac{dh}{dx} = -2(2x) + 15 = -4x + 15$

Stationary points are found when $\dfrac{dh}{dx} = 0$.

$$\dfrac{dh}{dx} = 0 \Rightarrow -4x + 15 = 0$$

Solve the equation to find x.

$$4x = 15$$
$$x = 3.75$$

At $x = 3.75$, $h = -2 \times 3.75^2 + 15 \times 3.75 + 12$
$$= 40.125$$

Substitute back into the original equation to find the corresponding value of h.

                               40.125   m

[5 marks]

(margin label: Extended)

Exam Questions

3 f is a function such that $f(x) = \dfrac{3}{2x+5}$.

a) Find f(7.5)

....
[1 mark]

b) Find the inverse function f^{-1} in the form $f^{-1}(x)$. Show your working clearly.

$f^{-1}(x) =$ ....
[3 marks]

c) Show that $ff^{-1}(x) = x$.

[3 marks]

4 A rectangular airfield has a length of $(5x + 1)$ km and a width of $(5 - 2x)$ km, where $-0.2 < x < 2.5$.

a) Write an equation for the area, A km², of the airfield. Expand and simplify your answer.

....
[2 marks]

b) Find $\dfrac{dA}{dx}$.

....
[2 marks]

c) Find the maximum possible area of the airfield.

.... km²
[3 marks]

5 Use differentiation to find the x-coordinates of both turning points of the graph of $y = x^3 - 12x - 2$, and to determine the nature of the turning points. Show your working.

....
[7 marks]

Revision Questions for Section Three

Section Three is finally done — try out these summary questions and see what you've learned.
- Try these questions and tick off each one when you get it right.
- When you've done all the questions for a topic and are completely happy with it, tick off the topic.

Coordinates (p.84) ☐

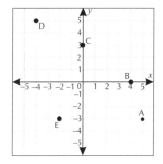

1) Give the coordinates of points A to E in the diagram on the right.

2) Find the midpoint of a line segment with endpoints B and C.

3) A parallelogram has vertices (2, 1), (6, 3) and (2, 7). Find the fourth vertex, given that it lies in the same quadrant as the other three.

Straight-Line Graphs and Gradients (p.85-89) ☐

4) Sketch the lines a) $y = -x$, b) $y = -4$, c) $x = 2$

5) Use the 'table of three values' method to draw the graph $y = x + \frac{1}{10}x$

6) Use the '$x = 0$, $y = 0$' method to draw the graph $y = 3x + 5$.

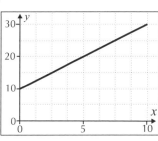

7) Find the gradient of the line on the right.

8) What do 'm' and 'c' represent in $y = mx + c$?

9) Find the equation of the graph on the right.

10) Line A has a gradient of 5.
   a) Line B is parallel to Line A. What is the gradient of Line B?
   b) Line C is perpendicular to line A. What is the gradient of line C?

Other Graphs (p.92-96) ☑

11) Plot the graph $y = x^2 + 2x - 8$ and use it to estimate the solutions to $-2 = x^2 + 2x - 8$ (to 1 d.p.).

12) Plot the following graphs between –3 and 3: a) $y = \frac{1}{x}$ b) $y = x^3 - 2x + 7$

13) Describe the shape of these graphs: a) $y = a^x$ where $a > 1$ b) $y = \tan x$

Real-Life Graphs (p.100-103) ☐

14) Candies'R'Yum sells chocolate drops. They charge $0.90 per 100 g for the first kg, then $0.60 per 100 g after that. Plot a graph to show the cost of buying up to 3 kg of chocolate drops.

15) What does a horizontal line mean on a distance-time graph?

16) The graph to the right shows the speed of a sledge on a slope. Find:
   a) an estimate of the total distance travelled by the sledge.
   b) the average acceleration between 6 and 14 seconds.
   c) the acceleration at 12 seconds.

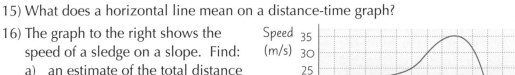
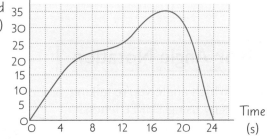

Functions and Differentiation (p.106-108) ☐

17) If f: $x \rightarrow 3x^2 - 2x$, find f(–1).

18) If f(x) = $6 - 2x$ and g(x) = $\frac{4}{x^2}$, find gf(–2).

19) Explain how you can find the inverse of a function.

20) Differentiate $3x^5 + 2x$, and then find the gradient of the graph of $y = 3x^5 + 2x$ at $x = 3$.

21) Find the coordinates of the turning point of each of these graphs. Say if each is a minimum or a maximum. a) $y = x^2 - 2x$ b) $y = -x^2 - 2x$.

Geometry

Before we really get going with all the excitement of angles and geometry, there are a few things you need to know. Nothing too scary — just some special angles and some fancy notation.

Special Angle Names

Some angles have special names. You might have to identify these angles in the exam.

Acute angles are less than 90°.

They're sharp and pointy

Right angles are exactly 90°.

They've got square corners

Obtuse angles are between 90° and 180°.

These ones are flatter

Reflex angles are more than 180°.

These bend back on themselves

4 Simple Rules

1) Angles in a triangle add up to 180°.

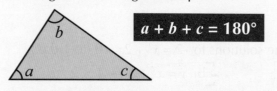

$$a + b + c = 180°$$

2) Angles on a straight line add up to 180°.

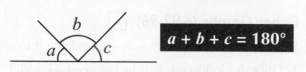

$$a + b + c = 180°$$

3) Angles in a quadrilateral add up to 360°.

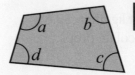

$$a + b + c + d = 360°$$

Remember that a quadrilateral is a 4-sided shape.

4) Angles round a point add up to 360°.

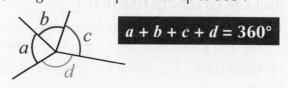

$$a + b + c + d = 360°$$

Three-Letter Angle Notation

The best way to say which angle you're talking about in a diagram is by using THREE letters. For example in the diagram, angle ACB = 25°.

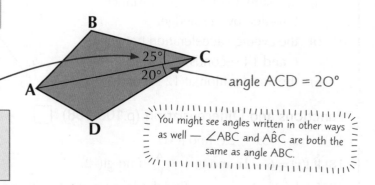

angle ACD = 20°

1) The middle letter is where the angle is.
2) The other two letters tell you which lines the angle is in between.

You might see angles written in other ways as well — ∠ABC and A B̂ C are both the same as angle ABC.

Four simple rules — make sure you learn them

Copy the four diagrams from the blue boxes above, then close the book and write the right rule next to each. You might need to use multiple rules in a question, so make sure you can spot them all.

Parallel Lines

Parallel lines are quite straightforward really. (They're also quite straight. And parallel.)
There are a few rules you need to learn — make sure you don't get them mixed up.

Angles Around **Parallel Lines**

When a line crosses two parallel lines, it forms special sets of angles.

1) The two groups of angles formed at the points
   of intersection are the same.

2) There are only actually two different angles involved
   (labelled *a* and *b* here), and they add up to 180°
   (from rule 2 on the previous page).

3) Vertically opposite angles (ones opposite each other) are equal
   (in the diagram, *a* and *a* are vertically opposite, as are *b* and *b*).

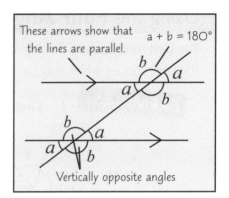

These arrows show that the lines are parallel.

$a + b = 180°$

Vertically opposite angles

Alternate, Allied and **Corresponding** Angles

The diagram above has some recognisable shapes to look out for — and each shape contains a
specific pair of angles. The angle pairs are known as alternate, allied and corresponding angles.

You need to spot the Z, C, U and F shapes:

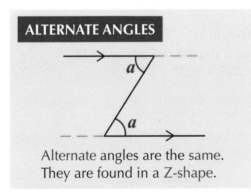

ALTERNATE ANGLES

Alternate angles are the same.
They are found in a Z-shape.

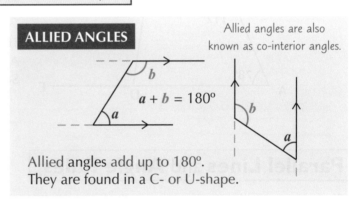

ALLIED ANGLES

Allied angles are also
known as co-interior angles.

$a + b = 180°$

Allied angles add up to 180°.
They are found in a C- or U-shape.

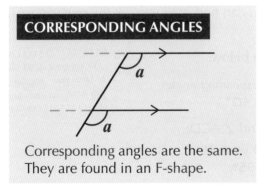

CORRESPONDING ANGLES

Corresponding angles are the same.
They are found in an F-shape.

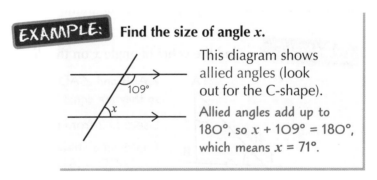

EXAMPLE: **Find the size of angle *x*.**

This diagram shows
allied angles (look
out for the C-shape).

Allied angles add up to
180°, so *x* + 109° = 180°,
which means *x* = 71°.

Parallelograms are quadrilaterals made from two sets of
parallel lines. You can use the properties above to show
that opposite angles in a parallelogram are equal, and
each pair of neighbouring angles add up to 180°.

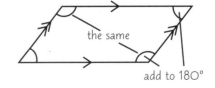

the same

add to 180°

Parallel lines are key things to look out for in geometry

Look out for parallel lines and Z, C, U and F shapes — extending the lines can make spotting them
easier. Learn how to recognise which pairs of angles are equal and which pairs add up to 180°.

Geometry Problems

As if geometry wasn't enough of a problem already, here's a page dedicated to geometry problems. Make sure you learn the four angle rules on p.112 — they'll help a lot on these questions.

Using the Four Angle Rules

The best method is to find as many angles as you can until you can work out the ones you're looking for. It's a bit trickier when you have to use more than one rule, but writing them all down helps a lot.

EXAMPLES:

1. Find the value of x.

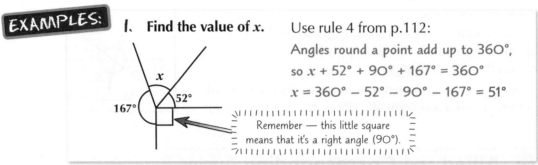

Use rule 4 from p.112:

Angles round a point add up to 360°, so x + 52° + 90° + 167° = 360°

x = 360° − 52° − 90° − 167° = 51°

Remember — this little square means that it's a right angle (90°).

2. Find the size of angle CDE.

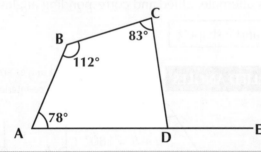

First use rule 3 from p.112:

Angles in a quadrilateral add up to 360°, so the fourth angle in the quadrilateral is 360° − 78° − 112° − 83° = 87°

Then use rule 2:

Angles on a straight line add up to 180°. So ∠CDE = 180° − 87° = 93°

Parallel Lines and Angle Rules

Sometimes you'll come across questions combining parallel lines and the four angle rules. These look pretty tricky, but like always, just work out all the angles you can find until you get the one you want.

EXAMPLE: **Find the value of angle x on the diagram below.**

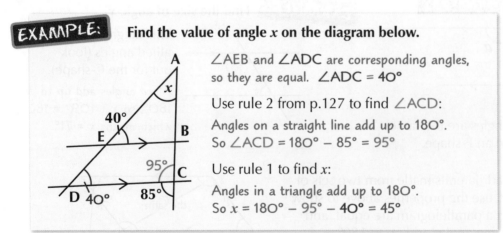

∠AEB and ∠ADC are corresponding angles, so they are equal. ∠ADC = 40°

Use rule 2 from p.127 to find ∠ACD:

Angles on a straight line add up to 180°. So ∠ACD = 180° − 85° = 95°

Use rule 1 to find x:

Angles in a triangle add up to 180°. So x = 180° − 95° − 40° = 45°

It's always a good idea to label your diagram as you work out each angle.

The most important rule of all — don't panic

EXAM TIP If you feel stuck in the exam, just write down every angle you can work out using the rules from the last two pages. Make sure you learn all the rules so you can use any of them when needed.

Bearings

Bearings. They'll be useful next time you go sailing. Or in your Maths exam.

Bearings

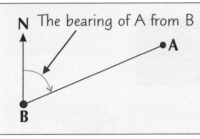

N   The bearing of A from B

1) A bearing is just a direction given as an angle in degrees.

2) All bearings are measured clockwise from the North line.

3) All bearings are given as 3 figures:
e.g. 060° rather than just 60°, 020° rather than 20° etc.

Three Words to Remember

To find or draw a bearing you must remember these three words:

1) 'FROM'

Find the word 'FROM' in the question, and put your pencil on the diagram at the point you are going 'from'.

2) NORTH LINE

At the point you are going FROM, draw in a NORTH LINE.

3) CLOCKWISE

Now draw in the angle CLOCKWISE from the NORTH LINE to the line joining the two points — this angle is the bearing.

EXAMPLES: **1. Find the bearing of Q from P.**

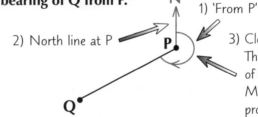

1) 'From P'

2) North line at P

3) Clockwise, from the N-line. This angle is the bearing of Q from P. Measure it with your protractor — **241°.**

2. The bearing of Z from Y is 110°.
Find the bearing of Y from Z.

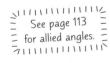

See page 113 for allied angles.

First sketch a diagram so you can see what's going on. Angles a and b are allied, so they add up to 180°.

Angle b = 180° − 110° = 70°
So bearing of Y from Z = 360° − 70° = 290°.

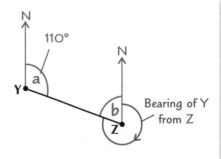

REVISION TIP

From a point, draw a North line then draw the angle clockwise

Make sure you've learned the three words above and the method that goes with them. When you answer a question on bearings, you might need to use some geometry rules at the same time.

Polygons

A polygon is a many-sided shape that can be regular or irregular. This page tells you the names of a few of them, plus some rules about their angles. Exciting, I know...

Regular Polygons

 KEY TERMS A polygon is a many-sided 2D shape that has only straight sides. A regular polygon is a polygon where all the sides are the same length and all of the angles are the same size.

In an irregular polygon, the sides and angles are not all the same.

Here are the first few regular polygons — the ones up to 10 sides:

EQUILATERAL TRIANGLE
3 sides

SQUARE
(regular quadrilateral)
4 sides

PENTAGON
5 sides

HEXAGON
6 sides

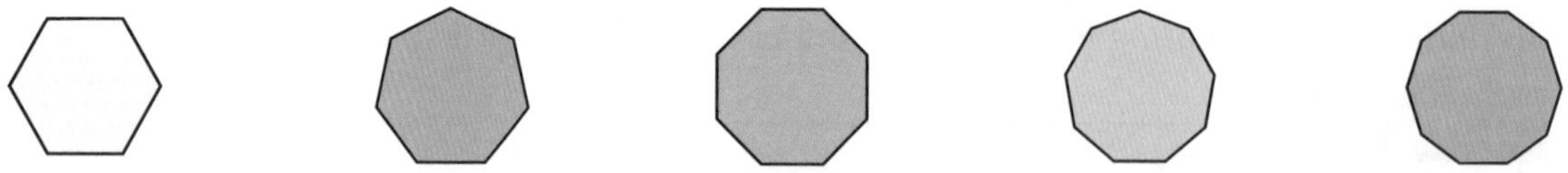

HEPTAGON
7 sides

OCTAGON
8 sides

NONAGON
9 sides

DECAGON
10 sides

Interior and Exterior Angles

Questions on interior and exterior angles often come up in exams — so you need to know what they are and how to find them. There are a couple of formulas you need to learn as well.

For REGULAR POLYGONS:

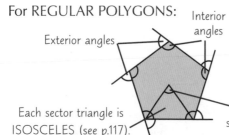

Exterior angles

Interior angles

Each sector triangle is ISOSCELES (see p.117).

This angle is always the same as the exterior angles.

$$\text{EXTERIOR ANGLE} = \frac{360°}{n}$$

$$\text{INTERIOR ANGLE} = 180° - \text{EXTERIOR ANGLE}$$

EXAMPLE: **The interior angle of a regular polygon is 165°. How many sides does the polygon have?**

First, find the exterior angle of the shape: exterior angle = $180° - 165° = 15°$

Use this value to find the number of sides: exterior angle = $\frac{360°}{n}$ so $n = \frac{360°}{\text{exterior angle}} = \frac{360°}{15°} = 24$ sides

For ANY POLYGON (regular or irregular):

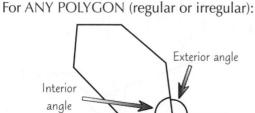

Exterior angle

Interior angle

$$\text{SUM OF EXTERIOR ANGLES} = 360°$$

$$\text{SUM OF INTERIOR ANGLES} = (n - 2) × 180°$$

 n is the number of sides

(left margin) Extended

(right margin) Extended

Four very simple and very important formulas

There are lots of questions examiners can ask on angles in polygons, but you can answer them all with the four formulas here. Check you've learned them and know which ones go with regular and irregular polygons.

Symmetry

This page is full with details about the TWO types of symmetry — and you need to learn them both.

Symmetry

Line Symmetry

MIRROR LINES go across a shape so that both sides fold exactly together. A regular polygon (see previous page) has the same number of lines of symmetry as its number of sides.

Regular pentagon — 5 lines of symmetry

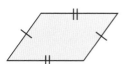

Parallelogram — no lines of symmetry

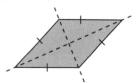

Rhombus — 2 lines of symmetry

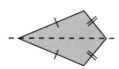

Kite — 1 line of symmetry

Rotational Symmetry

This is where you can rotate the shape into different positions that look exactly the same.
Again, regular polygons have the same order of rotational symmetry as their number of sides.

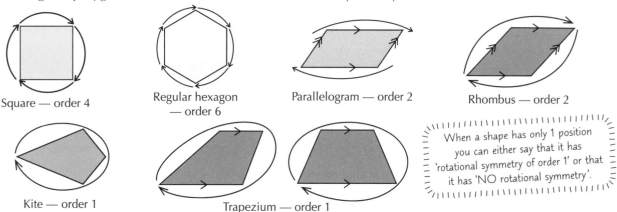

Square — order 4

Regular hexagon — order 6

Parallelogram — order 2

Rhombus — order 2

Kite — order 1

Trapezium — order 1

When a shape has only 1 position you can either say that it has 'rotational symmetry of order 1' or that it has 'NO rotational symmetry'.

The circle is a special case — it only has 1 side, but it has infinite lines of symmetry and rotational symmetry of infinite order.

Symmetry of **Triangles**

Triangles are a big part of geometry questions, so learn the symmetry properties of the different types:

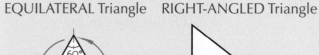

EQUILATERAL Triangle	RIGHT-ANGLED Triangle	ISOSCELES Triangle	SCALENE Triangle
		2 sides and 2 angles equal	No sides or angles equal

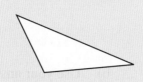

EQUILATERAL Triangle	RIGHT-ANGLED Triangle	ISOSCELES Triangle	SCALENE Triangle
3 lines of symmetry. Rotational symmetry order 3.	No lines of symmetry (unless the angles are 45° — then it's isosceles). Rotational symmetry order 1.	1 line of symmetry. Rotational symmetry order 1.	No lines of symmetry. Rotational symmetry order 1.

Make sure you learn the two different types of symmetry

Watch out for symmetry in geometry problems — you could use it to find a missing angle or side length.

Warm-Up and Worked Exam Questions

Don't just look at those lovely big diagrams — you need to work through the examples
in this section one by one to make sure that you've remembered all those rules...

Warm-Up Questions

1) Find the missing angles *a-d* below. State any angle laws used.

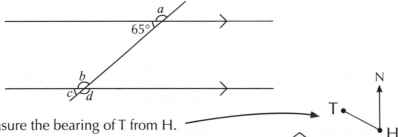

2) Measure the bearing of T from H.

3) How many sides does a hexagon have?

4) Write down the name of the shape to the right.

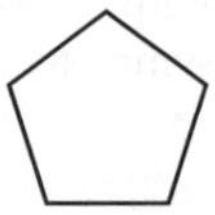

5) What is the size of an exterior angle of a regular 15-sided polygon?

6) A quadrilateral has 1 line of symmetry and 2 pairs of equal sides.
   What is the name of the quadrilateral?

Worked Exam Question

There'll probably be a question in the exam that asks you to find angles. That means you have
to remember all the different angle rules and practise using them in the right places...

1   *DEF* and *BEC* are straight lines that cross at *E*.
     AFB and *AC* are perpendicular lines.

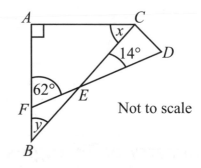

Not to scale

a)   Find angle *x*.
     Give a reason for each stage of your working.

Angles on a straight line add up to 180°,
so angle FEC = 180° − 14° = 166° ◄

Angles in a quadrilateral add up to 360°,
so x = 360° − 90° − 62° − 166° = 42°

Angle *x* is in quadrilateral ACEF,
so find the other missing angle
in ACEF, then you can find *x*.

$x =$ ....42............ °
[2 marks]

b)   Use your answer to part a) to show that *y* = 48°.

Angles in a triangle add up to 180°, so y = 180° − 90° − 42° = 48°

Angle *y* and angle *x* are
both in the triangle ABC.

[2 marks]

Exam Questions

2 Find the size of the angle marked *a*.
Give a reason for your answer.

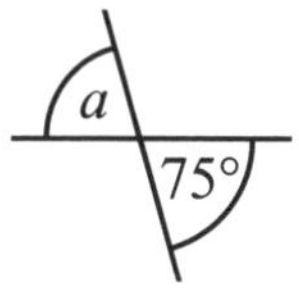

....

[2 marks]

3 *ABCD* is a quadrilateral.

Work out the size of angle *ADC*.

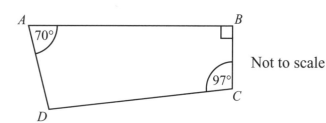

Not to scale

.... °
[2 marks]

4 Part of a regular polygon is on the right. Each interior angle is 150°.

Calculate the number of sides of the polygon.

Not to scale

....
[3 marks]

5 *BD* and *EF* are parallel straight lines.
AH is a straight line.

Work out the size of angle *x*.

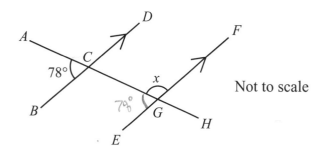

Not to scale

.... °
[2 marks]

6 The irregular polygon below has been divided into triangles as shown.

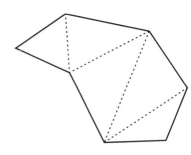

Use the triangles to show that the sum of the
interior angles of the polygon is 900°.

[2 marks]

Extended

Extended

Circle Geometry

It's time to start learning the good stuff — circle theorems. There's a lot to learn on these pages, but it's all very useful — particularly in exams...

Parts of a Circle

Here's a reminder of the names for the parts of a circle — you'll need to know what they all mean for the rules below...

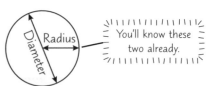

You'll know these two already.

KEY TERMS

A tangent is a straight line that just touches the outside of a circle.
A chord is a line drawn across the inside of a circle.
The circumference of a circle is the distance all the way around the outside.
An arc is just part of the circumference of a circle.

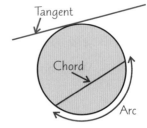

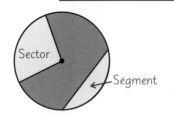

A sector is a wedge-shaped area (like a slice of cake) cut right from the centre.
A segment is the area between a chord and the outside of the circle.

Circle Rules to Learn

1) A TANGENT and a RADIUS meet at 90°.

A TANGENT always makes an angle of exactly 90° with the radius from where it touches the circle.

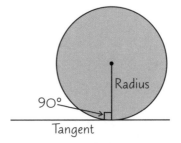

2) The ANGLE in a SEMICIRCLE is 90°.

A triangle drawn from the two ends of a diameter will ALWAYS make an angle of 90° where it hits the outer edge of the circle, no matter where it hits.

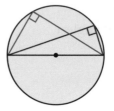

3) The PERPENDICULAR BISECTOR of a CHORD passes through the CENTRE of the circle.

No matter where you draw a chord, the line that cuts it exactly in half (at 90°), will go through the centre of the circle.

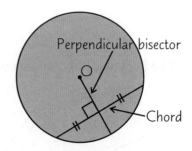

Extended

4) The angle at the CENTRE of a circle is TWICE the angle at the OUTER EDGE.

The angle made at the centre of a circle is EXACTLY DOUBLE the angle made at the outer edge of the circle from the same two points (two ends of the same chord).

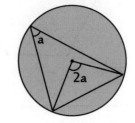

Circle Geometry

5) Angles in the SAME SEGMENT are EQUAL.

All triangles drawn from a chord will have the same angle where they touch the circumference. Also, the two angles on opposite sides of the chord add up to 180°.

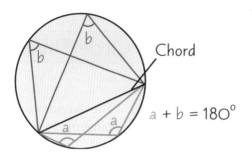

Chord

$a + b = 180°$

6) CHORDS of EQUAL LENGTH are EQUIDISTANT from the CENTRE.

Two chords that are the same length are always the same distance from the centre of the circle.

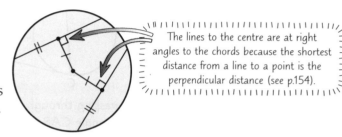

The lines to the centre are at right angles to the chords because the shortest distance from a line to a point is the perpendicular distance (see p.154).

7) OPPOSITE ANGLES in a CYCLIC QUADRILATERAL add up to 180°.

A cyclic quadrilateral is a 4-sided shape with every corner touching the circle. Both pairs of opposite angles add up to 180°.

$a + c = 180°$

$b + d = 180°$

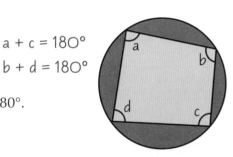

8) TANGENTS from the SAME POINT are the SAME LENGTH.

Two tangents drawn from an outside point are always equal in length, creating two congruent right-angled triangles as shown.

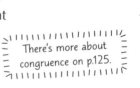

There's more about congruence on p.125.

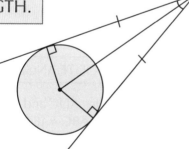

9) The ALTERNATE SEGMENT THEOREM.

The angle between a tangent and a chord is always equal to 'the angle in the opposite segment' (i.e. the angle made at the circumference by two lines drawn from the ends of the chord).

This is probably the hardest rule, so take care.

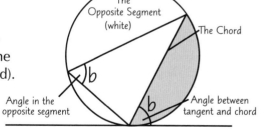

The Opposite Segment (white)

The Chord

b

Angle in the opposite segment

b

Angle between tangent and chord

REVISION TASK

Circle geometry already feels endless...

Sadly there's no way round it — you just need to learn all this stuff. Draw one circle for each of the circle properties you need to learn, then close the book and write one property on each.

Circle Geometry

After learning all of those rules you might wonder where you'll actually use them. Read on to find out...

Using the Circle Theorems

EXAMPLE: The diagram shows the triangle ABC, where lines BA and BC are tangents to the circle. Show that line AC is NOT a diameter.

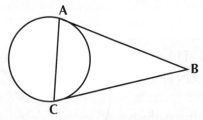

If AC was a diameter passing through the centre, O, then OA and OC would be radii, and angle CAB = angle ACB = 90° by rule 1:

1) A TANGENT and a RADIUS meet at 90°.

However, this would mean that ABC isn't a triangle as you can't have a triangle with two 90° angles, so AC cannot be a diameter.

If angles CAB and ACB were 90°, lines AB and BC would be parallel so would never meet.

EXAMPLE: A, B, C and D are points on the circumference of the circle, and O is the centre of the circle. Angle ADC = 109°. Work out the size of angles ABC and AOC.

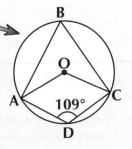

You'll probably have to use more than one rule to solve circle theorem questions — here, ABCD is a cyclic quadrilateral so use rule 7:

7) OPPOSITE ANGLES in a CYCLIC QUADRILATERAL add up to 180°.

Angles ADC and ABC are opposite, so:
angle ABC = 180° − 109° = 71°.

Now, angles ABC (which you've just found) and AOC both come from chord AC, so you can use rule 4:

4) The angle at the CENTRE of a circle is TWICE the angle at the CIRCUMFERENCE.

So angle AOC is double angle ABC, which means:
angle AOC = 71° × 2 = 142°.

Extended

Always stick to the rules with circle geometry

If you find this page isn't making much sense, you need to go back for another look at pages 120 and 121. Sometimes you'll find there's more than one way of finding the angle you want.

Warm-Up and Worked Exam Questions

Time to have a go at using all those great circle theorems. The only way this stuff is going to stay in your head is if you practise answering questions — luckily you've got two pages of them here...

Warm-Up Questions

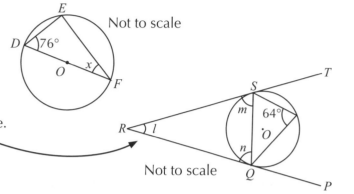

1) *DEF* is a triangle drawn in the circle. *DF* goes through the centre. Work out the missing angle, *x*.

Extended

2) *PQR* and *RST* are tangents to the circle. Find the missing angles *l*, *m* and *n*.

Worked Exam Question

Circle theorem questions can sometimes be a bit overwhelming, and it can be difficult to know where to start. The best approach is to keep finding any angles you can using the circle theorems and the angle rules from pages 112 and 113, until you have enough information to find the angle you want.

1   In the diagram, *O* is the centre of the circle. *A*, *B*, *C* and *D* are points on the circumference of the circle and *DE* and *BE* are tangents. Angle *DEB* is 80°.

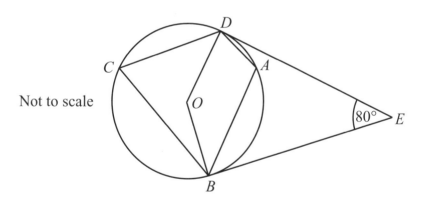

Not to scale

Work out the size of angle *DAB*, giving reasons for each step in your working.

Angles ODE and OBE are both 90°
because a tangent always meets a radius at 90°.

Angle DOB = 100° because angles in a quadrilateral add up to 360°.

Angle DCB = 50° because an angle at the centre is twice the angle at the circumference.

Angle DAB = 130° because opposite angles of a cyclic quadrilateral add up to 180°.

..........130.......°

[4 marks]

Exam Questions

2 The diagram on the right shows a circle with centre O.
Lines JK and KL are tangents to the circle.
Angle MON is 128°. Find angle JKL.

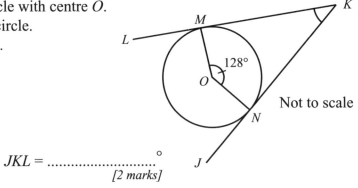

K
M
L
128°
O
Not to scale
N
J

JKL = ... °
[2 marks]

3 Line QR is a diameter of the circle shown below.
QS is a straight line that crosses the circle at P, and angle PRS is 32°. Find angle PSR.

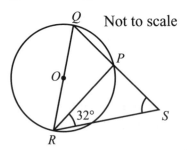

Q
Not to scale
P
O
32°
S
R

PSR = ... °
[3 marks]

4 The diagram below shows a circle with centre O. A, B, C and D are points on the circumference of the circle and AOC is a straight line.

B
x
C
O
62°
A
D
Not to scale

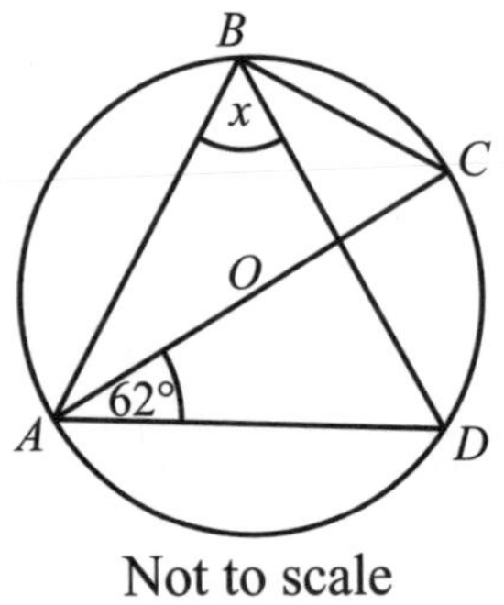

Work out the size of the angle marked x.

x = ... °
[3 marks]

5 Points A, B, C, D and E lie on the circumference of the circle shown in the diagram below.
Angle ABE is 37° and angle DCE is 53°. FG is the tangent to the circle at point E.

Prove that the chord AD passes through the centre of the circle.

F
E
A
G
37°
53°
B
D
C
Not to scale

[3 marks]

Extended

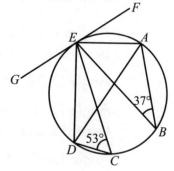

Congruence

Shapes can be congruent, which basically just means 'the same as each other'.
Luckily for you, here's a full page on congruence.

Congruent — Same Shape, Same Size

Congruence is another long maths word which sounds really complicated, but actually isn't.

KEY TERM

Congruent shapes are exactly the same — the same size and the same shape.

These shapes are all congruent:

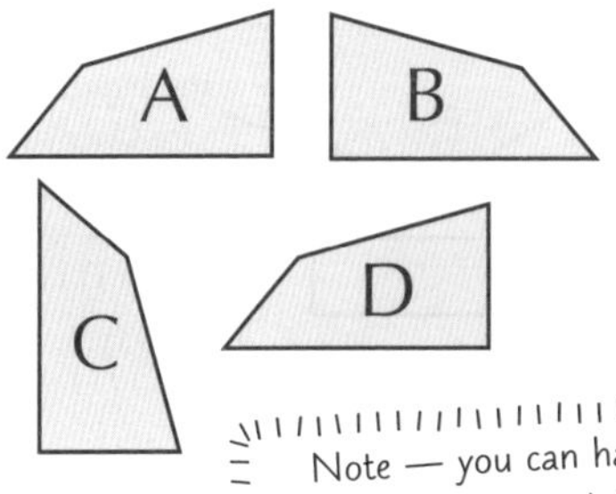

Note — you can have mirror images or rotations.

EXAMPLE: **Two of the triangles below are congruent. Write down the letters of the congruent triangles.**

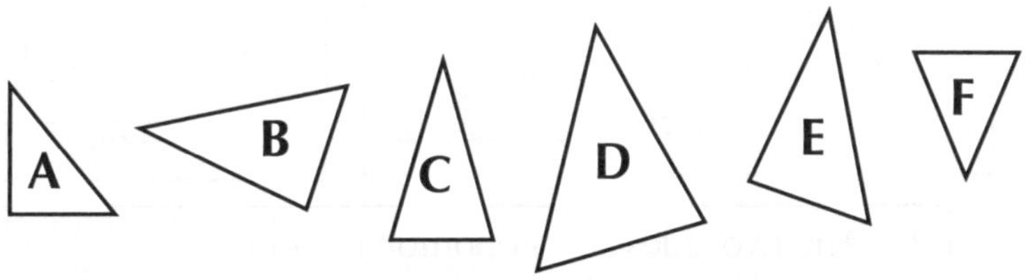

Just pick out the two triangles that are exactly the same — remember that the shape might have been rotated or reflected.
By eye, you can see that the congruent triangles are **B and E**.

Extended

Conditions for Congruent Triangles

Two triangles are congruent if one of the four conditions below holds true:

SSS	three sides are the same
AAS	two angles and a corresponding side match up
SAS	two sides and the angle between them match up
RHS	a right angle, the hypotenuse and one other side all match up

The hypotenuse is the longest side of a right-angled triangle — the one opposite the right angle.

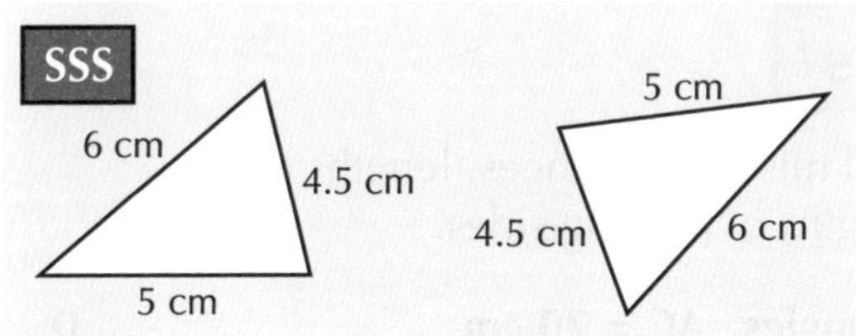

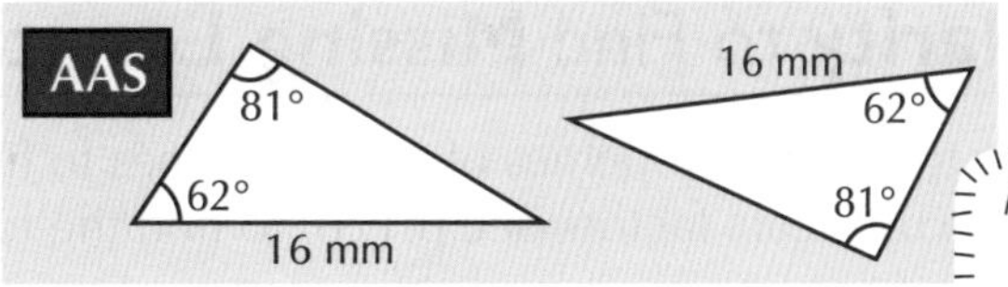

Make sure the sides match up — here, the side is opposite the 81° angle.

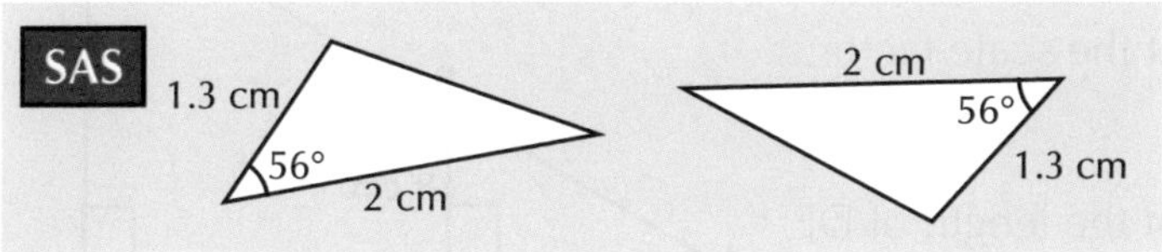

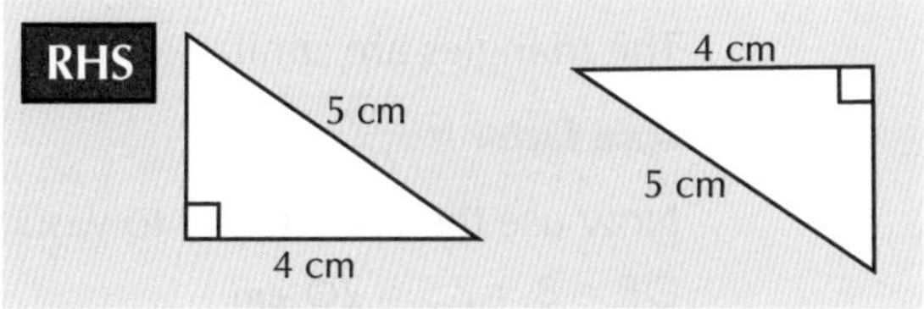

EXAM TIP

Congruent just means same size, same shape

When answering an exam question on conditions for congruent triangles, take your time and think carefully — make sure you're using the right sides and angles in each shape.

Similarity

Similar shapes are exactly the same shape, but can be different sizes (they can also be rotated or reflected).

e.g.

Similar Shapes Have the **Same Angles**

  Similar shapes have the same shape but a different size.

Generally, for two shapes to be similar, all the angles must match and the sides must be proportional. But for triangles, there are three special conditions — if any one of these is true, you know they're similar. Two triangles are similar if:

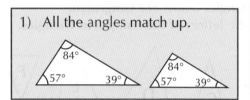

1) All the angles match up.

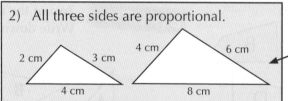

2) All three sides are proportional.

Here, the sides of the bigger triangle are twice as long as the sides of the smaller triangle.

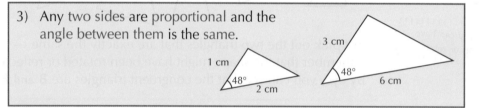

3) Any two sides are proportional and the angle between them is the same.

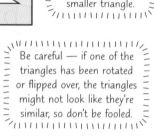

Be careful — if one of the triangles has been rotated or flipped over, the triangles might not look like they're similar, so don't be fooled.

EXAMPLE: Tony says, "Triangles ABC and DEF are similar." Is Tony correct? Explain your answer.

Check condition 3 holds — start by finding the missing angle in triangle DEF:

Angle DEF = 180° − 46° − 30° = 104° so angle ABC = angle DEF

Now check that AB and BC are proportional to DE and EF:

DE ÷ AB = 6 ÷ 2 = 3 and EF ÷ BC = 9 ÷ 3 = 3 so DE and EF are 3 times as long as AB and BC.

Tony is correct — two sides are proportional and the angle between them is the same so the triangles are similar.

Use **Similarity** to Find **Missing Lengths**

You might have to use the properties of similar shapes to find missing distances, lengths etc. — you'll need to use scale factors (see p.128) to find the lengths of missing sides.

EXAMPLE: ABC and ADE are similar right-angled triangles. AC = 20 cm, AE = 50 cm and BC = 8 cm. Find the length of DE.

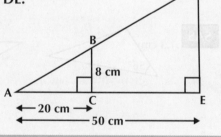

The triangles are similar, so work out the scale factor:

scale factor $= \frac{50}{20} = 2.5$

Now use the scale factor to work out the length of DE:

DE = 8 × 2.5 = 20 cm

Similar means the same shape but a different size

Make sure you know the difference between congruent and similar shapes — to help you remember, think 'similar siblings, congruent clones' — siblings are alike but not the same, clones are identical.

The Four Transformations

There are four transformations you need to know — translation, rotation, reflection and enlargement.

1) Translations

In a translation, a shape moves vertically and horizontally by a particular amount, which can be given as a vector (see p.162) written $\begin{pmatrix} x \\ y \end{pmatrix}$. For the vector, x is the horizontal movement (to the right) and y is the vertical movement (upwards). If the shape moves left and down, x and y will be negative.

EXAMPLE:

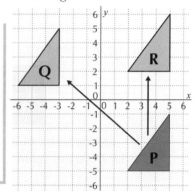

a) Describe the transformation that maps triangle P onto Q.
b) Describe the transformation that maps triangle P onto R.

a) To get from P to Q, you need to move 8 units left and 6 units up, so:

The transformation from P to Q is a **translation by the vector** $\begin{pmatrix} -8 \\ 6 \end{pmatrix}$.

b) The transformation from P to R is a **translation by the vector** $\begin{pmatrix} 0 \\ 7 \end{pmatrix}$.

2) Rotations

To describe a rotation, you must give 3 details:

1) The angle of rotation (usually 90° or 180°).
2) The direction of rotation (clockwise or anticlockwise).
3) The centre of rotation (often, but not always, the origin).

> For a rotation of 180°, it doesn't matter whether you go clockwise or anticlockwise, so you don't need to say.

EXAMPLE:  **a) Describe the transformation that maps triangle A onto B.**

The transformation from A to B is a rotation of 90° anticlockwise about the origin.

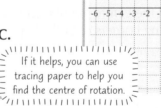

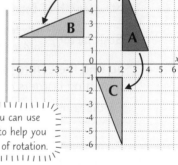

b) Describe the transformation that maps triangle A onto C.

The transformation from A to C is a rotation of 180° about the point (2, 0).

> If it helps, you can use tracing paper to help you find the centre of rotation.

3) Reflections

For a reflection, you must give the equation of the mirror line.

EXAMPLE:

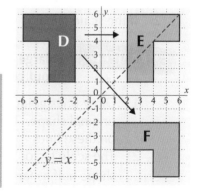

a) Describe the transformation that maps shape D onto shape E.

The transformation from D to E is a **reflection in the y-axis**.

b) Describe the transformation that maps shape D onto shape F.

The transformation from D to F is a **reflection in the line** $y = x$.

A rotation is specified by an angle, a direction and a centre

Translations, reflections and rotations of a shape are congruent. This is because their size and shape don't change when transformed — only their position and which way they face.

The Four Transformations

One more transformation coming up — enlargements. They're the trickiest, but also the most interesting.

4) Enlargements

For an enlargement, you must state:

> 1) The scale factor.
> 2) The centre of enlargement.

$$\text{scale factor} = \frac{\text{new length}}{\text{old length}}$$

1) The scale factor for an enlargement tells you how long the sides of the new shape are compared to the old shape. E.g. a scale factor of 3 means you multiply each side length by 3.

2) If you're given the centre of enlargement, it's vitally important where your new shape is on the grid.

> The scale factor tells you the relative distance of the
> old points and new points from the centre of enlargement.

So, a scale factor of 2 means the corners of the enlarged shape are twice as far from the centre of enlargement as the corners of the original shape.

Describing Enlargements

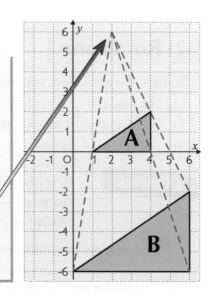

EXAMPLE: **Describe the transformation that maps triangle A onto triangle B.**

Use the formula to find the scale factor.
(Just do this for one pair of sides.)

Old length of triangle base = 3 units
New length of triangle base = 6 units

Scale factor = $\dfrac{\text{new length}}{\text{old length}} = \dfrac{6}{3} = 2$

To find the centre of enlargement, draw lines that go through matching corners of both shapes and see where they cross.

So the transformation is an **enlargement of scale factor 2, centre (2, 6)**.

Fractional Scale Factors

1) If the scale factor is bigger than 1 the shape gets bigger.
2) If the scale factor is smaller than 1 (e.g. ½) it gets smaller.

EXAMPLE: **Enlarge the shaded shape by a scale factor of $\frac{1}{2}$, about centre O.**

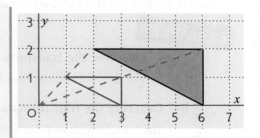

1) Draw lines going from the centre to each corner of the original shape. The corners of the new shape will be on these lines.
2) The scale factor is $\frac{1}{2}$, so make each corner of the new shape half as far from O as it is in the original shape.

An enlargement is given by a scale factor and a centre of enlargement

Enlargements of shapes are similar — the position and the size change, but the angles and ratios of the sides don't (see p.126). Remember that a scale factor smaller than 1 means the shape gets smaller.

The Four Transformations

Enlargements aren't just for graphs — you need to know how enlargements affect area and volume too. But there is one more type of enlargement on a graph you should know about first — negative scale factors.

Negative Scale Factors

If the scale factor is negative, the shape will move to the other side of the centre of enlargement. If the scale factor is –1, it's exactly the same as a rotation of 180°.

EXAMPLE: **Enlarge shape A below by a scale factor of –3, centre (1, 1). Label the transformed shape B.**

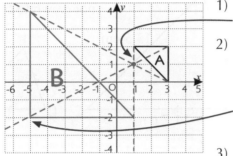

1) First, mark (1, 1) as the centre and draw lines going through it from each vertex of shape A.

2) Then, multiply the distance from each vertex to the centre of enlargement by 3, and measure this distance coming out the other side of the centre of enlargement. So on shape A, vertex (3, 2) is 2 right and 1 up from (1, 1) — so the corresponding point on shape B will be 6 left and 3 down from (1, 1). Do this for every point.

3) Join the points you've drawn to form shape B.

How Enlargement Affects Area and Volume

If a shape is enlarged by a scale factor (see previous page), its area, or surface area and volume (if it's a 3D shape), will change too. However, they don't change by the same value as the scale factor:

For a SCALE FACTOR n:		AS RATIOS:	
The SIDES are	n times bigger	Lengths	$a:b$
The AREAS are	n^2 times bigger	Areas	$a^2:b^2$
The VOLUMES are	n^3 times bigger	Volumes	$a^3:b^3$

$$n = \frac{\text{new length}}{\text{old length}} \qquad n^2 = \frac{\text{new area}}{\text{old area}}$$

$$n^3 = \frac{\text{new volume}}{\text{old volume}}$$

So if the scale factor is 2, the lengths are 2 times as long, the area is $2^2 = 4$ times as big, and the volume is $2^3 = 8$ times as big. As ratios, these enlargements are $1:2$ (length), $1^2:2^2 = 1:4$ (area) and $1^3:2^3 = 1:8$ (volume).

There's more on areas and volumes on p.139-140 and p.146-148.

EXAMPLE: **Cylinder A has surface area 6π cm², and cylinder B has surface area 54π cm². The volume of cylinder A is 2π cm³. Find the volume of cylinder B, given that B is an enlargement of A.**

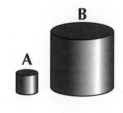

First, work out the scale factor, n: $n^2 = \dfrac{\text{Area B}}{\text{Area A}} = \dfrac{54\pi}{6\pi} = 9$, so $n = 3$

Use this in the volume formula: $n^3 = \dfrac{\text{Volume B}}{\text{Volume A}} \Rightarrow 3^3 = \dfrac{\text{Volume B}}{2\pi}$

$\Rightarrow$ Volume of B $= 2\pi \times 27 = 54\pi$ cm³

This shows that if the scale factor is 3, lengths are 3 times as long, the surface area is 9 times as big and the volume is 27 times as big.

You need to know all four types of transformation

EXAM TIP If an exam question asks you to describe a transformation, make sure you include all the important info. For rotations, state the centre of rotation, the angle and the direction. For reflections, give the equation of the mirror line. For enlargements, give the centre of enlargement and the scale factor.

Warm-Up and Worked Exam Questions

These warm-up questions cover some of the basics you'll need for the exam — use them to make sure you've learned all the key information properly before you move on to tackling some exam questions.

Warm-Up Questions

1) From the diagram to the right, pick out:
   a) a pair of congruent shapes
   b) a pair of similar (but not congruent) shapes

2) Triangles ABC and DEF are similar.
   a) Triangle DEF is an enlargement of triangle ABC. What is the scale factor of the enlargement?
   b) What is the length of DF?

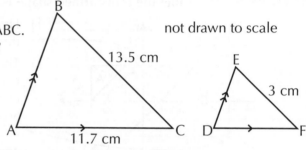

not drawn to scale

3) What translation would map the point (1, 3) onto (–2, 6)?

4) Point A is reflected in the *y*-axis to give point B.
   Given that point A is found at (3, 5), write down the coordinates of point B.

Worked Exam Question

Worked exam questions are the ideal way to get the hang of answering the real exam questions — make sure you understand the answer to this one.

1   Shapes **F** and **G** have been drawn on the grid below.

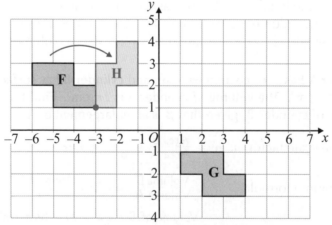

a)   Write down the vector which describes the translation that maps **F** onto **G**.

To get from F to G, the shape is moved 7 units to the right and 4 units down. $\begin{pmatrix} 7 \\ -4 \end{pmatrix}$

[2 marks]

b)   Rotate shape **F** by 90° clockwise about the point (–3, 1).
      Label your image **H**.   See the grid above — you might find it easiest
                                        to use tracing paper to draw rotations.

[2 marks]

Exam Questions

2   In the diagram below, **B** is an image of **A**.

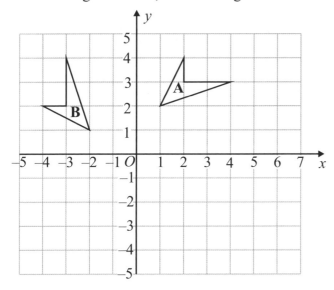

a)   Describe fully the single
transformation that maps **A** onto **B**.

....

....

....
[3 marks]

b)   Translate shape **B** by the vector $\begin{pmatrix} -1 \\ -4 \end{pmatrix}$.
Label the image as **C**.

[1 mark]

3   The shapes *ABCD* and *EFGH* are mathematically similar.

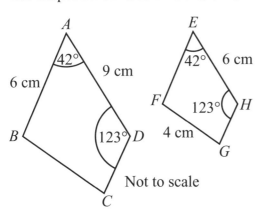

Not to scale

a)   Find the length of *EF*.

.... cm
[2 marks]

b)   Find the length of *BC*.

.... cm
[1 mark]

4   **A**, **B** and **C** are three solid cones which are mathematically similar. The surface area of each
cone is given below. The perpendicular height of **A** is 4 cm. The volume of **C** is 135π cm³.

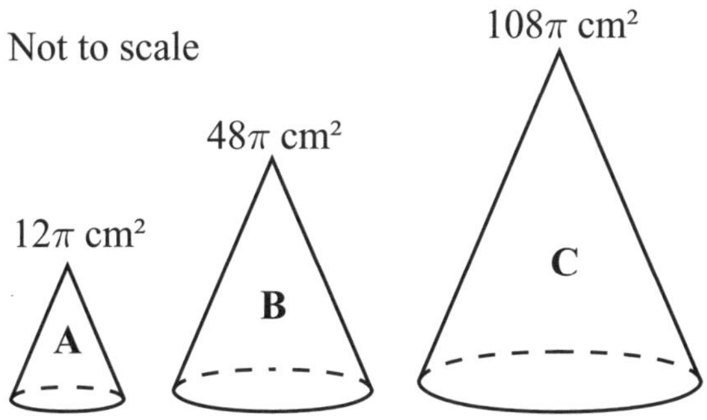

Not to scale

108π cm²

48π cm²

12π cm²

A

B

C

a)   Calculate the volume of **A**.

.... cm³
[4 marks]

b)   Calculate the perpendicular height of **B**.

.... cm
[4 marks]

Unit Conversions

Convert this page into knowledge by reading it and learning it. First up, metric units...

Metric Units

1) Length   mm, cm, m, km
2) Area mm^2, cm^2, m^2, km^2,
3) Volume mm^3, cm^3, m^3, ml, litres
4) Mass   g, kg, tonnes
5) Speed   km/h, m/s

COMMON UNIT CONVERSIONS

1 cm = 10 mm	1 tonne = 1000 kg
1 m = 100 cm	1 litre = 1000 ml
1 km = 1000 m	1 litre = 1000 cm^3
1 kg = 1000 g	1 cm^3 = 1 ml

EXAMPLE: **Convert 7 litres into ml.**

1) Write down the first conversion factor.   1 litre = 1000 ml, so conversion factor = 1000

2) Multiply the number of litres by 1000.   7 × 1000 = 7000 ml

EXAMPLE: **A whale is 18.6 m in length. How long is this in mm?**

Do this conversion in two steps — metres to cm then cm to mm.

1) Write down the first conversion factor.   1 m = 100 cm

2) Multiply the number of metres by 100.   18.6 × 100 = 1860 cm

3) Write down the second conversion factor.   1 cm = 10 mm

4) Multiply the number of cm by 10.   1860 × 10 = 18 600 mm

Always check your answer is sensible. E.g. 1 cm = 10 mm, so when you convert from cm to mm you should get a bigger number.

Currency Conversions

You could get asked to convert between any two currencies, but you'll be given the conversion factor.

EXAMPLE: **Using the exchange rate $1 = 6.7 Danish kroner, convert the following amounts:**

a) **$80 to kroner.** $80 = 80 × 6.7 = 536 kroner

b) **2010 kroner to dollars.**   2010 kroner = 2010 ÷ 6.7 = $300

Check your answers — $1 = 6.7 kroner, so the number of kroner should always be bigger than the equivalent number of dollars.

There's no way round it — you'll have to learn some conversions

There are a lot of conversions here, and you'll need to remember all of those metric unit conversions (you'll be given currency conversion factors so don't worry about that). Keep going until you've learned them all.

Area and Volume Conversions

Get ready to have a go at some trickier conversions now. There are a couple of methods for you to remember so that when it comes to the exam you can feel confident converting areas and volumes.

Converting **Areas**

You need to be really careful when converting areas — just because 1 m = 100 cm, it DOES NOT mean 1 m² = 100 cm². Follow this method to avoid slipping up:

$1 \text{ m}^2 = 100 \text{ cm} \times 100 \text{ cm} = 10\,000 \text{ cm}^2$
$1 \text{ cm}^2 = 10 \text{ mm} \times 10 \text{ mm} = 100 \text{ mm}^2$

1) Find the conversion factor — it'll be the same as for converting units (see p.132).
2) Multiply or divide by the conversion factor TWO TIMES.
3) Don't forget that the units come with a 'square', e.g. mm², cm².

EXAMPLE: The area of the top of a table is 0.6 m². Find its area in cm².

1) Find the conversion factor:

1 m = 100 cm ⟶ Conversion factor = 100

2) It's an area — multiply twice by the conversion factor:

0.6 × 100 × 100 = 6000 — 1 m = 100 cm — you expect more cm than m, so multiply.

3) Write down the correct units:

0.6 m² = 6000 cm²

Converting **Volumes**

$1 \text{ m}^3 = 100 \text{ cm} \times 100 \text{ cm} \times 100 \text{ cm} = 1\,000\,000 \text{ cm}^3$
$1 \text{ cm}^3 = 10 \text{ mm} \times 10 \text{ mm} \times 10 \text{ mm} = 1000 \text{ mm}^3$

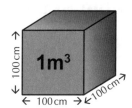

1) Conversion factor — it'll be the same as for converting units (see p.132).
2) Multiply or divide by the conversion factor THREE TIMES.
3) Don't forget that the units come with a 'cube', e.g. mm³, cm³.

EXAMPLE: A glass has a volume of 72 000 mm³. What is its volume in cm³?

1) Find the conversion factor:

1 cm = 10 mm ⟶ Conversion factor = 10

2) It's a volume — divide 3 times by the conversion factor:

72 000 ÷ 10 ÷ 10 ÷ 10 = 72 — 1 cm = 10 mm — you expect fewer cm than mm, so divide.

3) Write down the correct units:

72 000 mm³ = 72 cm³

Remember — area comes with a 2 and volume comes with a 3

Learn the rules for converting between units for areas and volumes. Always check your answer to see if it is sensible or not — common sense will get you a long way.

Time

Make sure you can handle time questions — they're simple and might get you a mark or two in the exam.

am means morning	
pm means afternoon or evening	

12 am (00:00) means midnight	
12 pm (12:00) means noon	

12-hour clock	24-hour clock
12.00 am	00:00
1.12 am	01:12
12.15 pm	12:15
1.47 pm	13:47
11.32 pm	23:32

The hour parts of times on 12- and 24-hour clocks are different after 1 pm:
add 12 hours to go from 12-hour to 24-hour, and subtract 12 to go the other way.

$$3.24 \text{ pm} \xrightarrow{+ 12 \text{ h}} 15{:}24$$
$$\xleftarrow{- 12 \text{ h}}$$

Break **Time** Calculations into **Simple Stages**

EXAMPLE: **Angela watched a film that started at 7.20 pm and finished at 10.05 pm. How long was the film in minutes?**

1) Split the time between 7.20 pm and 10.05 pm into simple stages.

7.20 pm ⟶ 9.20 pm ⟶ 10.00 pm ⟶ 10.05 pm
+ 2 hours   + 40 minutes   + 5 minutes

2) Convert the hours to minutes.   2 hours = 2 × 60 = 120 minutes

3) Add to get the total minutes.   120 + 40 + 5 = 165 minutes

> Avoid calculators — the decimal answers they give are confusing, e.g. 2.5 hours = 2 hours 30 mins, NOT 2 hours 50 mins.

Timetable Exam Questions

EXAMPLE:

Use the timetable to answer these questions:

a) How long does it take for the bus to get from Market Street to the hospital?

Bus Timetable					
Bus Station	18 45	19 00	19 15	19 30
Market Street	18 52	19 07	19 22	19 37
Long Lane Shops	19 01	19 16	19 31	19 46
Train Station	19 11	19 26	19 41	19 56
Hospital	19 23	19 38	19 53	20 08

Read times from the same column (I've used the 1st) — break the time into stages.

Market Street   Hospital
18 52 ⟶ 19 00 ⟶ 19 23
   + 8 mins   + 23 mins

8 + 23 = 31 minutes

b) Henriette wants to get a bus from the bus station to the train station in time for a train that leaves at 19:30. What is the latest bus that she can catch?

> This is the latest time she could arrive before 19 30.

1) Read along the train station row.   19 11   (19 26)   19 41   19 56

2) Move up this column to the bus station row and read off the entry.   The bus that gets to the train station at 19 26 leaves the bus station at 19 00.

This page might look easy, but make sure you learn it all

It's easy to go wrong when you're using your calculator for time questions, so be extra careful. Always try to split questions down into easier stages — that way you'll make fewer mistakes.

Speed, Density and Pressure

Let's see if you can speed through this page. You need to know the formulas and be able to substitute numbers into them — you should also be able to convert between different units (which is a bit harder).

Speed = Distance ÷ Time

 KEY TERM — Speed is the distance travelled per unit time. It's usually measured in m/s or km/h.

$$\text{SPEED} = \frac{\text{DISTANCE}}{\text{TIME}} \qquad \text{TIME} = \frac{\text{DISTANCE}}{\text{SPEED}} \qquad \text{DISTANCE} = \text{SPEED} \times \text{TIME}$$

A formula triangle is a very useful tool for remembering formulas. Here's the one for speed. To remember the order of the letters ($S^D T$) we have the words SaD Times. So if it's a question on speed, distance and time, just say SAD TIMES.

How DO YOU USE Formula Triangles?
1) COVER UP the thing you want to find and WRITE DOWN what's left.
2) Now PUT IN THE VALUES for the other two things and WORK IT OUT.

E.g. to get the formula for speed from the triangle, cover up S and you're left with $\frac{D}{T}$.

EXAMPLES:

1. Rob cycles 30 km in 2 hours. What is his average speed?

1) You want speed so covering S gives: $\quad S = \dfrac{D}{T}$

2) Put in the numbers — and don't forget the units. $\quad S = 30 \div 2$
$= 15 \text{ km/h}$

CHECK YOUR UNITS MATCH
Distance in km and time in hours give speed in km per hour.

2. A cheetah runs at a speed of 27 m/s for 20 s. What distance does it cover?

1) You want distance so covering D gives: $\quad D = S \times T$

2) Put in the numbers — and don't forget the units. $\quad D = 27 \times 20$
$= 540 \text{ m}$

UNITS CHECK: m/s and s go in the calculation, so m comes out.

Density = Mass ÷ Volume

 KEY TERM — Density is the mass per unit volume of a substance. It's usually measured in kg/m³ or g/cm³.

$$\text{DENSITY} = \frac{\text{MASS}}{\text{VOLUME}} \qquad \text{VOLUME} = \frac{\text{MASS}}{\text{DENSITY}} \qquad \text{MASS} = \text{DENSITY} \times \text{VOLUME}$$

Here's the formula triangle for density. Luckily, you don't need to learn this formula off by heart — you'll be given it in the question if you need it. You still need to know how to use it though...

EXAMPLE: A giant chocolate bar has a density of 1.3 g/cm³. If the bar's volume is 1800 cm³, what is the mass of the bar in grams?

1) You want the mass, so covering M gives: $\quad M = D \times V$

2) Put in the numbers — and remember the units.
$M = 1.3 \text{ g/cm}^3 \times 1800 \text{ cm}^3$
$= 2340 \text{ g}$

UNITS CHECK: g/cm³ and cm³ go in, so g comes out.

Speed, Density and Pressure

Pressure = Force ÷ Area

 KEY TERM Pressure is the amount of force acting per unit area. It's usually measured in N/m², or pascals (Pa).

'N' stands for 'newtons', which is the unit of force.

$$\text{PRESSURE} = \frac{\text{FORCE}}{\text{AREA}} \qquad \text{AREA} = \frac{\text{FORCE}}{\text{PRESSURE}} \qquad \text{FORCE} = \text{PRESSURE} \times \text{AREA}$$

Another formula triangle here — this one's for pressure. This formula will also be included in the question if you need to use it, but still make sure that you understand it properly.

EXAMPLE: A cuboid box with a weight of 200 N rests on horizontal ground. The side lengths of the face resting on the ground are 0.2 m and 0.8 m. Calculate the pressure exerted by the box on the ground.

1) Work out the area of the face in contact with the ground: 0.2 m × 0.8 m = 0.16 m²

2) Use the formula triangle — you want pressure so covering P gives: $P = \dfrac{F}{A}$

3) Put in the numbers. $P = \dfrac{200\,N}{0.16\,m^2}$

4) Check the units — you put in N and m² so you'll get N/m².   = 1250 N/m²

Converting **Speed, Density** and **Pressure**

1) Units of speed, density and pressure are made up of two measures — a distance and a time, a mass and a volume, or a force and an area.

2) So to convert units of speed, density or pressure, you might need to do two conversions — one for each measure.

EXAMPLE: A rabbit's top speed is 54 km/h. How fast is this in m/s?

1) First convert from km/h to m/h: 1 km = 1000 m, so conversion factor = 1000
      54 × 1000 = 54 000
      54 km/h = 54 000 m/h

2) Now convert from m/h to m/s: 1 hour = 60 minutes = 60 × 60 = 3600 seconds
      So conversion factor = 3600
      54 000 ÷ 3600 = 15
      54 km/h = 54 000 m/h = 15 m/s

Formula triangles are really helpful

Cover up the measurement you want to find, then write down what you can still see. Put the values in and your answer will come out. Make sure that the units make sense — you won't get a distance in seconds.

Warm-Up and Worked Exam Questions

Time to check that all that exciting revision has worked. Try these first to make sure you've learned it all:

Warm-Up Questions

1) a) Convert 12.7 kg into grams.   b) Convert 1430 cm into metres.
2) Change 3 m^3 to mm^3.
3) A cheetah runs 100 m in 4 seconds. What is its average speed in km per hour?
4) A cyclist travels for 0.75 hours at a speed of 12 km per hour. What distance does he travel?

The formula for density is: density = mass ÷ volume.

5) A lump of lead weighing 374 g has a volume of 33 cm^3.
   What is the approximate density of the lead (to 3 s.f.)?
6) A solid plastic building block measures 5 cm × 4 cm × 6 cm.
   The density of the plastic is 0.8 g/cm^3. What is the mass of the block?

Worked Exam Questions

Make sure you really know this stuff — read it thoroughly, and then once you're happy with it, have a go yourself to check you've understood it properly.

1   The cuboid below has three different faces (A, B and C).
    The cuboid has a weight of 40 N. [Pressure = $\frac{\text{Force}}{\text{Area}}$].

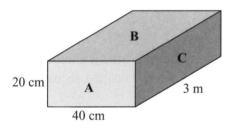

20 cm   A   40 cm   B   C   3 m

   a) Calculate the pressure, in N/m^2, that the cuboid exerts on horizontal ground when the cuboid is resting on face A.

   Area of A = 40 cm × 20 cm = 800 cm^2
              = 800 ÷ 100 ÷ 100 = 0.08 m^2
   Pressure = 40 N ÷ 0.08 m^2
            = 500 N/m^2

   ....500........ N/m^2
   [3 marks]

   b) Three of these cuboids are stacked directly on top of each other and the bottom cuboid is resting on face B. What pressure are they exerting on horizontal ground?

   Three cuboids would weigh = 3 × 40N = 120 N
   Area of B = 3 m × 0.4 m = 1.2 m^2
   Pressure = 120 N ÷ 1.2 m^2 = 100 N/m^2

   ....100........ N/m^2
   [3 marks]

2   In 2013 Mo ran a long-distance race and finished with time t.
    In 2014 he finished the same race but his time was 10% quicker.
    By what percentage did his average speed for the race increase? s_1 is Mo's speed in 2013,
    Give your answer to 2 decimal places. s_2 is Mo's speed in 2014

    In 2014 he finished with a time of 0.9t, so $s_1 = \frac{d}{t}$ and $s_2 = \frac{d}{0.9t}$

    So, because d is the same each year, $s_1 t = 0.9s_2 t \rightarrow s_2 = \frac{s_1}{0.9} = 1.11... × s_1$

    So s_2 is 111.11... % of s_1.

    His percentage increase was 11.11% (2 d.p.)

    ....11.11........ %
    [3 marks]

Exam Questions

3   Isaac and Ultan spent 13 days building a model robot.
     On the first 12 days they built from 4.30 pm till 7.15 pm and
     on the last day they built for a total of 7 hours 10 minutes.

     Find the total amount of time they spent building the robot.
     Give your answer in hours and minutes.

.... hours .... minutes

[4 marks]

4   Adam has been caught speeding by a pair of average speed cameras.
     The speed limit was 80 km/h. The cameras are 2500 m apart.

     The time taken for his car to pass between them was 102 seconds.

     a)   Work out Adam's average speed between the cameras.
          Give your answer to the nearest km/h.

.... km/h

[2 marks]

     b)   If Adam had been travelling within the speed limit, find the minimum time it should
          have taken him to pass between the cameras. Give your answer to the nearest second.

.... s

[2 marks]

5   The mass of a metal statue is 360 kg.
     The density of the metal alloy from which it is made is 1800 kg/m³. [Density = $\frac{\text{Mass}}{\text{Volume}}$]

     a)   Calculate the volume of the statue.

.... m³

[2 marks]

     b)   A new statue is made that has the same mass as the old one but a volume of 80 000 cm³.
          Calculate the density of the new statue in kg/m³.

.... kg/m³

[3 marks]

Perimeter and Area

Perimeter is the distance around the outside of a shape. Area is a bit trickier — you need to learn some formulas. You should already know that the area of a rectangle is $A = l \times w$ and the area of a square is $A = l^2$.

Area Formulas for Triangles and Quadrilaterals

Learn these formulas:

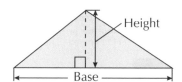

Area of triangle = ½ × base × vertical height

$$A = \tfrac{1}{2} \times b \times h$$

Note that in each case the height must be the vertical height, not the sloping height.

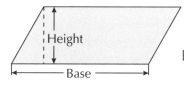

Area of parallelogram = base × vertical height

$$A = b \times h$$

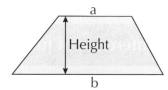

Area of trapezium = average of parallel sides × distance between them (vertical height)

$$A = \tfrac{1}{2}(a + b) \times h$$

Perimeter and Area Problems

You might have to use the perimeter or area of a shape to answer a slightly more complicated question (e.g. find the area of a wall, then work out how many rolls of wallpaper you need to wallpaper it).

EXAMPLE: **Greg is making a stained-glass window in the shape shown below.**

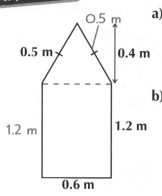

a) **Find the perimeter of the window.**

Label all the side lengths, then add them up:
0.5 m + 1.2 m + 0.6 m + 1.2 m + 0.5 m = 4 m

When you're adding side lengths, it's a good idea to mark them off as you go along to make sure you don't repeat or miss any.

b) **Coloured glass costs $82 per m². Work out the cost of the glass needed for the window.**

Split the shape into a triangle and a rectangle (as shown) to find the area:
Area of rectangle = length × width = 0.6 × 1.2 = 0.72 m²
Area of triangle = $\frac{1}{2}$ × base × height = $\frac{1}{2}$ × 0.6 × 0.4 = 0.12 m²
Total area of shape = 0.72 + 0.12 = 0.84 m²

Then multiply the area by the price to work out the cost:
Cost = area × price per m² = 0.84 × 82 = $68.88

Learn the area formulas

If you have a compound shape (a shape made up of different shapes stuck together), split it into triangles and quadrilaterals, work out the area of each bit and add them together.

Circles

Another page of formulas — this time on circles. You know the drill...

LEARN these Formulas

Area and Circumference of Circles

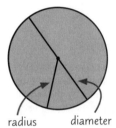

radius   diameter

Area of circle = $\pi \times$ (radius)^2
Remember that the radius is half the diameter.

$$A = \pi r^2$$

Circumference = $\pi \times$ diameter
= $2 \times \pi \times$ radius

$$C = \pi D = 2\pi r$$

For these formulas, use either the π button on your calculator or the value 3.142.

Arc Lengths and Areas of Sectors

These next ones are a bit more tricky — before you try to learn the formulas, make sure you remember what a sector and an arc are (see p.120 for a recap, but I've labelled the diagram below for you).

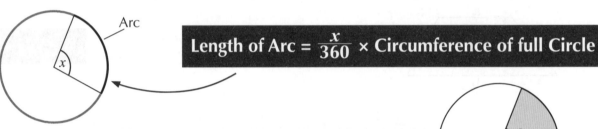

Arc

x

Length of Arc = $\dfrac{x}{360}$ × Circumference of full Circle

Area of Sector = $\dfrac{x}{360}$ × Area of full Circle

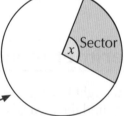

Sector

x

EXAMPLE:

1. The diagram shows a sector with angle 120° of a circle with radius 3 cm. Find the area of the shaded shape. Give your answer in terms of π.

Use the formula to find the area of the shaded sector:

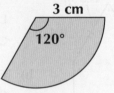

3 cm

120°

area of sector = $\dfrac{x}{360} \times \pi r^2 = \dfrac{120}{360} \times \pi \times 3^2$

$= \dfrac{1}{3} \times \pi \times 9 = 3\pi$ cm^2

2. The diagram shows an arc with angle 55° of a circle with radius 4 cm. Find the length of the arc.

Use the formula to find the length of the arc:

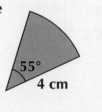

55°

4 cm

length of arc = $\dfrac{x}{360} \times 2\pi r = \dfrac{55}{360} \times 2 \times \pi \times 4$

= 3.84 cm (3 s.f.)

Extended

Make sure you answer the question fully

EXAM TIP

If an exam question asks you to find the perimeter of a semicircle or quarter circle, don't forget to add on the straight edges as well. It's an easy mistake to make, and it'll cost you marks.

Scale Drawings

Scales tell you what a distance on a map or drawing represents in real life. They can be written in various ways, but they're all basically something like "1 cm represents 5 km".

Map Scales

1 cm = 3 km — "1 cm represents 3 km"

1 : 2000 — 1 cm on the map means 2000 cm in real life.
Converting to m gives "1 cm represents 20 m".

 Use a ruler — the line's 2 cm long, so 2 cm means 1 km.
0　km　1　Dividing by 2 gives "1 cm represents 0.5 km".

Always make sure the scale is of the form "1 cm = ..." before you start working with it.

Converting from **Map** Distance to **Real Life** — **Multiply**

EXAMPLE: **This map shows a road between two cities, marked as P and W. Work out the length of the section of the road between P and W in km.**

1) Measure with a ruler: Distance on map = 2 cm

2) Read off the scale: Scale is 1 cm = 12 km

3) For real life, multiply by the map scale: Real distance is: 2 × 12 = 24 km
This looks sensible. ✓

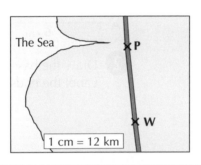

The Sea ✗P ✗W
1 cm = 12 km

Converting from **Real Life** to **Map Distance** — **Divide**

EXAMPLE: **Helmsley and Pickering are 18 km apart. How far apart would they be on a map with a scale of 1 cm = 6 km?**

Divide by the scale to find the map distance. Real-life distance = 18 km, Scale is 1 cm = 6 km
Distance on map = 18 ÷ 6 = 3 cm
This looks sensible. ✓

Scale Drawings

To convert between real life and scale drawings, replace the word 'map' with 'drawing' in the rules above.

EXAMPLE: **1 cm represents 1.5 m on the scale drawing of a room in Clare's house below. Her dining table is 0.9 m wide and 1.8 m long. Draw the table on the scale drawing.**

1) Divide to get the scale drawing dimensions.
Width on drawing = 0.9 ÷ 1.5 = 0.6 cm
Length on drawing = 1.8 ÷ 1.5 = 1.2 cm

2) Draw the table with a ruler in any sensible position and label it.

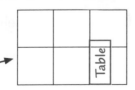

Table

REVISION TASK

Practise scale drawings by drawing maps of your house

Scale drawings can be a bit confusing at first, so practise them until you're confident with them. Try measuring a room in your house and drawing it as a scale drawing using a sensible map scale.

Triangle Constructions

How you construct a triangle depends on what information you're given about the triangle...

Three Sides — Use a **Ruler and Compasses**

EXAMPLE: **Construct the triangle ABC where AB = 6 cm, BC = 4 cm, AC = 5 cm.**

1 First, sketch and label a triangle so you know roughly what's needed. It doesn't matter which line you make the baseline.

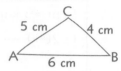

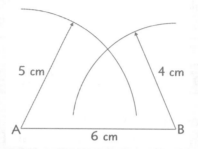

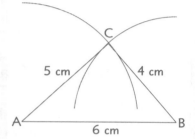

2 Draw the baseline. Label the ends A and B.

3 For AC, set the compasses to 5 cm, put the point at A and draw an arc. For BC, set the compasses to 4 cm, put the point at B and draw an arc.

4 Where the arcs cross is point C. Now you can finish your triangle.

Sides and Angles — Use a **Ruler and Protractor**

EXAMPLE: **Construct triangle DEF, where DE = 5 cm, DF = 3 cm and angle EDF = 40°.**

1 Roughly sketch and label the triangle.

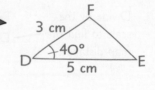

See p.112 if you're unsure how this notation works.

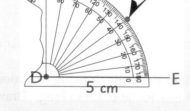

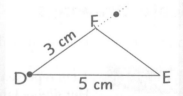

2 Draw the baseline.

3 Draw angle EDF (the angle at D) — place the centre of the protractor over D, measure 40° and put a dot.

4 Measure 3 cm towards the dot and label it F. Join up D and F. Now you've drawn the two sides and the angle. Just join up F and E to complete the triangle.

Don't forget your compasses and protractor for the exam

Constructing a triangle isn't difficult, as long as you learn the methods on this page — and remember to take your ruler, compasses and protractor into your exam, or you won't get very far.

Warm-Up and Worked Exam Questions

There are lots of formulas in this section. The best way to find out what you know is to practise these questions. If you find you keep forgetting the formulas, you need more practice.

Warm-Up Questions

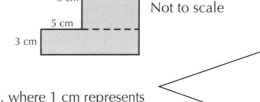

Not to scale

1) Find the perimeter of the shape shown on the right.

2) Give the formulas for:
   a) the area of a rectangle
   b) the circumference of a circle
   c) the area of a parallelogram

3) Calculate the area of a circle with radius 8 cm.

4) The diagram on the right is a scale drawing of a flag, where 1 cm represents 20 cm. Calculate the actual length of the vertical side of the flag.

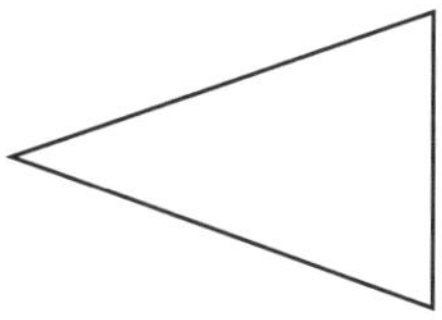

5) Construct a triangle with sides 3 cm, 4 cm and 5 cm. Check it by measuring the angles.

Worked Exam Questions

Here are two lovely worked exam questions for you. Work through each one step by step.

1   The diagram below shows a rectangle and a square.

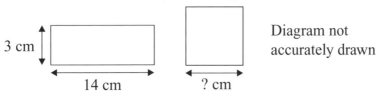

Diagram not accurately drawn

The ratio of the area of the rectangle to the area of the square is 6:7.
What is the area of the square?

Area of rectangle = 3 × 14 = 42 cm²

See p.28 for more
on scaling up ratios.

area of rectangle : area of square
                6 : 7
(×7)   42 : 49   (×7)
So area of the square = 49 cm²

......................49...................... cm²
[2 marks]

2   The diagram below shows a square with a circle inside. The circle touches each of the four sides of the square. Calculate the shaded area. Give your answer to 2 d.p.

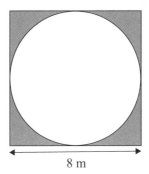

8 m

Area of square = 8 × 8 = 64 m²

Area of circle = π × 4² = 50.2654... m²

Shaded area = 64 − 50.2654...
            = 13.7345... m²

......................13.73...................... m²
[3 marks]

Exam Questions

3   A shape is made up from an isosceles triangle and a trapezium, as shown below.

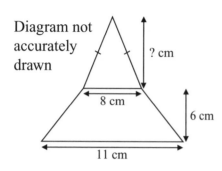

Diagram not accurately drawn

? cm

8 cm

6 cm

11 cm

The area of the trapezium is 3 times as big as the area of the triangle.

a)   Find the total area of the shape.

.... cm²
[3 marks]

b)   Find the height of the triangle.

.... cm
[2 marks]

4   Use a ruler and a protractor to construct a triangle with an angle of 40° between two sides of length 6 cm and 8 cm. Leave your construction marks.

[2 marks]

5   Look at the sector shown in the diagram below.

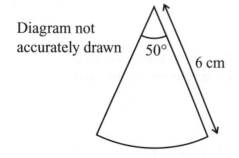

Diagram not accurately drawn

50°

6 cm

Find the perimeter and the area of the sector. Give your answers to 3 significant figures.

Don't forget to add the two radii to the arc length when finding the perimeter.

Perimeter = ... cm

Area = ... cm²
[5 marks]

3D Shapes

First up are some 3D shapes for you to learn, closely followed by a look at the different parts of solids.

Eight **Solids** to Learn

3D shapes are solid shapes. These are the ones you need to know:

There's more about prisms on p.147.

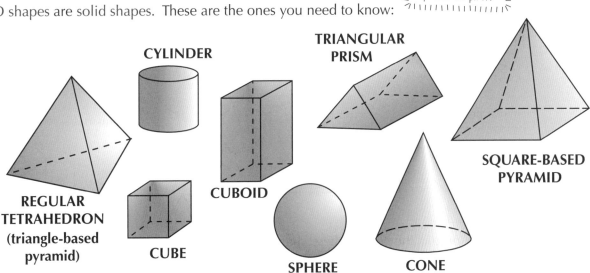

CYLINDER

TRIANGULAR PRISM

REGULAR TETRAHEDRON (triangle-based pyramid)

CUBOID

CUBE

SQUARE-BASED PYRAMID

SPHERE

CONE

Different Parts of Solids

There are different parts of 3D shapes you need to be able to spot. These are vertices (corners), faces (the flat bits) and edges. You might be asked for the number of vertices, faces and edges in the exam — just count them up, and don't forget the hidden ones.

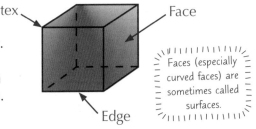

Vertex   Face

Faces (especially curved faces) are sometimes called surfaces.

Edge

Plane Symmetry

Just like 2D shapes can have mirror lines, solid 3D objects can have planes of symmetry.

KEY TERM

A plane of symmetry is a flat surface that splits a 3D shape into two symmetrical pieces.

A plane of symmetry can be drawn through many 3D shapes, but the shape must be exactly the same on both sides of the plane (i.e. mirror images), like these are:

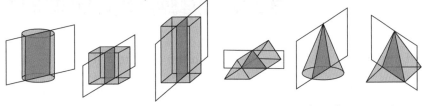

The shapes drawn here all have many more planes of symmetry, but there's only one drawn in for each shape — otherwise it would all get really messy and you wouldn't be able to see anything.

Extended

Make sure you can spot the vertices, faces and edges of 3D shapes

Remember the plural — 1 vertex, 2 vertices. They're tricky words that are (probably) designed to confuse you, so don't let them. You will also need to know the names of all the solid shapes on this page.

Surface Area and Nets

To find the surface area of a 3D shape, you need to find the area of each face and add them up. However, for some shapes there are some special formulas that you can use to save time.

Nets

A net is just a hollow 3D shape folded out flat.
Here are the nets of some common shapes — make sure you can recognise them.

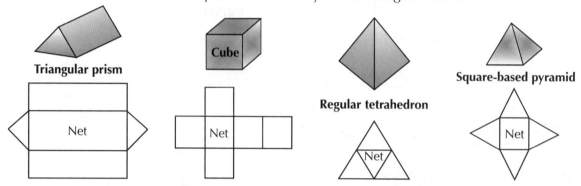

Triangular prism   **Cube**   **Regular tetrahedron**   **Square-based pyramid**

Note that these are just some of the nets for these shapes — there are many other nets that will produce the same shapes (particularly for a cube).

Surface Area

1) SURFACE AREA only applies to solid 3D objects — it's just the total area of all the faces added together.
2) SURFACE AREA OF SOLID = AREA OF NET. If it helps, imagine the net and add up the area of each bit.
3) There's a formula for the surface area of a CYLINDER:

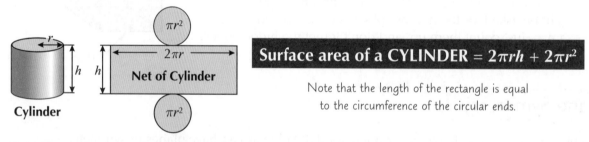

Surface area of a CYLINDER = $2\pi rh + 2\pi r^2$

Note that the length of the rectangle is equal to the circumference of the circular ends.

4) SPHERES and CONES have their own surface area formulas too:

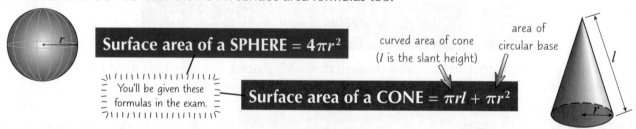

Surface area of a SPHERE = $4\pi r^2$

You'll be given these formulas in the exam.

curved area of cone (l is the slant height)   area of circular base

Surface area of a CONE = $\pi rl + \pi r^2$

EXAMPLE: **Find the surface area of the cylinder on the right to 1 d.p.**

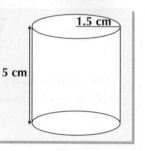

Just put the measurements into the formula and work it out carefully in stages:

Surface area of cylinder = 2πrh + 2πr²
$$= (2 \times \pi \times 1.5 \times 5) + (2 \times \pi \times 1.5^2)$$
$$= 47.123... + 14.137... = 61.261... = 61.3 \text{ cm}^2$$

To find the surface area of a solid, just add up the areas of each face

In a net all the faces are folded out flat — which makes it easier to see the shapes you're dealing with.

Volume

Here are two whole pages on the volumes of 3D shapes. You might see the word CAPACITY used in exam questions — it just means the same as volume.

Volumes of **Cuboids**

A cuboid is a rectangular block. Finding its volume is easy:

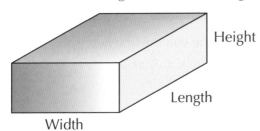

Height
Length
Width

Volume of Cuboid = Length × Width × Height

$$V = L \times W \times H$$

Volumes of **Prisms**

KEY TERM

A prism is a solid (3D) object which is the same shape all the way through — i.e. it has a constant area of cross-section.

The cross-section is the shape you get if you slice a solid perpendicular to its length.

VOLUME OF PRISM = CROSS-SECTIONAL AREA × LENGTH

$$V = A \times L$$

Triangular Prism

Constant Area of Cross-section

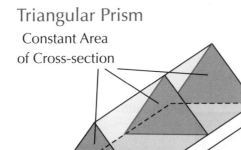

Length

Cylinder

Here the cross-section is a circle. So, using the formula from p.140 to find its area, the formula for the volume of a cylinder becomes:

$$V = \pi r^2 h$$

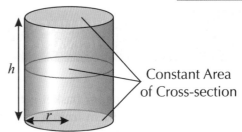

h

r

Constant Area of Cross-section

EXAMPLE:

Honey comes in cylindrical jars with radius 4.5 cm and height 12 cm. 1 cm³ of honey has a mass of 1.4 g. Work out the mass of honey in this jar to 3 s.f.

First, work out the volume of the jar — just use the formula above:

$V = \pi r^2 h = \pi \times 4.5^2 \times 12 = 763.41$ cm³

1 cm³ of honey has a mass of 1.4 g, so multiply the volume by 1.4:

mass of honey = 1.4 × 763.41 = 1068.8 = 1070 g (3 s.f.)

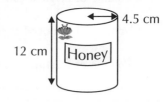
4.5 cm
12 cm
Honey

You have to remember what a prism is

It's the constant cross-section which is important — that's what makes a prism a prism. If you remember that, it makes perfect sense that to get the volume you just multiply that area by the length.

Volume

Another page on volumes now — it's the last page of new things to learn for this section.

Volumes of **Spheres**

$$\textbf{Volume of Sphere} = \tfrac{4}{3}\pi r^3$$

This formula will be given in the exam.

A hemisphere is half a sphere. So the volume of a hemisphere is just half the volume of a full sphere, $V = \tfrac{2}{3}\pi r^3$.

Volumes of **Pyramids** and **Cones**

A pyramid is a shape that goes from a flat base up to a point at the top. Its base can be any shape at all.

Cone

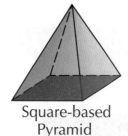

Square-based Pyramid

$$\textbf{Volume of Pyramid} = \tfrac{1}{3} \times \textbf{Base Area} \times \textbf{Vertical Height}$$
$$\textbf{Volume of Cone} = \tfrac{1}{3} \times \pi r^2 \times h$$

Make sure you use the vertical height in these formulas — don't get confused with the slant height, which you used to find the surface area of a cone.

You'll be given these formulas in the exam as well.

Volumes of **Frustums**

A frustum of a cone is what's left when the top part of a cone is cut off parallel to its circular base. You'll be given the formula for the volume of a cone in your exam, but you'll need to remember:

This bit is the frustum

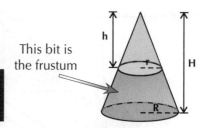

VOLUME OF FRUSTUM	=	VOLUME OF ORIGINAL CONE	−	VOLUME OF REMOVED CONE

A waste paper basket is the shape of a frustum formed by removing the top 10 cm from a cone of height 50 cm and radius 35 cm. Find the volume of the waste paper basket to 3 significant figures.

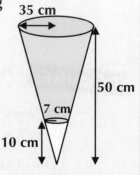

35 cm

50 cm

7 cm

10 cm

Use the formula for the volume of a cone above:

Volume of original cone $= \tfrac{1}{3} \times \pi \times 35^2 \times 50 = 64140.850...\ \text{cm}^3$

Volume of removed cone $= \tfrac{1}{3} \times \pi \times 7^2 \times 10 = 513.126...\ \text{cm}^3$

Volume of frustum $= 64140.850... - 513.126... = 63627.723... = 63600\ \text{cm}^3$ (3 s.f.)

Remember that a frustum is just a cone with the top chopped off

Learn the formula in the blue box above. It makes sense when you think about it — subtract the volume of the removed cone from the original volume, and you're left with the volume of the bit at the bottom.

Warm-Up and Worked Exam Questions

Make sure you're happy with all the properties of 3D shapes by trying these warm-up questions.

Warm-Up Questions

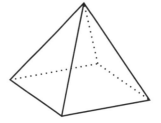

1) Look at the 3D shape on the right.
   a) What is this shape called?
   b) How many vertices does it have?
   c) How many planes of symmetry does it have?

2) a) The net of a regular tetrahedron consists of four equilateral triangles. Which of the shapes below could be this net?

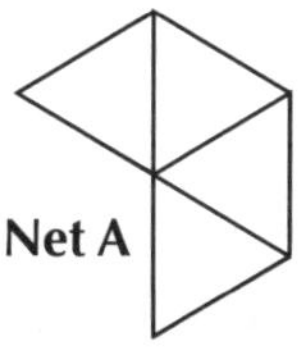

Net A

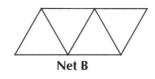

Net B

   b) Each triangle has base b and perpendicular height h. Find a simplified expression for the surface area of the tetrahedron in terms of b and h.

3) Calculate the volume of the triangular prism on the right.

4) The formula for the volume of a sphere is: Volume $= \frac{4}{3}\pi r^3$.
   Calculate the volume of a sphere with a radius of 7 metres.
   Give your answer to 3 s.f.

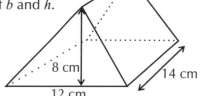

8 cm
14 cm
12 cm

Worked Exam Question

Work through this question carefully before having a go at the exam questions.

1   The dimensions of a cube and a square-based pyramid are shown in the diagram below.
The side length of the cube is 7 cm. The side length of the pyramid's base is 2 cm
and the slant height of the pyramid is 2 cm.

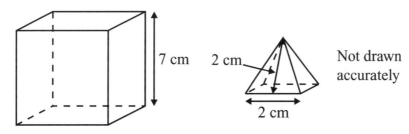

7 cm   2 cm.   Not drawn accurately

2 cm

Find the ratio of the surface area of the cube to the surface area of the pyramid in the form $n : 1$.

Surface area of cube = 6 × area of one face = 6 × 7 × 7 = 294 cm²

Surface area of square-based pyramid = area of base + (4 × area of one triangular face)
= 2 × 2 + (4 × ½ × 2 × 2) = 4 + 8 = 12 cm²

Surface area of cube : surface area of pyramid
= 294 : 12
= 294 ÷ 12 : 12 ÷ 12 = 24.5 : 1

Once you've found the surface area of each, set them as a ratio then divide to get the ratio in the form n:1.

24.5 : 1
....

[4 marks]

Exam Questions

2 The tank shown in the diagram below is completely filled with water.

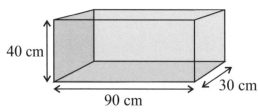

Not drawn accurately

40 cm
90 cm
30 cm

a) Calculate the volume of water in the tank.

.... cm³
[2 marks]

b) The water from this tank is then poured into a second tank with length 120 cm.
    The depth of the water is 18 cm. Find the width of the second tank.

.... cm
[2 marks]

3 A building block from a toy set is shown below. Calculate the surface area of the block.

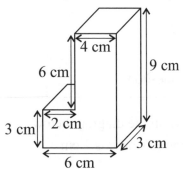

4 cm

6 cm

9 cm

3 cm

2 cm

3 cm

6 cm

.... cm²
[3 marks]

4 The diagram below shows a wooden spinning top made from a hemisphere and a cone.
   The hemisphere has a diameter of 14 cm. The slanting length of the cone is 12 cm
   and the radius of its base is 2 cm.

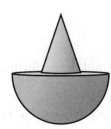

Work out the total surface area of
the spinning top. Give your answer
to 3 significant figures.

| Volume of sphere = $\frac{4}{3}\pi r^2$ |
| Volume of cone = $\frac{1}{3} \times \pi r^2 \times h$ |

.... cm²
[4 marks]

Revision Questions for Section Four

That wraps up Section 4 — time to put yourself to the test and find out how much you really know.
*   Try these questions and tick off each one when you get it right.
*   When you've done all the questions for a topic and are completely happy with it, tick off the topic.

Angles and Geometry Problems (p.112-115) ☐

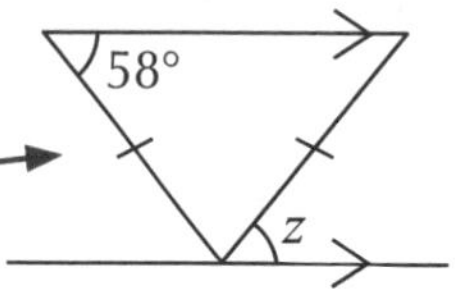

1) What is the name for an angle larger than 90° but smaller than 180°?
2) What do angles in a quadrilateral add up to?
3) Find the missing angle, z, in the diagram on the right.
4) Using the diagram on the right, find the bearing of Y from X.

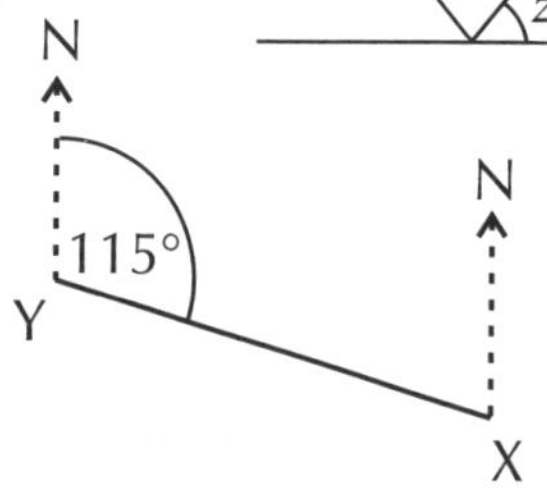

Polygons (p.116-117) ☐

5) Find the interior angle of a regular 20-sided polygon.
6) a) How many lines of symmetry does an equilateral triangle have?
    b) What is its order of rotational symmetry?

Circle Geometry (p.120-122) ☐

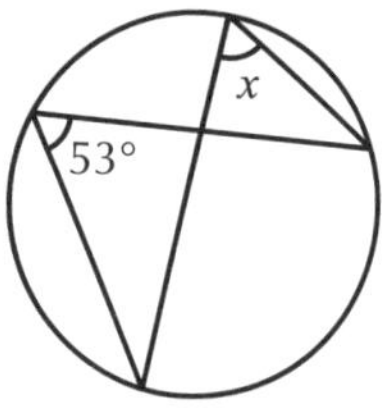

7) What angle is formed when a tangent meets a radius?
8) Find the missing angle, x, in the diagram on the right.

Congruence, Similarity and Transformations (p.125-129) ☐

9) What are congruent and similar shapes?
10) Carry out the following transformations on the triangle X, which has vertices (1, 1), (4, 1) and (2, 3):
    a) a rotation of 90° clockwise about (1, 1)   b) an enlargement of scale factor 2, centre (1, 1)
11) A shape with area 5 cm² is enlarged by a scale factor of 4. What is the area of the enlarged shape?

Unit Conversions, Time, Speed, Density and Pressure (p.132-136) ☐

12) Convert: a) 5.6 litres to cm³   b) 83 g to kg   c) 569 m² to cm²   d) 3 m/s to km/h
13) A concert starts at 19:30. The concert is 118 minutes long plus a 20 minute interval.
    What time does the concert finish? Give your answer in 12-hour time.
14) Find the area of an object in contact with horizontal ground, if the pressure it exerts on the ground
    is 120 N/m² and the force acting on the object is 1320 N. [Pressure = $\frac{\text{Force}}{\text{Area}}$]

Perimeter, Area, Scale Drawings and Constructions (p.139-142) ☐

15) Find the area of a parallelogram with base 9 cm and vertical height 4 cm.
16) Find the area of the shape on the right. 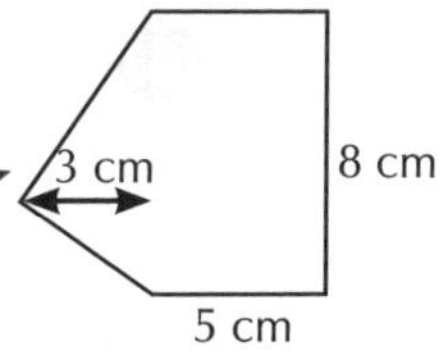
17) Find the area and perimeter of a quarter circle with radius 3 cm.
18) How do you use a map scale to go from a real-life distance to a distance on a map, and vice versa?
19) Construct a triangle with sides of lengths 4 cm, 7 cm and 8 cm.

3D Shapes, Surface Area and Volume (p.145-148) ☐

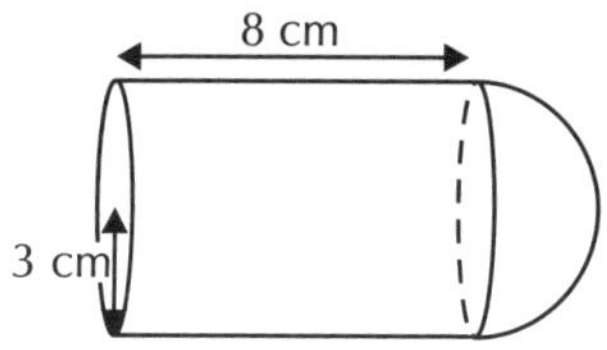

20) The shape on the right is made from a cylinder and a hemisphere.
    The formula for the surface area of a sphere is $4\pi r^2$.
    Find its surface area, giving your answer in terms of π.
21) Find the volume of a hexagonal prism with a cross-sectional area of 36 cm² and a length of 11 cm.

Pythagoras' Theorem

Pythagoras' theorem sounds hard but it's actually pretty simple.
It's also really important, so make sure you really understand it.

Pythagoras' Theorem — $a^2 + b^2 = c^2$

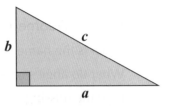

$$a^2 + b^2 = c^2$$

1) PYTHAGORAS' THEOREM only works for RIGHT-ANGLED TRIANGLES.
2) The theorem uses two sides to find the third side.
3) The BASIC FORMULA for Pythagoras' theorem is $a^2 + b^2 = c^2$.
4) Make sure you get the numbers in the RIGHT PLACE. c is the longest side (called the hypotenuse) and it's always opposite the right angle.
5) Always CHECK that your answer is SENSIBLE.

EXAMPLE:

ABC is a right-angled triangle.
AB = 6 m and AC = 3 m.
Find the length of BC.

1) Write down the formula.
2) Put in the numbers.
3) Rearrange the equation.
4) Take square roots to find BC.
5) Write your answer to 3 significant figures.

It's not always c you need to find — lots of people can go wrong here.

$a^2 + b^2 = c^2$
$BC^2 + 3^2 = 6^2$
$BC^2 = 6^2 - 3^2 = 36 - 9 = 27$
$BC = \sqrt{27} = 5.20$ m (3 s.f.)

Remember to check the answer is sensible — 5.20 is between 3 and 6, so that seems about right.

Use the **Theorem** to Find the **Distance Between Points**

You need to know how to find the straight-line distance between two points on a graph.
If you get a question like this, follow these rules and it'll all become simple:

1) **Draw a sketch to show the right-angled triangle.**
2) **Find the lengths of the shorter sides of the triangle.**
3) **Use the theorem to find the length of the hypotenuse. (That's your answer.)**

EXAMPLE:

Point P has coordinates (8, 3) and point Q has coordinates (−4, 8).
Find the length of the line PQ.

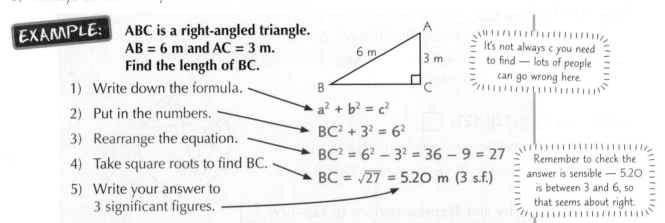

1

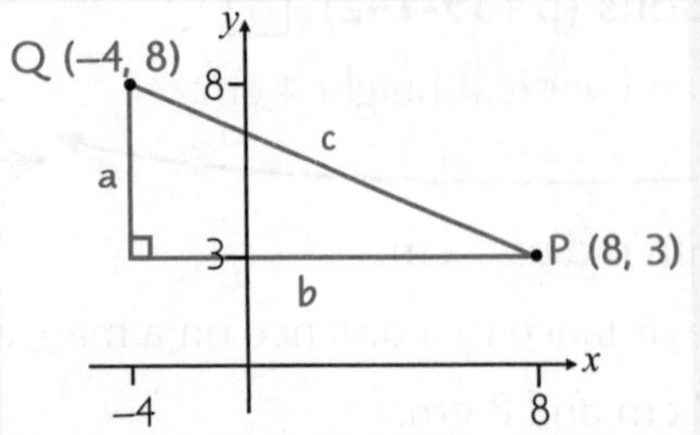

2 Length of side a = 8 − 3 = 5
Length of side b = 8 − (−4) = 12

3 Use Pythagoras' theorem to find side c:
$c^2 = a^2 + b^2 = 5^2 + 12^2 = 25 + 144 = 169$
So: $c = \sqrt{169} = 13$

Finding lengths in a right-angled triangle? Pythagoras is your man

EXAM TIP

Pythagoras' theorem is likely to come up on your exam, but it's unlikely that you'll be given the $a^2 + b^2 = c^2$ formula, so you need to learn it. Once you know it, it'll be as easy as a, b, c.

Trigonometry — Sin, Cos and Tan

Trigonometry — it's a big, scary word. It's important and always comes up in exams, but if you follow the method below it won't be a big scary topic.

The 3 Trigonometry Formulas

There are three basic trig formulas — each one links two sides and an angle of a right-angled triangle.

$$Sin\ x = \frac{Opposite}{Hypotenuse} \qquad Cos\ x = \frac{Adjacent}{Hypotenuse} \qquad Tan\ x = \frac{Opposite}{Adjacent}$$

KEY TERMS

The Hypotenuse is the longest side.
The Opposite is the side opposite the angle being used (x).
The Adjacent is the (other) side next to the angle being used.

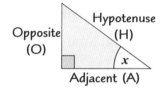

1) Whenever you come across a trig question, work out which two sides of the triangle are involved in that question — then pick the formula that involves those sides.

2) To find the angle, use the inverse, i.e. press **SHIFT** or **2ndF**, followed by sin, cos or tan (and make sure your calculator is in DEG mode) — your calculator will display $\sin^{-1}$, $\cos^{-1}$ or $\tan^{-1}$.

3) Remember, you can only use sin, cos and tan on right-angled triangles — you may have to add lines to the diagram to create one.

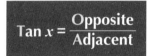
There's more about formula triangles on p.135 if you need a reminder.

Formula Triangles Make Things Simple

A useful way to answer trig questions is to convert the formulas into formula triangles. Then you can use the same method every time, no matter which side or angle is being asked for.

1) Label the three sides O, A and H (Opposite, Adjacent and Hypotenuse).

2) Write down from memory 'SOH CAH TOA'.

3) Decide which two sides are involved: O,H A,H or O,A and select SOH, CAH or TOA accordingly.

4) Turn the one you choose into a formula triangle:

   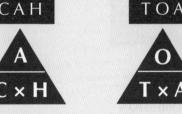

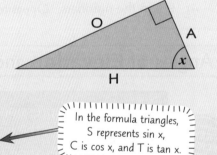
In the formula triangles, S represents sin x, C is cos x, and T is tan x.

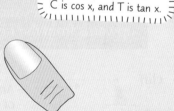

5) Cover up the thing you want to find (with your finger), and write down whatever is left showing.

6) Translate into numbers and work it out.

7) Finally, check that your answer is sensible.

REVISION TIP

H = longest, O = opposite and A = next to

You need to know all the formulas on this page. All you really have to do is learn SOH CAH TOA, then you can use that in the exam to come up with all of the formulas or the formula triangles.

Trigonometry — Sin, Cos and Tan

Here's an example using the method from the previous page — it'll help you learn the formulas.

Basic Example

EXAMPLE: **Find the length of x in the triangle on the right.**

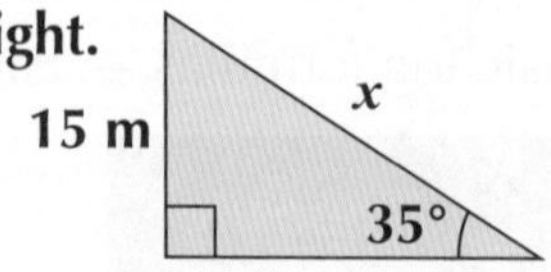

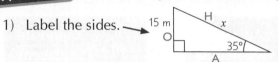

1) Label the sides.

2) Write down (SOH) CAH TOA . O and H are involved.

3) Write down the formula triangle.

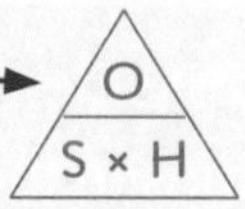

4) You want H so cover it up to give $H = \dfrac{O}{S}$.

5) Put in the numbers. $x = \dfrac{15}{\sin 35°} = 26.1517... \text{ m} = 26.2 \text{ m (3 s.f.)}$

Is it sensible? Yes, it's about twice as big as 15, as the diagram suggests.

The **Perpendicular** is the **Shortest Distance**

The perpendicular distance from a point to a line is the shortest distance to the line.
Draw the perpendicular line, then use trigonometry to find the distance.

EXAMPLE: **Work out the shortest distance from point P to line L.**

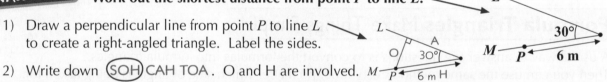

1) Draw a perpendicular line from point P to line L to create a right-angled triangle. Label the sides.

2) Write down (SOH) CAH TOA . O and H are involved.

3) You want O (opposite), so cover it up on the formula triangle to give Opposite = S × H.

4) Put in the numbers. Opposite = $\sin 30° \times 6 = 3$ m

Angles of **Elevation** and **Depression**

KEY TERMS

The angle of depression is the angle downwards from the horizontal.
The angle of elevation is the angle upwards from the horizontal.

EXAMPLE: **Find the angle of elevation of the cliff-top from the boat in the diagram.**

Just use trigonometry.
Call the angle of elevation x.

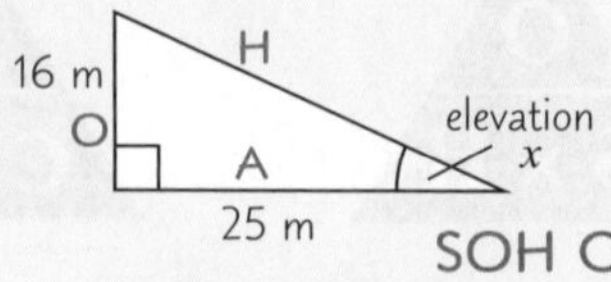

The angles of elevation and depression are equal.

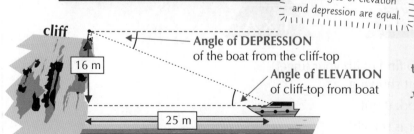

cliff

16 m

Angle of DEPRESSION of the boat from the cliff-top

Angle of ELEVATION of cliff-top from boat

25 m

SOH CAH (TOA)

$\tan x = \dfrac{O}{A} = \dfrac{16}{25} = 0.64$

$x = \tan^{-1}(0.64)$

$= 32.61...°$

$= 32.6°$ (to 1 d.p.)

Looking at the diagram, this seems sensible.

EXAM TIP

You need to have learned all seven steps on page 153

Sometimes an angle will be exact in trigonometry, but often it won't be. When an angle isn't exact, round it to 1 decimal place in the exam unless you're told to round it differently.

Extended

Warm-Up and Worked Exam Questions

Learning facts and practising exam questions is the path that will lead you to success.
That's what the questions on these pages are for. All you have to do... is do them.

Warm-Up Questions

1) A rectangular field is 250 m by 190 m. How far is it across diagonally?

2) Find the sin, cos and tan of each of these angles, giving your answers to 3 significant figures:
   a) 17°   b) 83°   c) 5°   d) 28°   e) 45°

3) In a right-angled triangle, the two shorter sides are 10 cm and 8.4 cm.
   Find: a) the length of the longest side,
           b) the smallest angle, correct to the nearest degree.

4) Find the length of x on the triangle to the right.

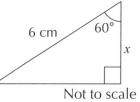

6 cm   60°
x
Not to scale

Worked Exam Questions

You need to apply the facts you've stored away in your brain to get marks in the exam.
These worked examples will really help you see how...

1   The diagram shows a right-angled triangle ABC.
    AC is 4 cm long. BC is 8 cm long.

    Calculate the length of AB.

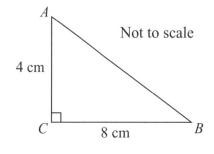

A
Not to scale
4 cm
C   8 cm   *B*

$4^2 + 8^2 = AB^2$ Use Pythagoras' Theorem:
                           $a^2 + b^2 = c^2$
$16 + 64 = 80 = AB^2$

$\sqrt{80} = AB$, so $AB = 8.94427... = 8.94$ cm (to 3 s.f.)

...........8.94........... cm
[2 marks]

2   The diagram shows a right-angled triangle.
    Find the size of the angle marked x.

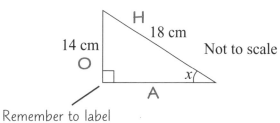

H
18 cm
14 cm   Not to scale
O
x
A

Remember to label
your triangle

 CAH   TOA

$S = \dfrac{O}{H}$

$\sin x = \dfrac{14}{18}$, so $x = \sin^{-1}(14 \div 18) = 51.05755... = 51.1°$ (to 1 d.p.)

...........51.1........... °
[2 marks]

Exam Questions

3   A ladder is 3.5 m long. For safety reasons, when the ladder is leant against a wall, the base should not be less than 2.1 m away from the wall.

Work out the maximum vertical height that the top of the ladder can safely reach to.

.... m

[3 marks]

4   The diagram shows a kite *ABCD*. *AB* is 28.3 cm long. *BC* is 54.3 cm long. *BE* is 20 cm long. Work out the perimeter of triangle *ABC*. Give your answer to 1 decimal place.

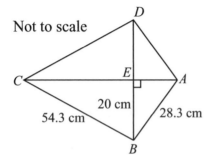

.... cm

[5 marks]

5   In the triangle on the right, *AB* = *BC* = 10 m and angle *C* = 34°.

a)   Calculate the height of the triangle.
Give your answer to 2 decimal places.

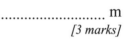

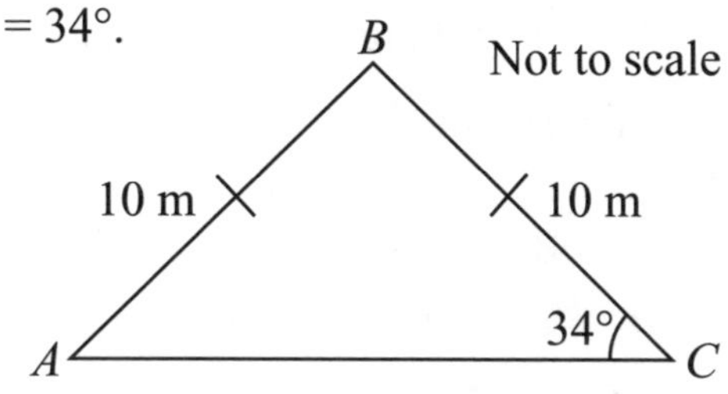

.... m

[2 marks]

b)   Calculate the length *AC*. Give your answer to 2 decimal places.

.... m

[3 marks]

6   The diagram on the right shows Person *A* in the window of a building and Person *B* standing on the ground. Person *A* is 94 m above Person *B* and Person *B* is 19 m away from the building. Calculate the angle of depression of Person *B* from Person *A*.

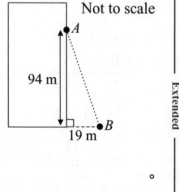

..........................°

[3 marks]

Extended

The Sine and Cosine Rules

Normal trigonometry using SOH CAH TOA can only be applied to right-angled triangles. This leaves us with the question of what to do with other-angled triangles. I present to you the sine and cosine rules...

Labelling the Triangle

This is very important. You must label the sides and angles properly so that the letters for the sides and angles correspond with each other. Use lower case letters for the sides and capital letters for the angles.

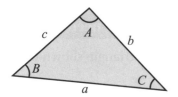

Remember, side a is opposite angle A, side b is opposite angle B and side c is opposite angle C.

It doesn't matter which sides you decide to call a, b and c, just as long as the angles are then labelled properly.

Three Formulas to Learn:

The Sine Rule

$$\frac{a}{\sin A} = \frac{b}{\sin B} = \frac{c}{\sin C}$$

You don't use the whole thing when you're doing a calculation — you just choose the two bits that you want:

e.g. $\dfrac{b}{\sin B} = \dfrac{c}{\sin C}$ or $\dfrac{a}{\sin A} = \dfrac{b}{\sin B}$

The Cosine Rule

The 'normal' form is...

$$a^2 = b^2 + c^2 - 2bc \cos A$$

...or this form is good for finding an angle (you get it by rearranging the 'normal' version):

$$\text{or } \cos A = \frac{b^2 + c^2 - a^2}{2bc}$$

Area of the Triangle

This formula is useful when you know two sides and the angle between them:

$$\text{Area of triangle} = \tfrac{1}{2} ab \sin C$$

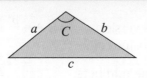

Of course, you already know a simple formula for calculating the area using the base length and height (see p.139). The formula here is for when you don't know those values.

EXAMPLE:

Triangle XYZ has XZ = 18 cm, YZ = 13 cm and angle XZY = 58°. Find the area of the triangle.

Label the sides and angle.

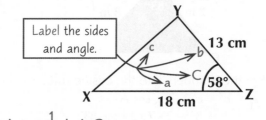

Area $= \dfrac{1}{2} ab \sin C$

$= \dfrac{1}{2} \times 18 \times 13 \times \sin 58°$

$= 99.2 \text{ cm}^2$ (3 s.f.)

Don't forget the units.

Label each side and angle of the triangle correctly

EXAM TIP The formulas won't work if your labels don't match up. You won't be given these formulas in the exam, so you'll need to learn them off by heart. Move on to the next page for some examples...

The Sine and Cosine Rules

There are four main question types where the sine and cosine rules would be applied.
So learn the exact details of these four examples and you'll be right on track.

The Four **Examples**

 TWO ANGLES given plus ANY SIDE — SINE RULE needed.

Find the length of AB for the triangle below.

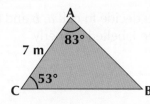

> The sine rule will always give you an acute angle — if the angle you're finding is obtuse, subtract the acute angle from 180° (see p.159).

1) Don't forget the obvious...
   $$B = 180° - 83° - 53° = 44°$$

2) Put the numbers into the sine rule.
   $$\frac{b}{\sin B} = \frac{c}{\sin C} \Rightarrow \frac{7}{\sin 44°} = \frac{c}{\sin 53°}$$

3) Rearrange to find c.
   $$c = \frac{7 \times \sin 53°}{\sin 44°} = 8.05 \text{ m (3 s.f.)}$$

 TWO SIDES given plus an ANGLE NOT ENCLOSED by them — SINE RULE needed.

Find angle ABC for the triangle shown below.

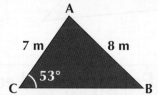

1) Put the numbers into the sine rule.
   $$\frac{b}{\sin B} = \frac{c}{\sin C} \Rightarrow \frac{7}{\sin B} = \frac{8}{\sin 53°}$$

2) Rearrange to find sin B.
   $$\sin B = \frac{7 \times \sin 53°}{8} = 0.6988...$$

3) Find the inverse
   $$B = \sin^{-1}(0.6988...) = 44.3° \text{ (1 d.p.)}$$

 TWO SIDES given plus the ANGLE ENCLOSED by them — COSINE RULE needed.

Find the length CB for the triangle below.

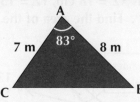

1) Put the numbers into the cosine rule.
   $$a^2 = b^2 + c^2 - 2bc \cos A$$
   $$= 7^2 + 8^2 - 2 \times 7 \times 8 \times \cos 83°$$
   $$= 99.3506...$$

2) Take square roots to find a.
   $$a = \sqrt{99.3506...}$$
   $$= 9.97 \text{ m (3 s.f.)}$$

> You might come across a triangle that isn't labelled ABC — just relabel it yourself to match the sine and cosine rules.

 ALL THREE SIDES given but NO ANGLES — COSINE RULE needed.

Find angle CAB for the triangle shown.

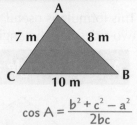

1) Use this version of the cosine rule.
   $$\cos A = \frac{b^2 + c^2 - a^2}{2bc}$$

2) Put in the numbers.
   $$= \frac{7^2 + 8^2 - 10^2}{2 \times 7 \times 8}$$

3) Take the inverse to find A.
   $$= \frac{49 + 64 - 100}{2 \times 7 \times 8}$$
   $$= \frac{13}{112} = 0.11607...$$
   $$A = \cos^{-1}(0.11607...)$$
   $$= 83.3° \text{ (1 d.p.)}$$

Learn which rule you need for each question type

REVISION TASK Cover the page and draw four triangles. Label two of the triangles with the angles and sides that use the sine rule. Label the other two triangles with the angles and sides that use the cosine rule.

Sin, Cos and Tan for Larger Angles

You need to know about sin, cos and tan of obtuse angles (they're the ones between 90° and 180°).

Cosine of Obtuse Angles

Values of cos x for obtuse angles are negative, but the cosine rule works just the same as for acute angles.

EXAMPLE: **Find the size of angle ACB.**

Angle ACB is obtuse, but the cosine rule still works:

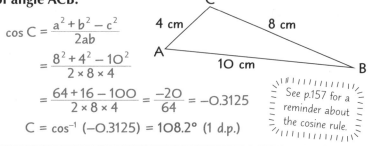

$$\cos C = \frac{a^2 + b^2 - c^2}{2ab}$$

$$= \frac{8^2 + 4^2 - 10^2}{2 \times 8 \times 4}$$

$$= \frac{64 + 16 - 100}{2 \times 8 \times 4} = \frac{-20}{64} = -0.3125$$

See p.157 for a reminder about the cosine rule.

$$C = \cos^{-1}(-0.3125) = 108.2° \text{ (1 d.p.)}$$

Sine of Obtuse Angles

1) You have to be a bit more careful with sine. Each value of sin x between 0 and 1 corresponds to 2 different values of x between 0° and 180°.

2) When you use your calculator's $\sin^{-1}$ function to find the size of the angle, it gives you the answer between 0° and 90°. If you know the angle is obtuse, you then have to subtract the calculator's answer from 180°.

EXAMPLE: **Find the size of angle ACB.**

1) Use the sine rule (see p.157):

$$\frac{a}{\sin A} = \frac{c}{\sin C}$$

$$\frac{8}{\sin 49.5°} = \frac{10}{\sin C}$$

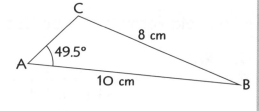

$$\sin C = \frac{10 \times \sin 49.5°}{8} = 0.9505...$$

2) Angle ACB is obtuse, so 71.9° is too small — subtract it from 180° to get the answer.

$$\sin^{-1}(0.9505...) = 71.8984...$$
$$180° - 71.8984°... = 108.1° \text{ (1 d.p.)}$$

Tan of Obtuse Angles

1) When you use your calculator's $\tan^{-1}$ function to find the size of an angle, it gives you an answer between −90° and 90°.

2) If you know the angle is obtuse, you then have to add 180°.

EXAMPLE: x **is an obtuse angle with tan x = −1. Find x.**

$$\tan^{-1}(-1) = -45°$$

It's an obtuse angle, so add 180°:

$$-45° + 180° = 135°$$

Check the answer is sensible — don't just copy your calculator

Remember the method for the three trig functions: cos works the same, sin is '180 – ' and tan is '180 +'. Keep in mind what size you expect your angle to be so you can see if it's correct.

Extended

3D Pythagoras

This is a 3D version of the 2D Pythagoras' theorem you saw on page 152. There's just one simple formula — learn it and you will have the skills to answer any Pythagoras question...

3D Pythagoras for **Cuboids** — $a^2 + b^2 + c^2 = d^2$

Cuboids have their own formula for calculating the length of their longest diagonal:

$$a^2 + b^2 + c^2 = d^2$$

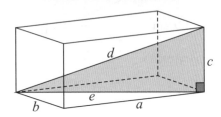

This is all stuff that you have seen before — it's just 2D Pythagoras' theorem being used twice:

1) a, b and e make a right-angled triangle so
$$e^2 = a^2 + b^2$$

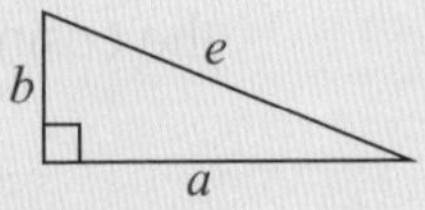

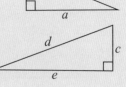

2) Now look at the right-angled triangle formed by e, c and d:
$$d^2 = e^2 + c^2 = a^2 + b^2 + c^2$$

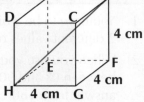

EXAMPLE: Find the length of the diagonal BH for the cube in the diagram.

1) Write down the formula. $a^2 + b^2 + c^2 = d^2$

2) Put in the numbers. $4^2 + 4^2 + 4^2 = BH^2$

3) Take the square root to find BH. $\Rightarrow BH = \sqrt{48} = 6.93$ cm (3 s.f.)

The Cuboid Formula Can be Used in **Other 3D Shapes**

EXAMPLE:

In the square-based pyramid shown, M is the midpoint of the base and A is vertically above M. Find the vertical height AM.

1) Label N as the midpoint of ED.

Then think of EN, NM and AM as three sides of a cuboid, and AE as the longest diagonal in the cuboid (like d in the section above).

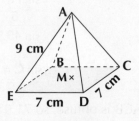

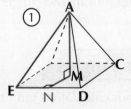

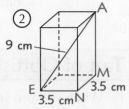

2) Sketch the full cuboid.

3) Write down the 3D Pythagoras formula. $a^2 + b^2 + c^2 = d^2$

4) Rewrite it using side labels. $EN^2 + NM^2 + AM^2 = AE^2$

5) Put in the numbers and solve for AM. $\Rightarrow 3.5^2 + 3.5^2 + AM^2 = 9^2$

$\Rightarrow AM = \sqrt{81 - 2 \times 12.25} = 7.52$ cm (3 s.f.)

$a^2 + b^2 + c^2 = d^2$ gives you the longest diagonal from the 3 edge lengths

Finding the length of the longest diagonal of a cuboid is pretty easy as long as you learn the formula. Other 3D shapes can be a little more tricky, but really you just need to work out where the formula fits.

Extended

Extended

3D Trigonometry

3D trig may sound tricky, and I suppose it is a bit... but it's actually just using the same rules.

Angle Between Line and Plane — Use a Diagram

Learn the 3-Step Method

1) Make a right-angled triangle between the line and the plane.

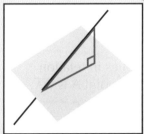

2) Draw a simple 2D sketch of this triangle and mark on the lengths of two sides (you might have to use Pythagoras to find one).

3) Use trig to find the angle.

Have a look at p.152-154 to jog your memory about Pythagoras' theorem and trigonometry.

EXAMPLE:

ABCDE is a square-based pyramid with M as the midpoint of its base. A is vertically above M. Find the angle the edge AE makes with the base.

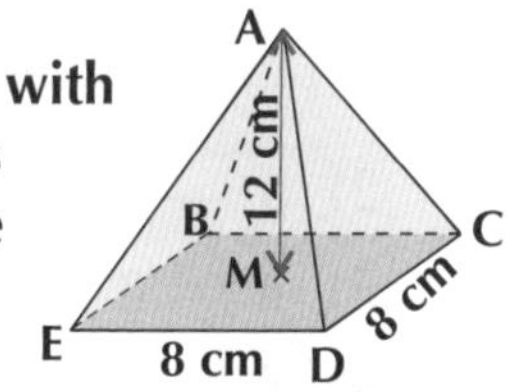

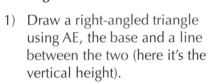

1) Draw a right-angled triangle using AE, the base and a line between the two (here it's the vertical height).

   Label the angle you need to find.

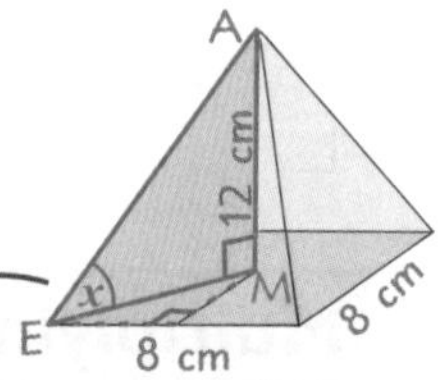

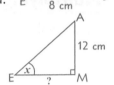

2) Now sketch this triangle in 2D and label it.

   Use Pythagoras (on the base triangle) to find EM.

   $EM^2 = 4^2 + 4^2 = 32$
   $\Rightarrow EM = \sqrt{32}\,cm$

3) Finally, use trigonometry to find x — you know the opposite and adjacent sides so use tan.

   $\tan x = \dfrac{12}{\sqrt{32}} = 2.1213...$

   $x = \tan^{-1}(2.1213...)$
   $= 64.8°$ (1 d.p.)

Extended

The Sine Rule and Cosine Rule Can Also be Used in 3D

For triangles inside 3D shapes that aren't right-angled you can use the sine and cosine rules (p.157).

EXAMPLE:

Find the size of angle AEH in the cuboid shown below.

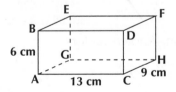

You could just use the rearranged version of the cosine rule at step 3 if you remembered it.

1) Draw the triangle AEH and label angle AEH as x.

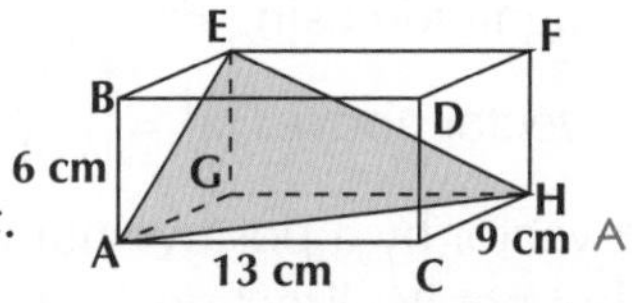

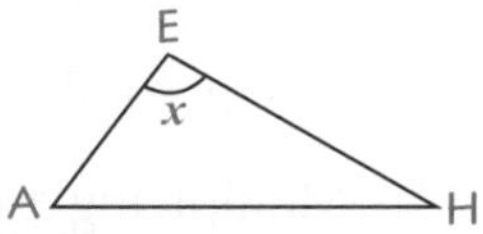

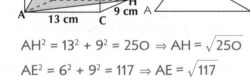

2) Use Pythagoras' theorem to find the lengths of AH, AE and EH.

   $AH^2 = 13^2 + 9^2 = 250 \Rightarrow AH = \sqrt{250}$
   $AE^2 = 6^2 + 9^2 = 117 \Rightarrow AE = \sqrt{117}$
   $EH^2 = 6^2 + 13^2 = 205 \Rightarrow EH = \sqrt{205}$

3) Find x using the cosine rule:
   Put in the numbers.
   Rearrange and take the inverse to find x.

   $AH^2 = AE^2 + EH^2 - 2 \times AE \times EH \times \cos x$
   $250 = 117 + 205 - 2\sqrt{117}\sqrt{205}\cos x$
   $x = \cos^{-1}\left(\dfrac{117 + 205 - 250}{2\sqrt{117 \times 205}}\right) = 76.6°$ (1 d.p.)

You can use the 2D trigonometry rules in 3D shapes too...

... you just need to work out where to apply the rules. If you're stuck in the exam, try redrawing it as a 2D triangle and see which lengths and angles you know and which ones you need to find.

Vectors

Vectors represent a movement of a certain size in a certain direction.

Vector **Notations**

There are several ways to write vectors...

1) Column vectors: $\begin{pmatrix} 2 \\ -5 \end{pmatrix}$ — 2 units right — 5 units down $\begin{pmatrix} -7 \\ 4 \end{pmatrix}$ — 7 units left — 4 units up

2) **a** ——— exam questions often use bold like this.

3) $\underline{a}$ or $\underset{\sim}{a}$ — you should always underline them.

4) $\overrightarrow{AB}$ —— this means the vector from point A to point B.

5) $\overrightarrow{OA}$ —— this is a position vector. It describes where a point lies in relation to the origin, O. For example, the position vector of point A is $\overrightarrow{OA}$.

Multiplying by a **Scalar**, **Adding** and **Subtracting**

To add column vectors, add the top to the top and the bottom to the bottom. ⟹ $\begin{pmatrix} 3 \\ -1 \end{pmatrix} + \begin{pmatrix} 5 \\ 3 \end{pmatrix} = \begin{pmatrix} 8 \\ 2 \end{pmatrix}$
You use the same method when subtracting.

To multiply a vector by a number, multiply both the top and the bottom by that number. The number is often called a scalar ⟹ $4 \times \begin{pmatrix} 3 \\ -1 \end{pmatrix} = \begin{pmatrix} 12 \\ -4 \end{pmatrix}$
— a measurement with size but no direction.

Vectors as **Directed Line Segments**

1) Vectors can be represented on a diagram by a line segment, e.g. $\mathbf{a} = \begin{pmatrix} -7 \\ 4 \end{pmatrix}$. The arrow shows the direction of the vector.

Magnitude only has length — no direction.

2) The length of the vector is called its magnitude.

KEY TERM The magnitude (or modulus) of a vector is its length.

The magnitude of a vector can be written as $|\mathbf{a}|$ or $|\overrightarrow{AB}|$. ⟵
You find the magnitude using Pythagoras' theorem (see p.152)

The lines around the vector are called modulus signs.

— e.g. for the vector above, $|\mathbf{a}| = \left| \begin{pmatrix} -7 \\ 4 \end{pmatrix} \right| = \sqrt{(-7)^2 + 4^2} = \sqrt{65} = 8.06$ (3 s.f.).

3) Multiplying a vector by a positive number changes the vector's size but not its direction — it scales the vector. If the number's negative then the direction gets switched.

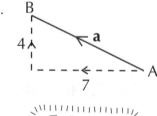

Vectors that are scalar multiples of each other are parallel.

4) You can describe movements between points by adding and subtracting known vectors.

- "**a** + **b**" means 'go along **a** then **b**'. ⟹
- "**c** – **d**" means 'go along **c** then backwards along **d**' (the minus sign means go the opposite way). ⟸

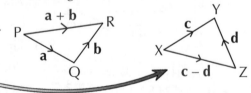

EXAMPLE:

In the diagram on the right, M is the midpoint of BC. Find vectors $\overrightarrow{AM}$ and $\overrightarrow{OC}$ in terms of a, b and m.

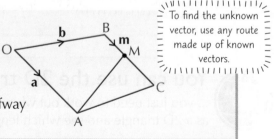

To find the unknown vector, use any route made up of known vectors.

$\overrightarrow{AM} = -\underline{a} + \underline{b} + \underline{m}$ —— A to M via O and B

$\overrightarrow{OC} = \underline{b} + 2\underline{m}$ ——— O to C via B and M — M's halfway between B and C, so $\overrightarrow{BC} = 2\mathbf{m}$

Vectors

Extra bits and pieces can crop up in vector questions — these examples will show you how to tackle them...

Vectors Along a Straight Line

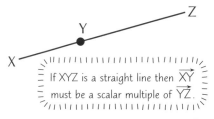

1) You can use vectors to show that points lie on a straight line.
2) You need to show that the vectors along each part of the line point in the same direction — that they're scalar multiples of each other.

If XYZ is a straight line then $\overrightarrow{XY}$ must be a scalar multiple of $\overrightarrow{YZ}$.

EXAMPLE:

In the diagram, $\overrightarrow{OB}$ = a, $\overrightarrow{AB}$ = 2b, $\overrightarrow{BD}$ = a – b and $\overrightarrow{DC}$ = $\frac{1}{2}$a – 4b.
Show that OAC is a straight line.

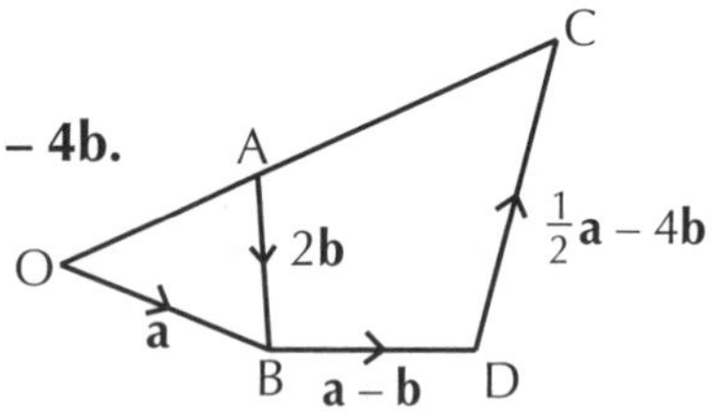

1) Work out the vectors along the two parts of OAC (OA and AC) using the vectors you know.

$$\overrightarrow{OA} = \underset{\sim}{a} - 2\underset{\sim}{b}$$

$$\overrightarrow{AC} = 2\underset{\sim}{b} + (\underset{\sim}{a} - \underset{\sim}{b}) + \left(\frac{1}{2}\underset{\sim}{a} - 4\underset{\sim}{b}\right)$$

$$= \frac{3}{2}\underset{\sim}{a} - 3\underset{\sim}{b} = \frac{3}{2}(\underset{\sim}{a} - 2\underset{\sim}{b})$$

2) Check that $\overrightarrow{AC}$ is a scalar multiple of $\overrightarrow{OA}$.

So, $\overrightarrow{AC} = \frac{3}{2}\overrightarrow{OA}$.

3) Explain why this means OAC is a straight line.

Therefore, $\overrightarrow{AC}$ is a scalar multiple of $\overrightarrow{OA}$, so OAC must be a straight line.

(margin: Extended)

Vector Questions Can Involve Ratios

Ratios are used in vector questions to tell you the lengths of different sections of a straight line. If you know the vector along part of that line, you can use this information to find other vectors along the line.

E.g.    XY:YZ = 2:3 tells you that $\overrightarrow{XY} = \frac{2}{5}\overrightarrow{XZ}$ and $\overrightarrow{YZ} = \frac{3}{5}\overrightarrow{XZ}$.

EXAMPLE: OABC is a parallelogram and O is the origin.
AB is parallel to OC and AO is parallel to BC. Point D
lies on AB, such that AD:DB = 3:1. $\overrightarrow{CB}$ = a and $\overrightarrow{CO}$ = b.
Find the position vector of D in terms of a and b.

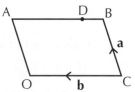

1) The position vector of D is $\overrightarrow{OD}$ — write this as a route along the parallelogram.

$$\overrightarrow{OD} = \overrightarrow{OA} + \overrightarrow{AD}$$

2) Use the parallel sides to find $\overrightarrow{OA}$ and $\overrightarrow{AB}$.

$$\overrightarrow{OA} = \overrightarrow{CB} = \underset{\sim}{a}$$
$$\overrightarrow{AB} = \overrightarrow{OC} = -\underset{\sim}{b}$$

3) Use the ratio to find $\overrightarrow{AD}$.

$$\overrightarrow{AD} = \frac{3}{4}\overrightarrow{AB}$$

4) Now use $\overrightarrow{OA}$ and $\overrightarrow{AD}$ to find $\overrightarrow{OD}$.

$$\overrightarrow{OD} = \overrightarrow{OA} + \overrightarrow{AD} = \underset{\sim}{a} - \frac{3}{4}\underset{\sim}{b}$$

Remember, parallel vectors are scalar multiples of each other

The only way to get good at vector questions is with lots of practice. Pick any two points on the diagrams in the examples above and try to find the vector between them in terms of **a** and **b**.

Warm-Up and Worked Exam Questions

Trigonometry and vector questions can be pretty tricky until you understand the basics. That's what these warm-up questions are for — work through them carefully and check anything you don't know.

Warm-Up Questions

Extended

1) In the triangle on the right, find the length of AC, correct to 1 decimal place.

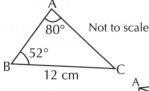

2) A triangle has sides of 4 cm, 6 cm and 8 cm. Calculate the largest angle.

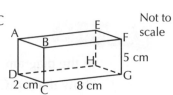

3) In the cuboid on the right, FG = 5 cm, CD = 2 cm and CG = 8 cm. Calculate the size of the angle FDG to 1 d.p.

4) If $90° < x < 180°$, find x to 1 d.p. when:
   a) $\sin x = 0.84$ b) $\sin x = 0.173$ c) $\tan x = -1$ d) $\tan x = -14.3$

5) If $\mathbf{f} = \begin{pmatrix} -2 \\ 1 \end{pmatrix}$ and $\mathbf{g} = \begin{pmatrix} 7 \\ -3 \end{pmatrix}$, find:
   a) $3\mathbf{g}$ b) $\mathbf{g} - \mathbf{f}$ c) the magnitude of $\mathbf{f} + \mathbf{g}$

Extended

6) ABCD is the parallelogram shown on the right. $\overrightarrow{AB} = 2\mathbf{a}$ and $\overrightarrow{AD} = 2\mathbf{d}$, L is the midpoint of AC, and M is the midpoint of BC. Write each of the following in terms of $\mathbf{a}$ and $\mathbf{d}$.
   a) $\overrightarrow{CD}$ b) $\overrightarrow{AC}$ c) $\overrightarrow{BL}$

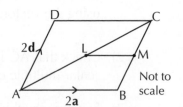

Worked Exam Question

Take the time to go through this example and make sure you understand it all.
If any of the facts are confusing you, it's not too late to take another look over the section.

Extended

1   In the triangle on the right, $AB = 10$ cm, $BC = 7$ cm and angle $ABC = 85°$.

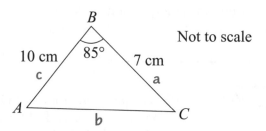

Label the sides of the triangle.

a) Calculate the length of *AC*.

Use the cosine rule to find b:

$b^2 = a^2 + c^2 - 2ac \cos B,$

$AC^2 = 7^2 + 10^2 - (2 \times 7 \times 10 \times \cos 85°)$

$AC = \sqrt{149 - 140 \times \cos 85°} = 11.69607... = 11.7$ cm (to 3 s.f.)

...........11.7........... cm

[4 marks]

b) Calculate the area of triangle *ABC*.

$\text{Area} = \dfrac{1}{2}ac \sin B$

$= \dfrac{1}{2} \times 7 \times 10 \times \sin 85°$

You know the length of two sides and the angle between them, so use the area formula from p.157.

$= 34.86681... = 34.9$ cm² (to 3 s.f)

...........34.9........... cm²

[2 marks]

Exam Questions

2   If $\mathbf{p} = \begin{pmatrix} 5 \\ -9 \end{pmatrix}$, $\mathbf{q} = \begin{pmatrix} -3 \\ 6 \end{pmatrix}$ and $\mathbf{r} = \begin{pmatrix} 8 \\ 1 \end{pmatrix}$, find $2\mathbf{p} + 3(\mathbf{q} - \mathbf{r})$.

....

[3 marks]

3   A castle drawbridge is supported by two chains, *AB* and *AC*. Using the information on the diagram below, calculate the total length of the drawbridge *BD*.

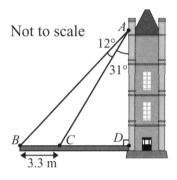

.... m

[6 marks]

4   A cuboid has a section removed from its top, creating the prism shown in the diagram. Calculate the angle *AGD*.

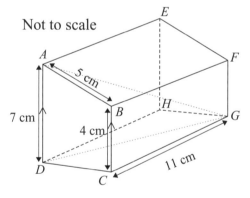

$\circ$

....

[5 marks]

5   *ABCD* is a parallelogram. $\overrightarrow{AB} = 3\mathbf{a}$ and $\overrightarrow{BW} = \mathbf{b}$.
   M is the midpoint of *CD* and *AX* = 2*XC*. *BW* : *WC* = 1 : 5

a)   Find $\overrightarrow{BX}$ in terms of **a** and **b**.

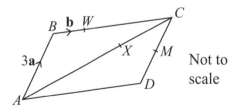

Not to scale

....

[3 marks]

b)   Hence show that *B*, *X* and *M* are three points on a straight line.

[2 marks]

Revision Questions for Section Five

There are lots of facts and formulas in this section, so use this page to check you're comfortable using them.
- Try these questions and tick off each one when you get it right.
- When you've done all the questions for a topic and are completely happy with it, tick off the topic.

Pythagoras' Theorem (p.152) ☐

1) What is the formula for Pythagoras' theorem? What do you use it for? ☑

2) A museum has a flight of stairs up to its front door (see diagram).
   A ramp is to be put over the top of the steps for wheelchair users.
   Calculate the length that the ramp would need to be. ☑

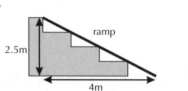
ramp
2.5m
4m

3) Point P has coordinates (–3, –2) and point Q has coordinates (2, 4).
   Calculate the length of the line PQ to 1 d.p. ☑

Trigonometry — Sin, Cos, Tan (p.153-154) ☐

4) Write down the three trigonometry formula triangles. ☑

5) Find the size of angle x in triangle ABC. ☑

B
9.1 cm
A x 7.6 cm C

6) A bird is sitting in a tree, 2.8 m above the ground.
   It sees a worm on the ground, 7.1 m away from the base of the tree.
   Calculate the angle of depression of the worm from the bird, correct to 1 d.p. ☑

7) Work out the shortest distance from point C to line B on this diagram. ☑

A C
15 cm
52°
B

The Sine and Cosine Rules (p.157-158) ☐

8) Write down the sine and cosine rules and the formula (involving sin) for the area of any triangle. ☑

9) List the 4 different types of sine/cosine rule questions and which rule you need for each. ☑

10) In triangle FGH, side FH = 8 cm, side GH = 9 cm and angle FHG = 47°.
    Find the length of side FG. ☑

11) Triangle PQR has side PQ = 12 cm, side QR = 9 cm and angle PQR = 63°. Find its area. ☑

Sin, Cos and Tan for Larger Angles (p.159) ☐

12) Triangle JKL has side JK = 6 cm, side JL = 11 cm and angle JLK = 28°.
    Find the size of the obtuse angle JKL. ☑

3D Pythagoras and Trigonometry (p.160-161) ☐

13) What is the formula for finding the length of the longest diagonal in a cuboid? ☑

14) Find the length of the longest diagonal in the cuboid measuring 5 m × 6 m × 9 m. ☑

15) Find the angle between the line BH and the plane ABCD in this cuboid. ☑

16) Find the size of angle WPU in the cuboid
    shown, to the nearest degree. ☑

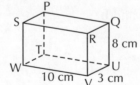
P
S Q
R
T 8 cm
W U
10 cm V 3 cm

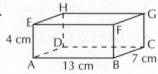
H G
E F
4 cm D C
A 13 cm B 7 cm

Vectors (p.162-163) ☐

17) $\mathbf{d} = \begin{pmatrix} 6 \\ 5 \end{pmatrix}$ and $\mathbf{e} = \begin{pmatrix} -8 \\ 3 \end{pmatrix}$. Work out: a) $\mathbf{d} + \mathbf{e}$, b) $4\mathbf{d}$. ☑

18) What is the magnitude of $\begin{pmatrix} 6 \\ -4 \end{pmatrix}$? ☑

19) OBCD is a quadrilateral with origin O. OXC is a straight line
    with OX : XC = 1 : 3. $\vec{XC} = \underset{\sim}{a}$, $\vec{DO} = \underset{\sim}{a} - \underset{\sim}{b}$ and $\vec{OB} = 3\underset{\sim}{a} - 2\underset{\sim}{b}$.
    a) Find the position vector of X.
    b) Find $\vec{DX}$ and $\vec{XB}$.
    c) Is DXB a straight line? Explain your answer. ☑

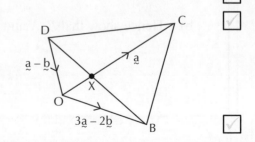
D C
$\underset{\sim}{a} - \underset{\sim}{b}$ $\underset{\sim}{a}$
X
O
$3\underset{\sim}{a} - 2\underset{\sim}{b}$ B

Probability Basics

A lot of people think probability is pretty tough. But if you learn the basics well, it will all make sense.

All **Probabilities** are **Between 0 and 1**

Probabilities are always between 0 and 1. The higher the probability of something, the more likely it is.

- A probability of zero means it will never happen.
- A probability of one means it definitely will. ←

You can't have a probability bigger than 1.

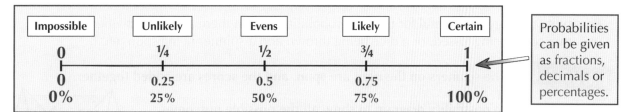

Probabilities can be given as fractions, decimals or percentages.

You Can Find **Some** Probabilities Using a **Formula**

Remember... the following formula only works if all the possible results are equally likely.

$$\text{Probability} = \frac{\text{Number of ways for something to happen}}{\text{Total number of possible results}}$$

'Fair' and 'at random' show that possible results are all equally likely. 'Biased' and 'unfair' mean the opposite (see p.175).

EXAMPLE: **Work out the probability of randomly picking a letter 'P' from the tiles below.**

APPLE PIE

1) There are 3 P's — so there are 3 different ways to 'pick a letter P'.

2) And there are 8 tiles altogether — each of these is a possible result.

$$\text{Probability} = \frac{\text{number of ways to pick a P}}{\text{total number of possible results}}$$

$$= \frac{3}{8} \text{ (or 0.375)}$$

Probabilities **Add Up to 1**

1) If only one possible result can happen at a time, then the probabilities of all the results add up to 1.

Probabilities always ADD UP to 1

2) So since something must either happen or not happen (i.e. only one of these can happen at a time):

P(event happens) + P(event doesn't happen) = 1

The probability of an event not happening equals 1 minus the probability of it happening.

EXAMPLE: **A spinner has different numbers of red, blue, yellow and green sections. What is the probability of spinning green?**

Colour	red	blue	yellow	green
Probability	0.1	0.4	0.3	

Only one of the results can happen at a time, so all the probabilities must add up to 1.

$$P(\text{green}) = 1 - (0.1 + 0.4 + 0.3) = 0.2$$

Probabilities are between 0 and 1

If you haven't fully understood this page, go back through it again until you are comfortable with the basics.

Listing Outcomes and Expected Frequency

For a lot of probability questions, a good place to start is with a list of all the things that could happen (also known as outcomes). Once you've got a list of outcomes, the rest of the question is easy.

Listing **All Outcomes**: **Two Coins, Dice, Spinners**

 KEY TERM A possibility diagram shows all the possible outcomes of two activities.

Possibility diagrams are useful for finding probabilities when there are two activities going on (e.g. two coins being tossed, or a dice being thrown and a spinner being spun, etc.).

EXAMPLE: **The spinners on the right are spun, and the scores are added together.**

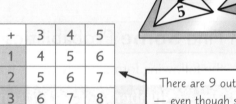

a) **Make a possibility diagram to show all the possible outcomes.**

1) All the scores from one spinner go along the top. All the scores from the other spinner go down the side.

2) Add the two scores together to get the different possible totals (the outcomes).

+	3	4	5
1	4	5	6
2	5	6	7
3	6	7	8

There are 9 outcomes — even though some of the totals are repeated.

b) **Find the probability of spinning a total of 6.**

There are 9 possible outcomes altogether, and 3 ways to score 6.

$$P(\text{total} = 6) = \frac{\text{ways to score 6}}{\text{total number of possible outcomes}} = \frac{3}{9} = \frac{1}{3}$$

Use Probability to Find the **Expected Frequency**

You can estimate how often you'd expect something to happen if you carry out an experiment *n* times.

 KEY TERM Expected frequency is the expected number of times an outcome will happen.
Expected frequency = probability × number of trials

EXAMPLE: **A game involves throwing a fair six-sided dice. The player wins if they score either a 5 or a 6. If one person plays the game 180 times, estimate the number of times they will win.**

1) First calculate the probability that they win each game.

$$\text{Probability of winning} = \frac{\text{number of ways to win}}{\text{total number of possible results}}$$
$$= \frac{2}{6} = \frac{1}{3}$$

2) Then estimate the number of times they'll win in 180 separate attempts.

$$\text{Expected number of wins} = \text{probability of winning} \times \text{number of trials}$$
$$= \frac{1}{3} \times 180$$
$$= 60$$

 REVISION TASK ## Expected frequency estimates how many times it will happen

Estimate the number of 1s you would expect to roll if you rolled a six-sided dice 30 times. Then, if you have a dice, try rolling it 30 times and see how the results compare to the estimate.

The AND/OR Rules

This page is also about when you have more than one thing happening at a time.

Combined Probability — Two or More Events

1) **Always break down a complicated-looking probability question into A SEQUENCE of SEPARATE EVENTS.**
2) **Find the probability of EACH of these SEPARATE EVENTS.**
3) **Apply the AND/OR rule.**

And now for the rules. If you have two events, A and B...

The **AND Rule** Gives **P(Both Events Happen)**

$$P(A \text{ and } B) = P(A) \times P(B)$$

This only works when the result of one event does not affect the other event.

This says: The probability of Event A AND Event B BOTH happening is equal to the two separate probabilities MULTIPLIED together.

 **Dave picks one ball at random from each of bags X and Y. Find the probability that he picks a yellow ball from both bags.**

1) Write down the probabilities of the different events.

$P(\text{Dave picks a yellow ball from bag X}) = \frac{4}{10} = 0.4.$

$P(\text{Dave picks a yellow ball from bag Y}) = \frac{2}{8} = 0.25.$

2) Use the formula.

So $P(\text{Dave picks a yellow ball from both bags}) = 0.4 \times 0.25 = 0.1$

The **OR Rule** Gives **P(At Least One Event Happens)**

$$P(A \text{ or } B) = P(A) + P(B)$$

This only works when the two events can't both happen at the same time.

This says: The probability of EITHER Event A OR Event B happening is equal to the two separate probabilities ADDED together.

 **A spinner with red, blue, yellow and green sections is spun. The probability of it landing on each colour is shown in the table. Find the probability of spinning either red or green.**

Colour	red	blue	yellow	green
Probability	0.25	0.3	0.35	0.1

1) Write down the probabilities of the different events.

$P(\text{lands on red}) = 0.25$ and $P(\text{lands on green}) = 0.1$

2) Use the formula.

So $P(\text{lands on either red or green}) = 0.25 + 0.1 = 0.35$

 ## Two rules to learn here

Make sure you learn the AND/OR rules — if you keep mixing them up, just remember that they're the wrong way round — AND <u>doesn't</u> go with '+'. It's 'AND with ×' and 'OR with +'.

Warm-Up and Worked Exam Questions

A few nice warm-up questions for you here. If you have any problems with these,
go back and have another look at the last few pages before moving on to the exam questions.

Warm-Up Questions

1) Calculate the probability of the fair spinner on the right landing on 4.

2) If the probability of spinning red on a spinner is 0.8,
   find the probability of spinning any colour except red.

3) Two fair 6-sided dice are thrown, and their scores added together.
   a) Find the probability of throwing a total of 7.
   b) If the pair of dice are thrown 300 times, how many times would you expect a total of 7?

4) I pick a candy from a bag of 26 candies. 18 of the candies are yellow, 2 of them are blue
   and the rest are pink. Find the probability that the candy I pick is blue or pink.

Worked Exam Question

Look through this worked exam question and make sure you understand it.

1   Here is a 5-sided spinner. The spinner is biased.

The probability that the spinner will land on each of
the numbers 1 to 4 is given in the table below.

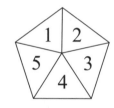

Number	1	2	3	4	5
Probability	0.3	0.15	0.2	0.25	

The spinner is spun once.

a) Work out the probability the spinner will not land on 2.

$$P(\text{not } 2) = 1 - P(2) = 1 - 0.15 = 0.85$$

.........0.85.........
[2 marks]

b) Work out the probability the spinner will land on an odd number.

$$P(\text{even}) = P(2 \text{ or } 4) = 0.15 + 0.25 = 0.4$$
$$\text{So } P(\text{odd}) = 1 - P(\text{even}) = 1 - 0.4 = 0.6$$

You could also work out P(5) first by doing
$1 - (0.3 + 0.15 + 0.2 + 0.25) = 0.1$
Then P(odd) = P(1 or 3 or 5) = 0.3 + 0.2 + 0.1

.........0.6.........
[3 marks]

The spinner is spun twice.

c) Work out the probability that the spinner will land on 3 both times.

$$P(3 \text{ both times}) = P(3 \text{ first time and } 3 \text{ second time})$$
$$= P(3) \times P(3) = 0.2 \times 0.2 = 0.04$$

.........0.04.........
[2 marks]

Exam Questions

2   There are 10 balls in a bag. Four of the balls are blue and the remaining balls are red.
    One ball is picked out at random.

    a)   Work out the probability that the ball picked is red.
    Give your answer as a fraction in its lowest terms.

        ....
    [2 mark]

    b)   What is the probability that the ball picked is green?

        ....
    [1 mark]

3   The total number of students in a school is 834.

    Work out an estimate for the number of students who were born on a Tuesday.

*The answer has to be a
whole number of students,
so you'll need to round.*

        .... students
    [3 marks]

4   Josie has six different cards, shown below.

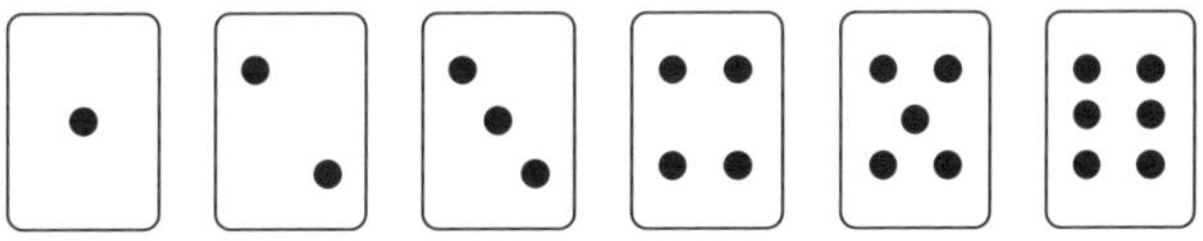

    a)   Find the probability that a randomly chosen card will have fewer than 3 dots on it.

        ....
    [1 mark]

    b)   Josie picks a card, replaces it and picks
    another card. She adds the results from
    the two cards together.

        Complete the possibility diagram
    to show all the possible outcomes.

	1	2	3	4	5	6
1	2	3	4	5		
2	3	4	5	6		
3	4	5				
4	5	6				
5						
6						

[2 marks]

    c)   What is the probability that the total number of dots
    on the two cards that Josie picks will be 4?

        ....
    [2 marks]

Tree Diagrams

Tree diagrams can really help you work out probabilities when you have a combination of events.

Remember These **Four** Key **Tree Diagram Facts**

1) On any set of branches which meet at a point, the probabilities must add up to 1.

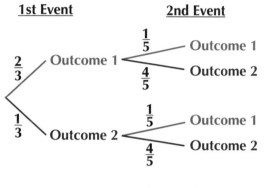

1st Event   **2nd Event**

2) Multiply along the branches to get the end probabilities.

$\frac{2}{3} \times \frac{1}{5} = \frac{2}{15}$

$\frac{2}{3} \times \frac{4}{5} = \frac{8}{15}$

3) If you work out all the end probabilities they should add up to 1.

$\frac{1}{3} \times \frac{1}{5} = \frac{1}{15}$

$\frac{1}{3} \times \frac{4}{5} = \frac{4}{15}$

Total = 1

4) Pick the probability you need to answer the question.

EXAMPLE: A box contains only red and green discs. A disc is taken at random and replaced. A second disc is then taken. The tree diagram below shows the probabilities of picking each colour.

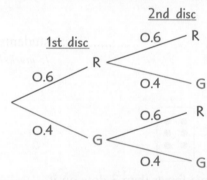

a) **What is the probability that both discs are red?**

Multiply along the branches to find the probability you want:

P(both discs are red) = P(red, red) = 0.6 × 0.6 = 0.36

b) **What is the probability that you pick a green disc then a red disc?**

Multiply along the branches to find the probability you want:

P(green, red) = 0.4 × 0.6 = 0.24

Tree diagrams can also show conditional probabilities — for these ones, you'll get different probabilities on different sets of branches.

 KEY TERM

The conditional probability of A given B is the probability of event A happening, given that event B happens.

EXAMPLE: Florence travels to work by either walking or driving. The probability that she walks is 0.3. If she walks, the probability that she is late is 0.8. If she drives, the probability that she is late is 0.1.

a) **Complete the tree diagram below.**

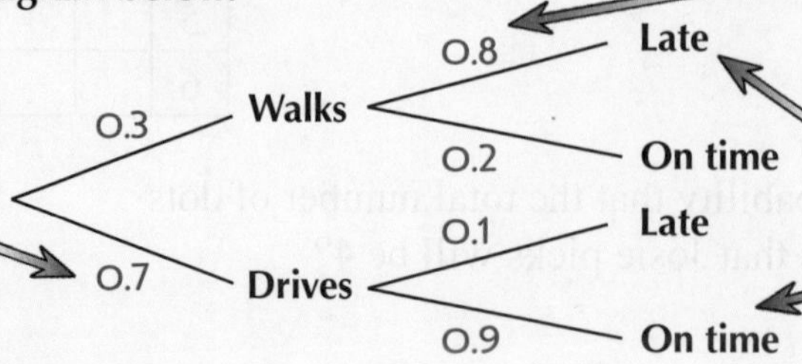

This is a conditional probability — the probability of being late given that she walks.

Fill in the empty branches so they add to 1.

0.3 — **Walks**
0.8 — Late
0.2 — On time
0.7 — **Drives**
0.1 — Late
0.9 — On time

The probabilities of being late or on time depend on whether she walks or drives — they are dependent events.

b) **Find the probability that she is late.**

Multiply along the branches to find the probabilities you want. Then add the probabilities.

P(late) = P(walks and is late) + P(drives and is late)

= (0.3 × 0.8) + (0.7 × 0.1)

= 0.24 + 0.07 = 0.31

Extended

Tree Diagrams

Four Extra Details for the Tree Diagram Method:

1) Always split the question into a sequence of separate events.

You need a sequence of events to be able to draw any sort of tree diagram.
For example... '3 coins are tossed at the same time' — just split it into 3 separate events.

2) You don't always have to draw complete tree diagrams.

For example... 'What is the probability of throwing a fair six-sided dice 3 times and getting 2 sixes followed by an even number?'

The diagram on the right is all you need to get the answer: $\frac{1}{6} \times \frac{1}{6} \times \frac{1}{2} = \frac{1}{72}$

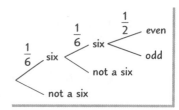

3) With 'AT LEAST' questions, it's always (1 − probability of 'LESS THAN that many'):

For example... 'I throw 3 fair six-sided dice. Find the probability of throwing AT LEAST one six.'

There are in fact quite a few different ways of 'throwing AT LEAST one six', and you could spend a long time working out all the different probabilities.

The clever trick you should know is this:
The probability of 'AT LEAST something or other' is just: 1 − probability of 'less than that many'.
So: P(at least one six) = 1 − P(less than one six) = 1 − P(no sixes).

4) Watch out for conditional probabilities.

This is where the probabilities on a set of branches change depending on the result of the previous event. For example... if you're picking things at random (e.g. cards from a pack, or balls out of a bag) without replacing your earlier picks.

See the last example on the previous page.

Extended

EXAMPLE: The following letters are placed in a hat:

'With replacement' means the first tile was put back in the bag before the second one was picked out.

Two letters are picked out at random and written down, with replacement.

a) Complete the tree diagram below to show whether or not each of the letters picked is a 'B'.

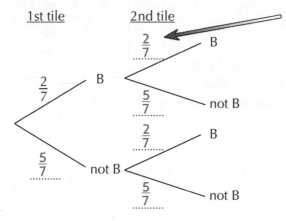

1st tile   2nd tile

The tiles are replaced, so the probabilities for the 2nd tile aren't affected by what you pick for the 1st tile.

b) **Calculate the probability that at least one of the selected tiles is a 'B'.**

P(at least 1 tile is B) = 1 − P(less than 1 tile is B)

$\qquad\qquad\qquad\quad = 1 - P(\text{neither tile is B})$

$\qquad\qquad\qquad\quad = 1 - \frac{5}{7} \times \frac{5}{7}$

$\qquad\qquad\qquad\quad = 1 - \frac{25}{49} = \frac{24}{49}$

See how useful tree diagrams are

Tree diagrams are an excellent tool for working out probabilities. If you feel stuck on an exam question about combined events, drawing a tree diagram for them can be a good place to start.

Probability from Venn Diagrams

If you can't remember everything about Venn diagrams and need a reminder, head back to pages 43-44. Once you've done that, read on to find out how they can be used to calculate probabilities.

Finding Probabilities from **Venn Diagrams**

Venn diagrams can be used to show the number of things in different groups or that share something in common. You can easily work out probabilities by counting up the things you're interested in.

EXAMPLE: In a class of 30 students, 8 of them like mustard, 24 of them like ketchup and 5 of them like both mustard and ketchup.

a) **Complete the Venn diagram below to show this information.**

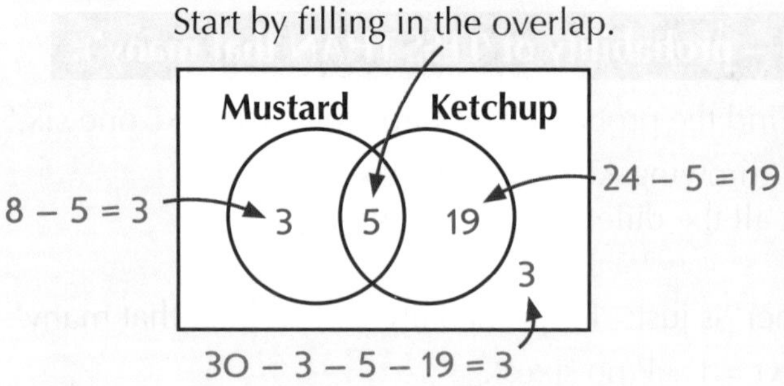

Start by filling in the overlap.

$8 - 5 = 3$

$24 - 5 = 19$

$30 - 3 - 5 - 19 = 3$

b) **How many students like mustard or ketchup?**

This is the number of students in the union of the two sets.

$3 + 5 + 19 = 27$

c) **What is the probability that a randomly selected student will like mustard and ketchup?**

5 out of 30 students are in the intersection.

$\frac{5}{30} = \frac{1}{6}$

You could get a question in your exam about finding probabilities from a Venn diagram with three circles. Don't panic — it works the same as one with two circles, but the calculations are a bit trickier.

EXAMPLE: The Venn diagram below shows the number of children competing at a school sports day in the 100 metre race (R), the high jump (H) and crocodile wrestling (C).

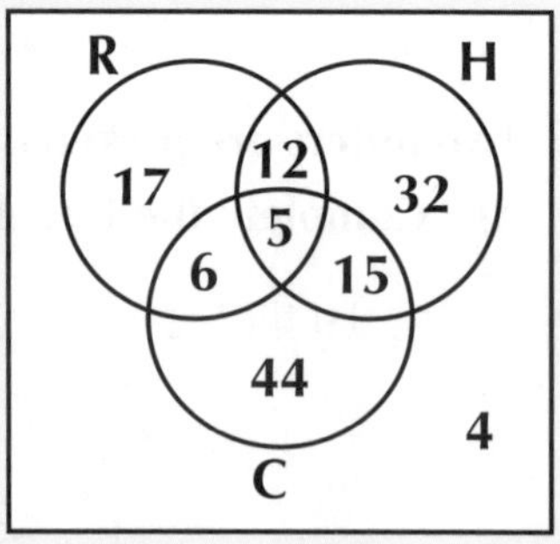

a) **Find the probability that a randomly selected child is not competing in the crocodile wrestling.**

$n(\text{children}) = 4 + 44 + 15 + 5 + 6 + 17 + 12 + 32 = 135$

$n(\text{not competing in crocodile wrestling}) = 17 + 12 + 32 + 4 = 65$

$P(\text{not competing in crocodile wrestling}) = \frac{65}{135} = \frac{13}{27}$

b) **Given that a randomly selected child is competing in the 100 metre race, find the probability that they are also competing in both the high jump and the crocodile wrestling.**

$n(\text{competing in 100 metre race}) = 17 + 12 + 5 + 6 = 40$

$n(\text{competing in all three events}) = 5$

Remember, the number in the middle is how many are in all three categories.

$P(\text{competing in all three events given they're competing in 100 metre race}) = \frac{5}{40} = \frac{1}{8}$ or 0.125

Make sure you can remember all set notation from Section One

All the stuff about intersections and unions on page 43 relates to the AND/OR rules in probability. To find P(A and B), look for A ∩ B on your Venn diagram. For P(A or B), look for A ∪ B. If you're asked to find a probability given an event, only consider the bits inside the circle for that event.

Relative Frequency

The formula on page 167 only works when the outcomes are equally likely. If they're not equally likely, you can use the results from previous experiments to estimate the probability of each outcome.

Do the Experiment **Again** and **Again**...

You need to do an experiment over and over again and count how many times each outcome happens (its frequency). Then you can calculate the relative frequency using this formula:

$$\text{Relative frequency} = \frac{\text{Frequency}}{\text{Number of times you tried the experiment}}$$

An experiment could just mean rolling a dice.

You can use the relative frequency of a result as an estimate of its probability.

 **EXAMPLE:** The spinner on the right was spun 100 times. Use the results in the table below to estimate the probability of getting each of the scores.

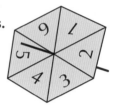

Score	1	2	3	4	5	6
Frequency	3	14	41	20	18	4

Divide each of the frequencies by 100 to find the relative frequencies.

Score	1	2	3	4	5	6
Relative Frequency	$\frac{3}{100} = 0.03$	$\frac{14}{100} = 0.14$	$\frac{41}{100} = 0.41$	$\frac{20}{100} = 0.2$	$\frac{18}{100} = 0.18$	$\frac{4}{100} = 0.04$

The MORE TIMES you do the experiment, the MORE ACCURATE your estimate of the probability should be.

E.g. if you spun the above spinner 1000 times, you'd get a better estimate of the probability for each score.

Fair or Biased?

 KEY TERMS

A fair object (e.g. coin, spinner, dice) is one where all outcomes are equally likely. A biased or unfair object is one where certain outcomes have a higher probability of happening.

1) If the dice/spinner/coin/etc. is fair, then the relative frequencies of the results should roughly match the expected probabilities you'd get using the formula on p.167.
2) If the relative frequencies are far away from those probabilities, you can say it's probably biased.

 **EXAMPLE:** Do the results from the example above suggest the spinner is biased?

Yes, because the relative frequency of 3 is much higher than you'd expect, while the relative frequencies of 1 and 6 are much lower.

For a fair 6-sided spinner, you'd expect all the relative frequencies to be around $1 \div 6 = 0.167$ (3 s.f.).

 REVISION TIP

More experiments mean a more accurate probability estimate

Learn the formula for calculating relative frequency — you can then use the relative frequency of a result as an estimate of its probability. If something is biased, this just means it isn't fair. But remember — even with a fair dice you're unlikely to get the expected result exactly.

Warm-Up and Worked Exam Questions

Probability is not that difficult once you understand it, but it's important to do loads of practice, so try these warm-up questions. Take a look back at anything you're unsure about.

Warm-Up Questions

1) A bag contains 6 red balls and 4 black ones. Two balls are picked at random (with replacement). Use a tree diagram to find the probability that they're different colours.

2) The numbers 1 to 21 are put in a lottery draw. A machine selects the numbers randomly (without replacement). Use a tree diagram to find the probability that out of the first two numbers selected: a) at least one is even,   b) one is odd and one is even.

3) 50 birdwatchers were looking for two types of bird — pigeons and seagulls. 28 of them saw a pigeon, 15 of them saw both birds and 10 of them didn't see either bird.
a) Show this information on a Venn diagram.
b) Find the probability that a randomly selected birdwatcher saw a seagull.

4) Sandro rolled a dice 1000 times and got the results shown in the table below.

Score	1	2	3	4	5	6
Frequency	140	137	138	259	161	165

Find the relative frequencies for each of the scores 1-6. Do you think the dice is biased?

Worked Exam Question

Have a good look at this worked exam question. Make sure you understand each part — you'll usually get at least one probability question in the exam.

1   Suda has a six-sided dice. The sides are numbered 1 to 6.

Suda rolls the dice 50 times. Her results are shown in the table below.

Number	1	2	3	4	5	6
Relative Frequency	0.32	0.12	0.24	0.14	0.06	0.12

a)   How many times did she roll a 6?

$$50 \times 0.12 = 6$$

                                                      6
[2 marks]

b)   Is Suda's dice fair? Explain your answer.

On a fair dice, the theoretical probability of throwing each number is 0.166...,

so as 1 has a much higher relative frequency and 5 has a much lower relative

frequency, the dice is probably not fair.

[2 marks]

c)   She rolls the dice another 50 times. Should she expect the same results? Explain your answer.

No, each dice roll is random, so in a small number of

trials like 50 she is likely to get different results.

[1 mark]

Exam Questions

2   A married couple are both carriers of a gene that causes a disease.
    If they have a child, the probability that the child will carry the gene is 0.25.

   a)   The couple have two children. Draw a tree diagram to show the probabilities
         of each child carrying or not carrying the gene.

[2 marks]

   b)   Find the probability that both children will carry the gene.

....
[2 marks]

3   The Venn diagram on the right shows the number
    of female contestants (F) and singers (S)
    in a talent competition.

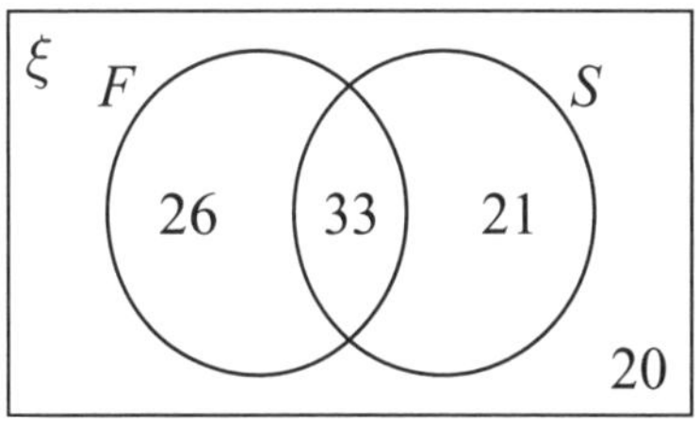

   a)   Find the probability that a randomly selected
         contestant isn't a singer.

....
[1 mark]

   b)   Find the probability that a randomly selected contestant
         isn't female, given that they're a singer.

....
[1 mark]

4   A box of chocolates contains 12 chocolates. 7 are milk chocolate and
    5 are white chocolate. Two chocolates are chosen at random without replacement.

   a)   Given that the first chocolate is a milk chocolate,
         what is the probability that the second chocolate is a milk chocolate?

....
[1 mark]

   b)   Calculate the probability that one milk chocolate
         and one white chocolate are chosen in any order.

....
[2 marks]

Collecting Data

Data you collect yourself is called primary data. If you use data that someone else has collected, e.g. you get it from a website, it's called secondary data. You need to record primary data in a way that's easy to analyse and suitable for the type of data you've got.

There are **Different Types** of **Data**

Qualitative data is descriptive. It uses words, not numbers.

E.g. pets' names — Smudge, Snowy, Dave, etc., flavours of ice cream — 'vanilla', 'chocolate', etc.

Quantitative data measures quantities using numbers.

E.g. heights of people, times taken to finish a race, numbers of goals scored in football matches, etc.

There are two types of quantitative data.

Discrete data — the numbers can only take certain exact values.

E.g. the number of customers in a shop each day has to be a whole number — you can't have half a person.

Continuous data — the numbers can take any value in a range.

E.g. heights and weights are continuous measurements.

You can **Organise** your **Data** into **Classes**

1) To record data in a table, you often need to group it into classes to make it easier to work with. Discrete data classes should have 'gaps' between them, e.g. '0-1 goals', '2-3 goals' (it jumps from 1 to 2 because there are no values in between). Continuous data classes should have no 'gaps', so they are often written using inequalities (see p.181).

2) Whatever data you have, make sure none of the classes overlap and that they cover all the possible values.

When you group data, you lose some accuracy because you don't know the exact values any more.

EXAMPLE: **Jonty wants to find out about the ages (in whole years) of people who use his local library. Design a table he could use to collect his data.**

Include columns for: the data values, 'Tally' to count the data and 'Frequency' to show the totals.

Use non-overlapping classes with gaps because the data is discrete.

Include classes like '...or over', '...or less' or 'other' to cover all options in a sensible number of classes.

Age (whole years)	Tally	Frequency
0-19		
20-39		
40-59		
60-79		
80 or over		

Questionnaires should be **Designed Carefully**

Another way to record data is to ask people to fill in a questionnaire. Your questions should be:

Watch out for response boxes that could be interpreted in different ways, that overlap, or that don't allow for all possible answers.

1) Clear and easy to understand
2) Easy to answer
3) Fair — not leading or biased

A question is 'leading' if it guides you towards picking a particular answer.

Tables are a really good way to record data

You need to know what type of data you've got so you can record and display it in a suitable way. If an exam question asks you to draw a table, make sure you clearly label each of the columns.

Mean, Median, Mode and Range

Mean, median, mode and range are really important in statistics — make sure you know what they are.

The Four Definitions

Mode = Most common value
Median = Middle value (when values are in order of size)
Mean = Total of items ÷ number of items
Range = Difference between highest and lowest

The mode, median and mean are all types of average, but when people say 'average' they're usually talking about the mean.

The Golden Rule There's one important step for finding the median that lots of people forget:

Always REARRANGE the data in ASCENDING ORDER

'Ascending order' just means from lowest to highest.

You must do this when finding the median,
but it's also really useful for working out the mode too.

EXAMPLE: **Find the median, mode, mean, and range of these numbers:**
2, 5, 3, 2, 6, –4, 0, 9, –3, 1, 6, 3, –2, 3

Check that you still have the same number of entries after you've rearranged them.

The MEDIAN is the middle value, so rearrange the numbers in order of size.
When there are two middle numbers,
the median is halfway between the two.

–4, –3, –2, 0, 1, 2, (2, 3) 3, 3, 5, 6, 6, 9
← seven numbers this side   seven numbers this side →
Median = 2.5

An even number of values means there will be two middle numbers.

MODE (or modal value) is the most common value. ⟶ Mode = 3

Data sets can have more than one mode.

$$\text{MEAN} = \frac{\text{total of items}}{\text{number of items}} \longrightarrow \frac{-4-3-2+0+1+2+2+3+3+3+5+6+6+9}{14}$$

$$= 31 \div 14 = 2.214... = 2.21 \text{ (3 s.f.)}$$

RANGE = distance from lowest to highest value, i.e. from –4 up to 9. ⟶ 9 – (–4) = 13

Choose the Best Average

The mean, median and mode all have their advantages and disadvantages — learn them:

	Advantages	Disadvantages
Mean	Uses all the data. Usually most representative.	Isn't always a data value. May be distorted by extreme data values.
Median	Easy to find in ordered data. Not distorted by extreme data values.	Isn't always a data value. Not always a good representation of the data.
Mode	Easy to find in tallied data. Always a data value.	Sometimes there's more than one mode, or no mode. Not always a good representation of the data.

Mean, median, mode & range — easy marks for learning four words

The maths involved in working these out is pretty simple — as long as you learn the definitions.
Practise using the golden rule: when finding the median, always arrange the data from lowest to highest.

Frequency Tables

The word frequency means 'how many', so a frequency table is just a 'How many in each category' table. You saw how to find averages and range on p.179 — it's the same idea here, but with the data in a table.

Find **Averages** from **Frequency Tables**

1) The MODE is just the CATEGORY with the MOST ENTRIES.

2) The RANGE is found from the HIGHEST and LOWEST entries in the first column.

3) The MEDIAN is the CATEGORY with the middle value in the second column.

4) To find the MEAN, you have to WORK OUT A THIRD COLUMN by multiplying the first two columns.

Then the MEAN is: **3rd Column Total ÷ 2nd Column Total**

Categories   How many

Number of cats	Frequency	
0	19	
1	14	
2	5	
3	2	

Third column for working out the mean

EXAMPLE: **Some people were asked how many sisters they have. The table opposite shows the results.**
Find the mode, the range, the mean and the median of the data.

Number of sisters	Frequency
0	7
1	15
2	12
3	8
4	4
5	0

1 The mode is the category with the most entries — i.e. the one with the highest frequency:

The highest frequency is 15 for '1 sister', so MODE = 1.

2 The range is the difference between the highest and lowest numbers of sisters — that's 4 sisters (no one has 5 sisters) and no sisters, so:

RANGE = 4 – 0 = 4

3 To find the mean, add a 3rd column to the table showing 'number of sisters × frequency'. Add up these values to find the total number of sisters of all the people asked.

You can label the first column x and the frequency column f, then the third column is $x \times f$.

Number of sisters (x)	Frequency (f)	No. of sisters × Frequency $(x \times f)$
0	7	0
1	15	15
2	12	24
3	8	24
4	4	16
5	0	0
Total	46	79

3rd column total

$$\text{MEAN} = \frac{\text{total number of sisters}}{\text{total number of people asked}} = \frac{79}{46} = 1.72 \text{ (3 s.f.)}$$

2nd column total

4 The median is the category of the middle value. Work out its position, then count through the 2nd column to find it.

It helps to imagine the data set out in an ordered list:
0000000111111111111111222222222222223333333334444

median

There are 46 values, so the middle value is halfway between the 23rd and 24th values. There are a total of (7 + 15) = 22 values in the first two categories, and another 12 in the third category takes you to 34. So the 23rd and 24th values must both be in the category '2 sisters', which means the MEDIAN is 2.

Mode is most, median is middle and mean is average

When finding the mean, divide by the total of the <u>frequency column</u>. Now, use the frequency table for 'Number of cats' at the top of the page to show that the mean of the data is 0.75 cats.

Grouped Frequency Tables

Grouped frequency tables group together the data into classes.
They look like ordinary frequency tables, but they can be a little trickier than that...

For continuous data (see p.178):
- Use inequality symbols to cover all possible values.
- Here, 10 would go in the 1st class, but 10.1 would go in the 2nd class.

Height (h mm)	Frequency
$5 < h \leq 10$	12
$10 < h \leq 15$	15

If h in the table was discrete and had to be a whole number, you could just have classes like '6-10', '11-15', etc.

To find mid-interval values:
- Add together the end values of the class and divide by 2.
- E.g. $\dfrac{5+10}{2} = 7.5$

Find Averages from Grouped Frequency Tables

Unlike with ordinary frequency tables, you don't know the actual data values, only the classes they're in. So you have to estimate the mean, rather than calculate it exactly. Again, you do this by adding columns:

> **Add a 3rd column and enter the mid-interval value for each class.**
> **Add a 4th column to show 'frequency × mid-interval value' for each class.**

You might also be asked to find the modal class — this is just the class with the highest frequency.

EXAMPLE: This table shows information about the weights, in kilograms, of 60 school children.

a) Write down the modal class.
b) Calculate an estimate for the mean weight.

Weight (w kg)	Frequency
$30 < w \leq 40$	8
$40 < w \leq 50$	16
$50 < w \leq 60$	18
$60 < w \leq 70$	12
$70 < w \leq 80$	6

a) The modal class is the one with the highest frequency.

Modal class is $50 < w \leq 60$

b) 1) Add extra columns for 'mid-interval value' (3rd column) and 'frequency × mid-interval value' (4th column).

2) Add up the values in the 4th column to estimate the total weight of the 60 children.

3) Then divide the total weight of the children by the number of children — just like you would to find the exact value of the mean.

Weight (w kg)	Frequency (f)	Mid-interval value (x)	fx
$30 < w \leq 40$	8	35	280
$40 < w \leq 50$	16	45	720
$50 < w \leq 60$	18	55	990
$60 < w \leq 70$	12	65	780
$70 < w \leq 80$	6	75	450
Total	60	—	3220

You don't need to add up the mid-interval values.

$\text{Mean} \approx \dfrac{\text{total weight}}{\text{number of children}}$ ← 4th column total ← 2nd column total

$= \dfrac{3220}{60}$

$= 53.7$ kg (3 s.f.)

This time there are two columns to add

With frequency tables there was just one column to add, but with grouped frequency tables there are two. It's still not too difficult as long as you remember what the columns are and how to find them.

Extended

Warm-Up and Worked Exam Questions

When you have collected this knowledge, try the warm-up questions below. If there's anything you're struggling with, look back over the previous pages before moving on to the exam questions.

Warm-Up Questions

1) State whether the data below is qualitative, discrete or continuous:
   a) The number of people watching a rugby match at a stadium.
   b) A list of the different colours of stones on a beach.
   c) The hottest daily temperatures recorded by a thermometer.

2) Find the mode, median, mean and range of the following numbers:
   1, 2, –2, 0, 1, 8, 3, –3, 2, 4, –2, 2

3) The data in the table below shows the number of cars owned by 124 households in a survey. Find the: a) mean,   b) median,   c) mode,   d) range.

Number of cars	0	1	2	3	4	5	6
Frequency	1	24	36	31	22	9	1

4) The grouped frequency table below represents data from 79 random people.

Height (cm)	$145 \le x < 155$	$155 \le x < 165$	$165 \le x < 175$	$175 \le x < 185$
Frequency	18	22	24	15

   a) Estimate the mean.   b) State the modal group.

Extended

Worked Exam Question

This worked exam question is just like one that could come up in the exam.
But the one in the exam won't have the answers filled in, so make the most of it now.

1   50 people were asked how many times a week they play sport. The table to the right shows the results.

No. of times sport played (x)	Frequency (f)	No. of times played sports × Frequency (x × f)
0	8	0
1	15	15
2	17	34
3	6	18
4	4	16
5 or more	0	0
Total	50	83

a) Find the mode.

The highest frequency is 17 for playing sports 2 times a week.

........**2**........
[1 mark]

b) Find the median.

$50 \div 2 = 25$, so the median is halfway between the 25th and 26th values, so it lies in the category containing the 25th and 26th values, which is 2.

........**2**........
[2 mark]

c) Calculate the mean.

Add a column to the table to work out x × f.

Mean = $\frac{83}{50}$ = 1.66

........**1.66**........
[2 marks]

Exam Questions

2   In a class, 15 boys and 13 girls took a Maths test. The mean mark for the boys was b.
In the same test the mean mark for the girls was g.

Write down an expression for the mean mark of all 28 students.

....

[3 marks]

3   For her homework, Vanessa collected information about the number of text messages that
36 students in her school sent one day. She recorded her results in the frequency table below.
Use the table to calculate the mean number of text messages sent.

Number of messages	Frequency
0	2
2	4
3	7
5	11
7	6
8	3
10	3
Total	36

....

[3 marks]

4   During a science experiment, 10 seeds were planted and
their growth was measured to the nearest cm after 12 days.
The results were recorded in the table on the right.

Use the table to find:

a)   the modal class,

Growth in cm	Number of plants
$1 \leq x \leq 3$	2
$4 \leq x \leq 6$	4
$7 \leq x \leq 9$	3
$10 \leq x \leq 12$	1

....

[1 mark]

b)   an estimate of the mean growth.

.... cm

[4 marks]

Extended

Simple Charts

There are lots of ways to display data, including pictograms, bar charts and stem-and-leaf diagrams...

Pictograms Show Frequencies Using **Symbols**

Every pictogram has a key telling you what one symbol represents.

With pictograms, you must use the key.

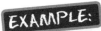

EXAMPLE: **This pictogram shows how many peaches were sold in a shop on different days.**

Key:
represents 4 peaches
Monday
Tuesday
Wednesday
Thursday
Friday

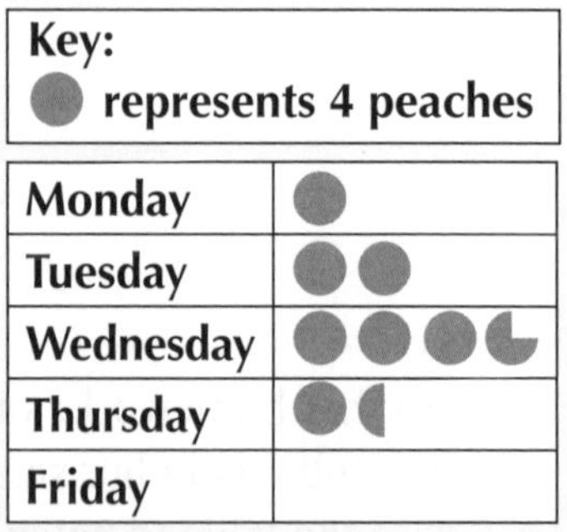

a) **How many peaches were sold on Tuesday?**
Each circle represents 4 peaches. There are 2 circles for Tuesday.
4 × 2 = 8 peaches

b) **10 peaches were sold on Friday.**
Use this information to complete the diagram.
You need 2 whole circles (= 8 peaches),
plus another half circle (= 2 peaches).

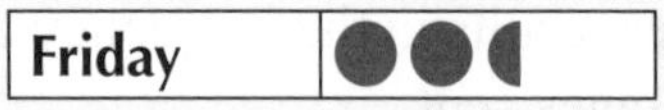

Friday

Bar Charts Show Frequencies Using **Bars**

1) Bar charts are very similar to pictograms. Frequencies are shown by the heights of the different bars.
2) Dual bar charts show two things at once — they're good for comparing different sets of data.

EXAMPLE: **This dual bar chart shows the number of men and women visiting a coffee shop on different days.**

a) **How many men visited the coffee shop altogether?**
Men are shown by the red bars.
Add up the numbers shown by the heights.
4 + 3 + 6 + 2 = 15 men

b) **On which day did the most women visit the coffee shop?**
Find the tallest green bar. Tuesday

Bars representing different categories are separated by gaps.
Men
Women
Number of people
0
1
2
3
4
5
6
7
Monday
Tuesday
Wednesday
Thursday
Day
Both axes on a bar chart must be labelled.

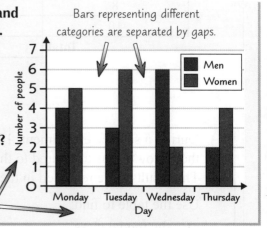

Stem-and-Leaf Diagrams put data in **Order**

An ordered stem-and-leaf diagram shows a set of data in order of size.
This makes it easy to find things like the median and range (see p.179).

EXAMPLE: **This stem-and-leaf diagram shows the ages of some school teachers.**

3	3	5			
4	0	5	7	8	
5	1	4	9		
6	1	3			

Key: 5 | 4 = 54 years

a) **How old is the oldest teacher?**
Use the key to help you read off the diagram. 6 | 3 = 63 years old

b) **What is the median age?**
The median is the middle value.
Find its position, then read off the value.
There are 11 values, so the median is the 6th value.
So median age is 4 | 8 = 48 years

Pie Charts

They might seem pretty simple, but examiners can turn pie charts into tricky exam questions. Just remember the Golden Pie Chart Rule...

The TOTAL of Everything = 360°

1) **Fraction** of the Total = **Angle ÷ 360°**

EXAMPLE: **This pie chart shows the colour of all the cars sold by a dealer. What fraction of the cars were red?**

Just remember that 'everything = 360°'.

$$\text{Fraction of red cars} = \frac{\text{angle of red cars}}{\text{angle of everything}} = \frac{72°}{360°} = \frac{1}{5}$$

2) Find a **Multiplier** to Calculate Your **Angles**

EXAMPLE: **Draw a pie chart to show this information about the types of animal in a petting zoo.**

Animal	Geese	Hamsters	Guinea pigs	Rabbits	Ducks
Number	12	20	17	15	26

1) Find the total by adding. 12 + 20 + 17 + 15 + 26 = 90

2) 'Everything = 360°' — so find the multiplier (or divider) that turns your total into 360°.   Multiplier = 360 ÷ 90 = 4

3) Now multiply every number by 4 to get the angle for each sector.

Angle	12 × 4 = 48°	20 × 4 = 80°	17 × 4 = 68°	15 × 4 = 60°	26 × 4 = 104°	Total = 360°

4) Draw your pie chart accurately using a protractor.

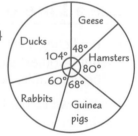

3) Find **How Many** by Using the Angle for **1 Thing**

EXAMPLE: **The pie chart on the right shows information about the types of animals liked most by different students. There were 9 students altogether.**

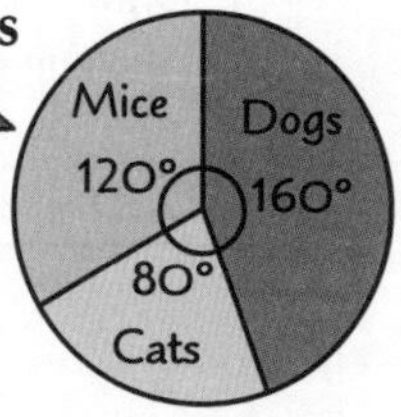

a) **Work out the number of students who liked dogs most.**

1) 'Everything = 360°', so: ⟶ 9 students = 360°

2) Divide by 9 to find: ⟶ 1 student = 40°

3) The angle for dogs is 160°, and 160° ÷ 40° = 4: ⟶ 4 students = 160° — 4 students liked dogs most

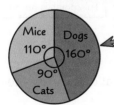

b) **The pie chart on the left shows information about the types of animals liked most by a different group of students. Dafydd says, "This means that 4 students in this group like dogs most." Explain why Dafydd is not correct.**

We don't know how many students in total the pie chart represents, so we can't work out how many students liked dogs most.

It's important to know the uses of each graph and chart

Knowing the type of data shown on different graphs and charts will help you to interpret them.

Scatter Diagrams

A scatter graph tells you how closely two things are related — the fancy word is CORRELATION.

Scatter Graphs Show **Correlation**

 KEY TERM | If two data sets are correlated, it means there's a relationship between them.

1) If you can draw a line of best fit pretty close to most of your data points, the two things are correlated. If the points are randomly scattered, and you can't draw a line of best fit, then there's no correlation.

2) Strong correlation is when your points make a fairly straight line — the two things are closely related. Weak correlation is when your points don't line up so nicely, but you can still draw a line of best fit.

3) If the points form a line sloping up from left to right, then there is positive correlation. If the line slopes down from left to right, then there is negative correlation.

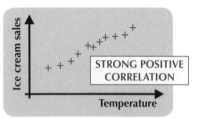
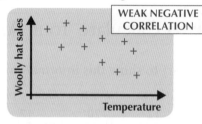
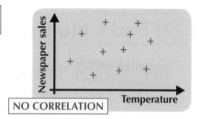

Use a **Line of Best Fit** to Make **Predictions**

1) Predicting a value within the range of data you have should be reliable. But if you extend your line outside the range of data your prediction might be unreliable, because the pattern might not continue.

2) Also watch out for outliers — data points that don't fit the general pattern. Outliers can drag your line of best fit away from the other values, so it's best to ignore them when you're drawing the line.

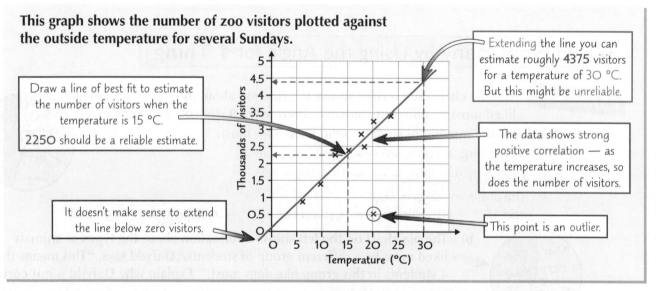

This graph shows the number of zoo visitors plotted against the outside temperature for several Sundays.

Extending the line you can estimate roughly **4375** visitors for a temperature of 30 °C. But this might be unreliable.

Draw a line of best fit to estimate the number of visitors when the temperature is 15 °C. **2250** should be a reliable estimate.

The data shows strong positive correlation — as the temperature increases, so does the number of visitors.

It doesn't make sense to extend the line below zero visitors.

This point is an outlier.

BE CAREFUL with correlation — if two things are correlated, it doesn't mean that one causes the other. There could be a third factor affecting both, or it could just be a coincidence.

 EXAM TIP | ## Correlation means there's a relationship between two things

Learn the terms so you can answer any exam question that asks you to describe a scatter graph. Make sure you can recognise if there's positive or negative correlation, or no correlation at all.

Histograms

Histograms are a way to show continuous data. When the classes are equal, they're pretty straightforward.

Histograms Can Have **Equal** Class Widths

1) Histograms display continuous data (see p.178) from a grouped frequency table. On this page, the class widths of the groups are all equal.

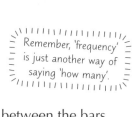

Remember, 'frequency' is just another way of saying 'how many'.

2) To draw a histogram for data with equal class widths, put frequency on the *y*-axis and a suitable scale for your data on the *x*-axis — then draw a bar for each class.

3) They look a lot like bar charts, but there's one key difference — there are no gaps between the bars. This is because the scale on the *x*-axis is continuous and each class ends at the start of the next one.

4) You might need to complete a grouped frequency table from a histogram — you'll be given the frequency of one class, which you use to label the *y*-axis on the histogram and read off the values.

EXAMPLE: The heights of students in Class C are shown in the histogram.
a) **Use the histogram to complete the frequency table.**

The first bar is 5 units tall and has a frequency of 20, so **1 unit = 20 ÷ 5 = 4 students**.
Use this to complete the *y*-axis and then read off the frequencies to complete the table.

Height (cm)	Frequency
$140 < h \le 150$	20
$150 < h \le 160$	28
$160 < h \le 170$	32
$170 < h \le 180$	16

The sideways 'z' on the histogram shows that some of the x-axis is hidden.

5) You can use histograms to identify the class with the highest or lowest frequency, estimate the frequency above or below a certain value and comment on the distribution of the data (see p.195).

EXAMPLE: b) **Use the histogram to estimate the number of students in Class C who are shorter than 155 cm.**

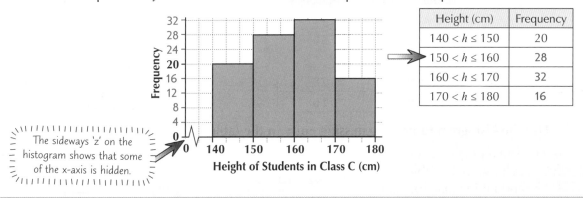

Draw a vertical line on the histogram at 155 cm.
The number of students shorter than 155 cm is all of the $140 < h \le 150$ bar and half of the $150 < h \le 160$ bar. Using the table from above:

20 + (28 ÷ 2) = 20 + 14 = **34 students**

This is an estimate because you don't know the exact data values — in the $150 < h \le 160$ class there might not actually be 14 students between 150 and 155 cm tall.

Histograms — a good old-fashioned diagram...

Histograms present data from grouped frequency tables, so any data read from a histogram is often an estimate. It's useful for talking about the data as a whole, but not for individual data values.

Histograms

A histogram can also have bars of different widths. Read on to find out how...

Unequal Class Widths use Frequency Density

1) When a grouped frequency table uses classes with unequal class widths, the bars on the histogram are different widths too.

2) The vertical axis (y axis) on this type of histogram is the frequency density. You work it out using this formula:

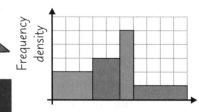

KEY TERM

> Frequency Density = Frequency ÷ Class Width

3) You can rearrange this formula to work out how many of something a bar represents:

> **Frequency = Frequency Density × Class Width = AREA of bar**

EXAMPLE:

This table and histogram show the lengths of beetles found in a garden.

Length (mm)	Frequency
$0 < x \leq 10$	32
$10 < x \leq 15$	36
$15 < x \leq 18$	
$18 < x \leq 22$	28
$22 < x \leq 30$	16

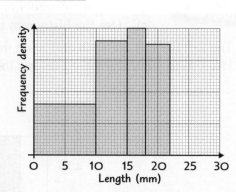

a) Use the histogram to find the missing entry in the table.

1) Add a frequency density column to the table and fill in what you can using the formula.

Frequency density
32 ÷ 10 = 3.2
36 ÷ 5 = 7.2
28 ÷ 4 = 7
16 ÷ 8 = 2

2) Use the frequency densities to label the vertical axis of the graph.

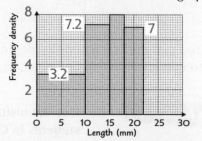

3) Now use the 3rd bar to find the frequency for the class '$15 < x \leq 18$'.
Frequency density = 8 and class width = 3.
So frequency = frequency density × class width = 8 × 3 = 24

b) Use the table to add the bar for the class '$22 < x \leq 30$' to the histogram.

Frequency density = frequency ÷ class width = $\frac{16}{8}$ = 2

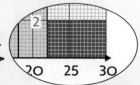

c) Estimate the number of beetles between 7.5 mm and 12.5 mm in length.

Use the formula frequency = frequency density × class width — multiply the frequency density of the class by the width of the part of that class you're interested in.
So the estimated number of beetles between 7.5 mm and 12.5 mm is:

3.2 × (10 − 7.5) + 7.2 × (12.5 − 10) = 3.2 × 2.5 + 7.2 × 2.5 = 8 + 18 = 26

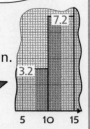

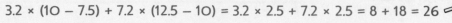

You need to use the height and width of a bar to find its frequency

Although they look very similar to nice and easy bar charts, histograms can be pretty unpleasant. Make sure you understand the method above so you know exactly what to do if you see it in the exam.

Extended

Warm-Up and Worked Exam Questions

Well that was a lot of charts and graphs... And here are some more for you — you're welcome.
Start with the warm-up questions, then test your knowledge by trying the exam questions.

Warm-Up Questions

1) This pictogram shows the different types of CDs that Javier owns, but the key is missing. Javier owns 20 blues CDs.
   a) How many jazz CDs does Javier own?
   b) He owns 5 opera CDs. Complete the pictogram.

Rock	●
Blues	● ●
Opera	
Jazz	● ◗

2) Draw an ordered stem-and-leaf diagram for this data:
   17, 12, 4, 19, 23, 29, 12, 25, 31, 2, 39, 9.

3) The table on the right shows the different types of DVD that Diana owns. She wants to create a pie chart using this data. Work out the angles that she will need for each type of DVD.

Type of DVD	Number
Comedy	23
Western	25
Action	12

4) Decide what type of correlation best describes the two scatter graphs below.

a)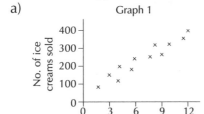

b)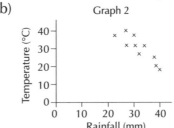

Worked Exam Question

It's no good learning all these facts if you don't know how to answer a real exam question.
This exam question shows how to turn those facts into good answers — and earn yourself marks.

1   A survey was carried out at a leisure centre to find out which sport
     people prefer to do. The results are shown in the pie chart.

a)   What fraction of people prefer to do fitness training?

$90° = \frac{1}{4}$ of a circle

$\frac{1}{4}$
....
[1 mark]

60 people said they prefer to play football.

b)   How many people prefer to play badminton?

Badminton = 360° − 180° − 90° − 30° = 60°

Football = 180°, so 60 people = 180°

Find the angle that represents 1 person. → 1 person = 180° ÷ 60 = 3°

Number of people who prefer badminton = 60° ÷ 3°
Divide the angle of 'badminton' by the angle for '1 person'. → = 20

20
....
[2 marks]

Exam Questions

2   A museum records the arrival times of their visitors one day, as shown in the table.
    Show this information as a histogram on the grid below.

Arrival Time (x)	Number of Visitors
$10:00 \leq x < 11:00$	190
$11:00 \leq x < 12:00$	100
$12:00 \leq x < 13:00$	70
$13:00 \leq x < 14:00$	280
$14:00 \leq x < 15:00$	150

[4 marks]

3   The scatter graph below shows the heights and weights of players in a rugby team.

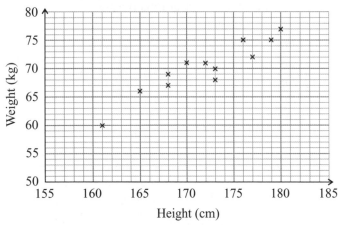

Two more players join the team. Their heights and weights are shown in this table.

Player	Height (cm)	Weight (kg)
13	169	70
14	183	76

a)   Add the information in the table to the scatter graph.

[1 mark]

b)   Describe the relationship between the height and weight of the players.

....

[1 mark]

4   100 students were each given a potato. The table below shows how long it took the students
    to peel their potato. Use the information in the table to draw a histogram on the grid below.

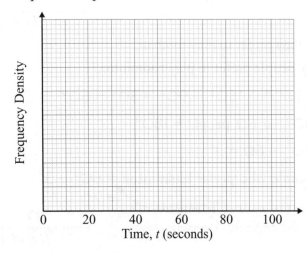

Time, t (s)	Frequency
$0 < t \leq 20$	15
$20 < t \leq 30$	35
$30 < t \leq 40$	30
$40 < t \leq 60$	15
$60 < t \leq 100$	5

[3 marks]

Extended

Extended

Box and Whisker Plots

A box and whisker plot might not look very sophisticated, but it gives you a useful summary of a data set.

Extended

Box and Whisker Plots show the **Spread** of a Data Set

1) The lower quartile Q_1, the median Q_2 and the upper quartile Q_3 are the values that lie 25% ($\frac{1}{4}$), 50% ($\frac{1}{2}$) and 75% ($\frac{3}{4}$) of the way through an ordered set of data.
2) If a set of data has n values, you can work out the positions of the quartiles using the formulas: **Q_1: (n + 1)/4 Q_2: (n + 1)/2 Q_3: 3(n + 1)/4**
3) The INTERQUARTILE RANGE (IQR) is the difference between the upper quartile and the lower quartile and contains the middle 50% of values.
4) A box and whisker plot tells you the quartile values and the range. The range is shown by the 'whiskers', which go from the lowest value to the highest value. However, the plot doesn't tell you the individual data values.

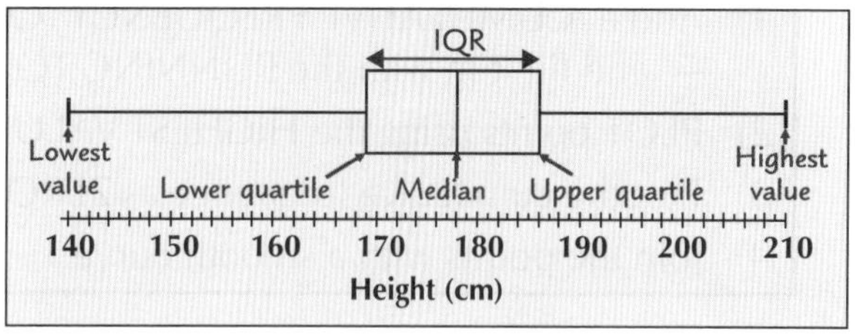

EXAMPLE: **This table gives information about the numbers of rainy days last year in some cities. On the grid below, draw a box plot to show the information.**

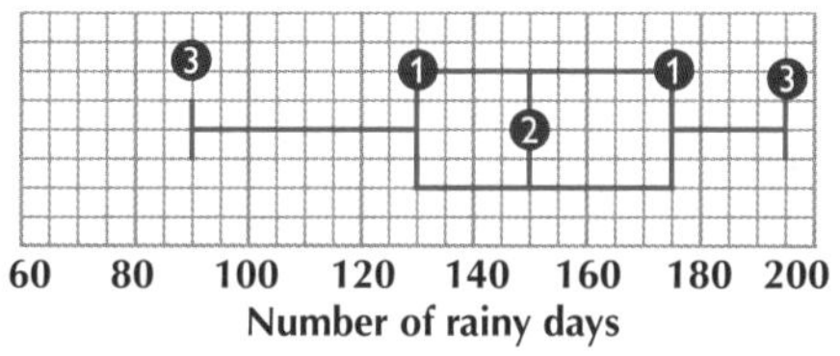

❶ Mark on the quartiles and draw the box.

❷ Draw a line at the median.

❸ Mark on the minimum and maximum points and join them to the box with horizontal lines.

Minimum number	90
Maximum number	195
Lower quartile	130
Median	150
Upper quartile	175

Box plots show two measures of spread — range (highest – lowest) and interquartile range ($Q_3 - Q_1$).
The range is calculated from the lowest and highest data values, so it can be affected by outliers — data values that don't fit the general pattern (i.e. that are a long way from the rest of the data).
The IQR is based on only the middle 50% of the data values, so it isn't affected by outliers.
This means it can be a more reliable measure of spread than the range.

EXAMPLE: **This box plot shows a summary of the heights of a group of gymnasts.**

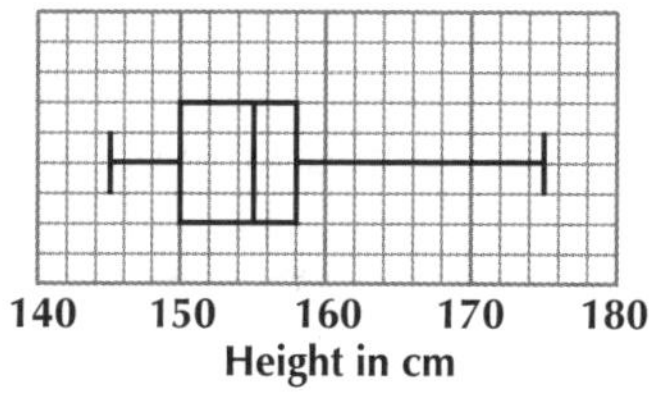

a) **Work out the range of the heights.**
Range = highest – lowest = 175 – 145 = 30 cm

b) **Work out the interquartile range for the heights.**
Q_1 = 150 cm and Q_3 = 158 cm, so IQR = 158 – 150 = 8 cm

c) **Do you think the range or the interquartile range is a more reliable measure of spread for this data? Give a reason for your answer.**
The IQR is small and 75% of the values are less than 158 cm, so it's likely that the tallest height of 175 cm is an outlier. The IQR doesn't include the tallest height, so the IQR should be more reliable.

d) **Explain whether it's possible to work out the number of gymnasts represented by the box plot.**
The box plot gives no information about the number of values it represents, so it isn't possible to work out the number of gymnasts.

Extended

REVISION TASK

The edges of the box show the lower and upper quartiles

Cover up this page and draw a box plot. Label the range, median, lower and upper quartiles and the interquartile range. Once you can do this without checking the page, you'll be an expert.

Cumulative Frequency

A cumulative frequency graph shows cumulative frequency up the side and the data values along the bottom. You might be asked to draw one in the exam, so learn the stuff below...

Drawing the Graph

KEY TERM — Cumulative frequency is the sum of the frequencies up to a given point.

'Running total' just means the total up to that point.

1) Add a 'CUMULATIVE FREQUENCY' COLUMN to the grouped frequency table — and fill it in with the RUNNING TOTAL of the frequency column.
2) PLOT points using the HIGHEST VALUE in each class and the CUMULATIVE FREQUENCY.
3) Plot the cumulative frequency as ZERO at the lowest value of the first class.
4) Join the points with a smooth curve.

EXAMPLE: The table below shows information about the heights of a group of people.

a) Draw a cumulative frequency graph for the data.

1) Fill in the cumulative frequency column:

For the first class, it's the same as the frequency.

For the other classes, add the frequency for that class to the cumulative frequency of the class above.

Height (h cm)	Frequency	Cumulative Frequency
$140 < h \leq 150$	4	4
$150 < h \leq 160$	9	4 + 9 = 13
$160 < h \leq 170$	20	13 + 20 = 33
$170 < h \leq 180$	33	33 + 33 = 66
$180 < h \leq 190$	36	66 + 36 = 102
$190 < h \leq 200$	15	102 + 15 = 117
$200 < h \leq 210$	3	117 + 3 = 120

2) Plot the points using the highest value in each class, i.e. (150, 4), (160, 13), etc.

3) Plot zero at the lowest value in the first class, i.e. (140, 0).

4) Join up the points with a nice smooth curve.

You might have to use your curve to do some other calculations (see the next page), so make sure you draw it really carefully.

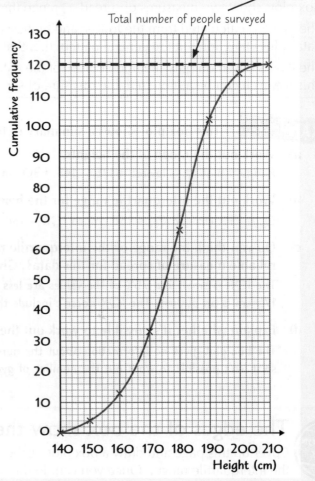

Total number of people surveyed

Cumulative Frequency

Continuing with the example from the previous page...

EXAMPLE: b) Use the graph drawn in part a) to estimate the median, the interquartile range and the 10th percentile of the heights.

To **Find** the **Vital Statistics**...

1) MEDIAN — go halfway up the side, across to the curve, then down and read off the bottom scale.

2) LOWER AND UPPER QUARTILES — go ¼ and ¾ up the side, across to the curve, then down and read off the bottom scale.

3) INTERQUARTILE RANGE — the distance between the lower and upper quartiles.

4) PERCENTILES — e.g. to find the 10th percentile, go up the side to 10% of the total, across to the curve, then down and read off the bottom scale.

> A percentile is the data value corresponding to that percentage of the cumulative frequency, e.g. the lower quartile = the 25th percentile.

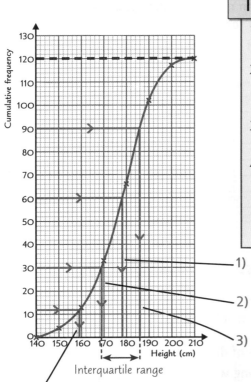

1) The halfway point is at ½ × 120 = 60.
Reading across and down gives a median of 178 cm.

2) ¼ of the way up is at ¼ × 120 = 30.
Reading across and down gives a lower quartile of 169 cm.

3) ¾ of the way up is at ¾ × 120 = 90.
Reading across and down gives an upper quartile of 186 cm.
The interquartile range = 186 − 169 = 17 cm.

4) The 10th percentile is at 120 × 0.1 = 12. Reading across and down gives a 10th percentile of 159 cm.

c) Use the graph to estimate the number of people who have a height greater than 195 cm.

More **Estimating**...

To estimate the number of things with a value less than or greater than a given value:

- Go along the bottom scale to the given value, up to the curve, then across to the cumulative frequency.
  This gives you the number of things with a value less than the given value.

- To find the number of things with a value greater than the given value, subtract this from the frequency total.

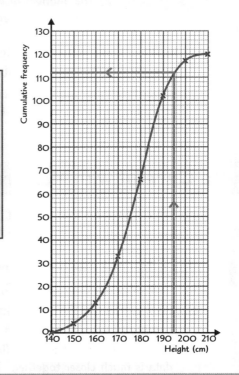

1) Read off the curve (along the green line) to find the number of people with height up to 195 cm:

   No. of people with height 195 cm or less = 112

2) Subtract from total frequency:

   No. of people with height greater than 195 cm
   = 120 − 112 = 8

Plot the points using the highest value in each class

Remember — when you plot points on a cumulative frequency graph, use the upper limit for each class. You only use the mid-interval value when finding an estimate of the mean of grouped data.

Interpreting Data

This page is about getting information from data and recognising when it might be misleading.

You can **Find Averages** from **Diagrams**

**EXAMPLE:** This vertical line graph shows information on the number of pairs of penguin slippers a shop sells each day for 50 consecutive days.

Calculate the mean number of pairs sold each day.

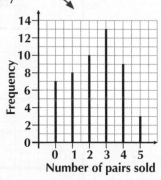

Fill in a frequency table and add a third column to find the total number of pairs sold — see p.180.

$$\text{Mean} = \frac{\text{total number of pairs sold}}{\text{total number of days}}$$

$$= \frac{118}{50} = 2.36$$

Number of pairs	Frequency	No. of pairs × Frequency
0	7	0
1	8	8
2	10	20
3	13	39
4	9	36
5	3	15
Total	50	118

Watch Out for **Misleading Diagrams**

When you first look, a diagram might seem perfectly fine.
But if you look again, it might not be quite as fine as you first thought...

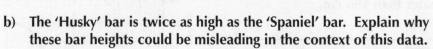**EXAMPLE:** This bar chart shows the numbers of dogs of different breeds at a rescue centre.

a) **Write down three things that are wrong with the bar chart.**

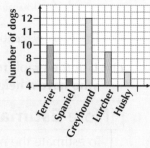

1) The 'number of dogs' axis doesn't start at zero.
2) The 'number of dogs' axis has inconsistent numbering.
3) The 'breed of dog' axis has no label.

b) **The 'Husky' bar is twice as high as the 'Spaniel' bar. Explain why these bar heights could be misleading in the context of this data.**

The bar heights suggest that there are twice as many Huskies as Spaniels.
But reading the scale, there are 6 Huskies and 5 Spaniels.

Be Careful with Measures of **Average** and **Range**

Outliers are data values that don't fit the general pattern — they're a long way from the rest of the data.
Outliers can have a big effect on the mean or range of a data set, so you get a misleading value.

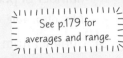**EXAMPLE:** The data below shows the number of songs Fred downloads each week for ten weeks.

0, 1, 3, 3, 5, 6, 7, 8, 8, 20

See p.179 for averages and range.

a) **Fred works out that the range of his data is 20.**
Comment on this value as a measure of the spread.

A range of 20 isn't a true reflection of the spread of the whole data set, because most of the data is much closer together. The highest value of 20 has a big effect on increasing the range.

b) **Explain why the mode isn't a helpful measure of average for this data.**

The data has two modes, 3 and 8, so this doesn't give you a good idea of the average value.

Comparing Data Sets

You can compare data sets using averages and range, or by drawing suitable diagrams.

Compare Data Sets Using **Averages** and **Range**

Say which data set has the higher/lower value and what that means in the context of the data.

EXAMPLE: **Some children take part in a 'guess the weight of the baby hippo' competition. Here is some information about the weights they guess.**

Compare the distributions of the weights guessed by the boys and the girls.

Boys:	Girls:
Mean = 40 kg	Mean = 34 kg
Median = 43 kg	Median = 33 kg
Range = 42 kg	Range = 30 kg

1)   Compare averages:
The boys' mean and median values are higher than the girls', so the boys generally guessed heavier weights.

2)   Compare ranges:
The boys' guesses have a bigger range, so the weights guessed by the boys show more variation.

Compare Data Sets Using **Diagrams**

The type of diagram you should use depends on what you want to show.

EXAMPLE: **Habiba carried out a survey into whether or not people like olives. She draws these pie charts to show her results.**

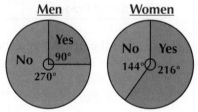

a)   **Can you tell from the pie charts whether more women said 'yes' than men? Explain your answer.**

No, you can't tell whether more women said 'yes'. You can see that a higher proportion of women said 'yes' but you don't know how many men and women the pie charts represent.

b)   **Habiba surveyed 20 men and 20 women. Draw a suitable diagram to compare the numbers of men and women giving each answer.**

A dual bar chart is suitable — it shows the numbers of men and women side by side.

Use the pie charts to work out the frequency of each answer. E.g. find the fraction of the total, then multiply by 20.

Men: 'Yes' = $\frac{90}{360} \times 20 = 5$,   'No' = $\frac{270}{360} \times 20 = 15$

Women: 'Yes' = $\frac{216}{360} \times 20 = 12$,   'No' = $\frac{144}{360} \times 20 = 8$

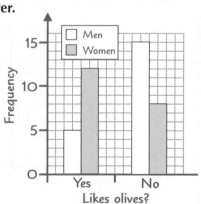

You could be asked to compare any type of chart or diagram

Make sure you know about all the different types of chart and diagram. In the exam you might be asked to compare two diagrams (or two different types of diagram). You might also need to work out the values of the averages and range (see p.179) before comparing data sets.

Warm-Up and Worked Exam Questions

Check that you know how to present and interpret data as well as draw conclusions from the data.

Warm-up Questions

Extended

1) A large amount of data is analysed and the following conclusions are made: The minimum and maximum values are 5 and 22, 50% of the values are less than 12, 75% of the values are less than 17 and the IQR is 8. Draw a box and whisker plot for this data.

2) The table on the right shows data on the lengths of slugs in a garden.
   a) Using this data, draw a cumulative frequency diagram.
   b) Work out the median from your cumulative frequency diagram.

Length (x mm)	Frequency
$0 < x \leq 40$	30
$40 < x \leq 60$	55
$60 < x \leq 75$	75
$75 < x \leq 100$	20

3) The following temperatures were recorded in a city eight times during a year: 12°C, 30°C, 30°C, 8°C, 17°C, 11°C, 4°C, 15°C
   Explain why the mode is not a good average to use for this data.

Worked Exam Question

To get you started, I've worked through this question for you. Read it all to make sure you understand it, then move on to the exam questions I've left blank for you...

1 The cumulative frequency table below gives information about the length of time it takes to travel between Udderston and Trundle on the main road each morning.

Journey Time (t mins)	$0 < t \leq 20$	$0 < t \leq 25$	$0 < t \leq 30$	$0 < t \leq 35$	$0 < t \leq 45$	$0 < t \leq 60$
Cumulative Frequency	7	22	36	45	49	50

a) On the graph paper below, draw a cumulative frequency graph for the table.

The table gives you the cumulative frequency already, so you don't need to work it out yourself.

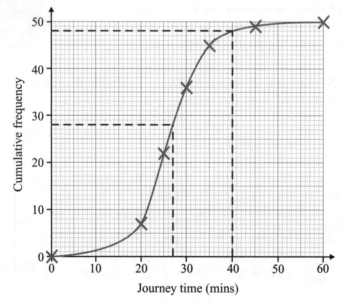

[2 marks]

b) Use your graph to estimate the number of journeys that took between 27 and 40 minutes.

Draw lines on the graph at 27 mins and 40 mins. $48 - 28 = 20$

.........20......... journeys

[2 marks]

Exam Questions

2   This data shows the amount of rainfall in mm that
    fell on an island during a 12-day period in June.

Key
0 | 8 means
8 mm of rain

```
0 | 8
1 | 7 9
2 | 3 6 9
3 | 0 1 4 7 8
4 |
5 |
6 | 3
```

a)   Work out the range of the rainfall and comment
     on this value as a measure of the spread of the data.

....

....

[3 marks]

In November the median amount of rainfall was 22 mm and the range was 20 mm.

b)   Compare the rainfall in June with the rainfall in November.

....

....

....

[3 marks]

3   120 students in a year group sit an examination at the end of the year.
    Their results are given in the table below.

Exam mark (%)	≤ 20	≤ 30	≤ 40	≤ 50	≤ 60	≤ 70	≤ 80	≤ 100
Cumulative Frequency	3	13	25	49	91	107	116	120

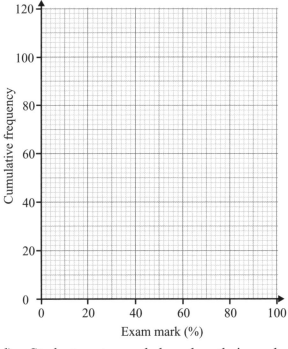

a)   Use the table to draw a cumulative
     frequency graph on the graph paper.

[3 marks]

b)   Use your graph to find an
     estimate for the median.

.... %
[1 mark]

c)   Use your graph to find an estimate
     for the interquartile range.

.... %
[2 marks]

d)   Students got a grade based on their mark. Four times as many students got grade 5 or
     higher than those who got a lower grade. Estimate the lowest mark needed to get grade 5.

....

....

[3 marks]

Revision Questions for Section Six

That's the end of Section 6 — time to put yourself to the test and find out how much you really know.
- Try these questions and tick off each one when you get it right.
- When you've done all the questions for a topic and are completely happy with it, tick off the topic.

Probability Basics, Expected Frequency and the AND/OR Rules (p.167-169) ☑

1) I pick a random integer between 1 and 50. Find the probability that my number is a multiple of 6. ☑

2) What do the probabilities of all possible outcomes of an experiment add up to
(if none of them can happen together)? ☑

3) I flip a fair coin twice. HT means Heads on the first flip and Tails on the second.
a) Complete this possibility diagram showing all the possible results.
b) Use your diagram to find the probability of getting 2 Heads. ☑

	Second flip	
First flip	Heads	Tails
Heads		HT
Tails		

4) Write down the formula to estimate how many times you'd expect something to happen in n trials. ☑

5) I throw a fair six-sided dice twice. Find P(I throw a 6 and then an even number). ☑

6) I throw a fair six-sided dice. Find P(I throw either a 5 or a multiple of 3). ☑

Tree Diagrams, Venn Diagrams and Relative Frequency (p.172-175) ☑

7) I have a bag of 52 balls. Four balls are red and the rest are white. I pick one at random, note it, put
it back, then I pick another ball. Use a tree diagram to find the probability that I pick two red balls. ☑

8) 100 people were asked whether they like tea or coffee. Half the people said they like coffee,
34 people said they like tea, 20 people said they like both.
a) Show this information on a Venn diagram.
b) If one of the 100 people is randomly chosen, find the probability of them liking tea or coffee. ☑

9) When might you need to use relative frequency to find a probability? ☑

Collecting Data, Finding Averages and Frequency Tables (p.178-181) ☑

10) Is 'eye colour' qualitative, discrete or continuous data? ☑

11) Find the mode, median, mean and range of this data: 2, 8, 11, 15, 22, 24, 27, 30, 31, 31, 41 ☑

12) For this grouped frequency table showing the lengths of some pet alligators:
a) find the modal class,   b) estimate the mean. ☑

Length (y m)	Frequency
$1.4 \leq y < 1.5$	4
$1.5 \leq y < 1.6$	8
$1.6 \leq y < 1.7$	5
$1.7 \leq y < 1.8$	2

Graphs and Charts (p.184-193) ☑

13) As well as counting the number of symbols on a pictogram, you need to check
one other thing before you can find a frequency. What's the other thing? ☑

14) The numbers of students in different years at a village school
are shown in this table. Draw a bar chart to show this data. ☑

School Year	7	8	9	10	11
No. of students	40	30	40	45	25

15) Sketch graphs to show: a) weak positive correlation, b) strong negative correlation, c) no correlation ☑

16) What is the formula for frequency density? ☑

17) a) Draw a box and whisker plot to represent the data in Q11.
b) Draw a cumulative frequency diagram for the data in Q12. ☑

Interpreting and Comparing Data Sets (p.194-195) ☑

18) Explain the effect that outliers can have on the mean and range of data. ☑

19) These pie charts show the results of a survey on the colour of people's cars.
Compare the popularity of each colour of car amongst men and women. ☑

Practice Papers

Once you've been through all the questions in this book, you should feel pretty confident about the exams. As final preparation, here is a set of **practice exams** to really get you ready for the real thing.

Cambridge International GCSE Mathematics

Core Paper 1

In addition to this paper you should have:
- A pen and pencil.
- A ruler, protractor and pair of compasses.
- A calculator.

Centre name					
Centre number					
Candidate number					

Time allowed:
- 1 hour

Candidate name
Candidate signature

Instructions to candidates
- Write your name and other details in the spaces provided above.
- Use blue or black ink to write your answers.
- Answer all questions in the spaces provided.
- You may use tracing paper.
- In calculations, show clearly how you worked out your answers.
- Non-exact answers should be rounded to 3 significant figures or 1 decimal place for angles, unless it is specified in the question.
- For π, use the button on your calculator or 3.142.

Information for candidates
- The marks available are given in brackets at the end of each question part.
- There are 56 marks available for this paper.

Answer ALL the questions.

Write your answers in the spaces provided.

You must show all of your working.

1   Write one of the signs <, =, or > to make this statement correct.

7% 0.7

[1]

2   Write the ratio 40 : 25 in its simplest form.

....

[1]

3   Eight points are shown plotted on the grid.

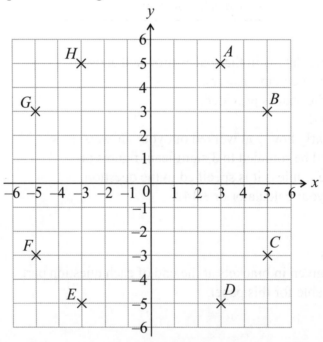

(a) Write down the letter of the point that has coordinates (−5, −3).

....

[1]

(b) Give the equation of the straight line that passes through points *A* and *D*.

....

[1]

4 Karl has five number cards.

$$\boxed{-6} \quad \boxed{6} \quad \boxed{-8} \quad \boxed{-12} \quad \boxed{2}$$

(a) Write Karl's number cards in order, starting with the lowest.

lowest ...., ..., ..., ..., ... highest

[1]

(b) Write two of Karl's number cards in this calculation to make it correct.

.... − .... = 10

[1]

5 (a) Convert 3.97 km into m.

.... m

[1]

(b) Convert 4 m³ into cm³.

.... cm³

[1]

6 Put a ring around the vector that translates a shape 5 units **left**.

$$\begin{pmatrix} -5 \\ 0 \end{pmatrix} \qquad \begin{pmatrix} 5 \\ 0 \end{pmatrix} \qquad \begin{pmatrix} 0 \\ 5 \end{pmatrix} \qquad \begin{pmatrix} 0 \\ -5 \end{pmatrix}$$

[1]

7 (a) Draw a line to match each shape to its number of **surfaces**.

cone   4

                   3

sphere

                   2

cylinder   1

[2]

(b) Write down the number of **vertices** for a triangular prism.

....

[1]

8

> If you add a multiple of 3 to a multiple of 6, you always get a multiple of 9.

Give an example to show that this statement is not true.

....

....

[1]

9 (a) Simplify $11a + 5b - 2a + 2b$

....

[1]

(b) Simplify $2a \times 3a$

....

[1]

10 Put a ring around the number that is both a square number and a cube number.

$$16 \qquad 27 \qquad 64 \qquad 25 \qquad 8 \qquad 100$$

[1]

11 The ages (in years) of seven children are

$$6 \qquad 12 \qquad 9 \qquad 6 \qquad 5 \qquad 7 \qquad 11$$

(a) Find the median age.

.... years

[1]

(b) Find the mean age.

.... years

[2]

12 Write 594 000 000 000 in standard form.

....

[1]

13 (a) Calculate

$$\sqrt{12.2} + (1.1 + 3.6)^3$$

Write down all the digits on your calculator.

....

[1]

(b) Round your answer to (a) to two decimal places.

....

[1]

14 Here are the names of four types of quadrilateral.

| Parallelogram | Square | Trapezium | Kite |

Choose from this list the quadrilateral that has:

(a) exactly one pair of parallel sides,

....

[1]

(b) no lines of symmetry, but rotational symmetry of order 2.

....

[1]

15 The diagram on the right shows a circle with its centre at O.
The line AB is a tangent to the circle. Angle AOB is $50°$.

Explain how you know angle $OBA = 40°$.

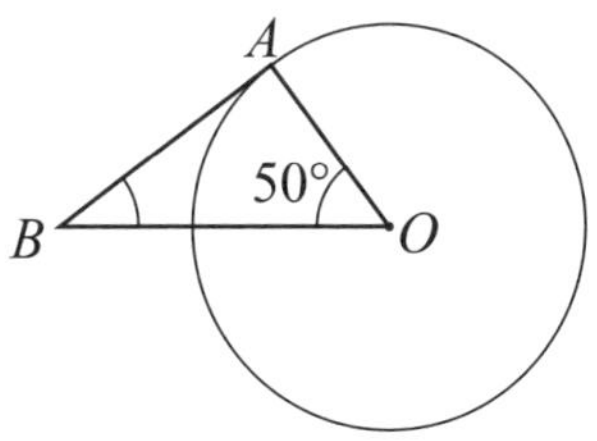

....

....

....

[1]

16 Write down the gradient of the line $y = 7 - 2x$.

....

[1]

17 The diameter of a sphere is 6 cm.
Work out the volume of this sphere in terms of π.
[The volume, V, of a sphere with radius r is $V = \frac{4}{3}\pi r^3$]

.... cm³
[2]

18 Put a ring around the fraction which is equivalent to 0.113.

$$\frac{113}{100} \qquad \frac{113}{10\,000} \qquad \frac{113}{1000} \qquad \frac{13}{100}$$

[1]

19 Work out the value of k if

$$k \times 3^{-2} = 4$$

$k = $ ....
[2]

20 Enlarge triangle A by scale factor 3, centre P.

Label the image B.

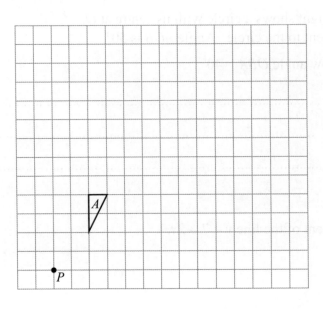

[2]

21 George has two fair spinners.

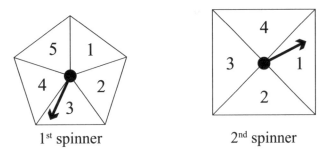

1st spinner   2nd spinner

He spins each spinner once and records whether the score is an odd or an even number.

(a) Complete the tree diagram to show the probabilities.

1st spinner   2nd spinner

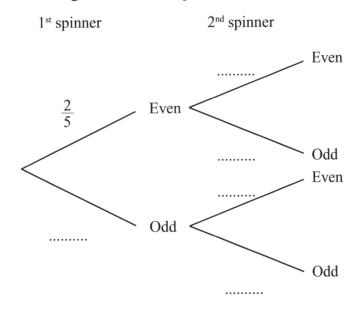

[2]

(b) Work out the probability that George spins two odd numbers.

....

[2]

22 ξ = {1, 2, 3, …, 10}
A = {3, 4, 5, 6}
B = {$x : x$ is a factor of 12}

Complete the Venn diagram to show the elements of each set.

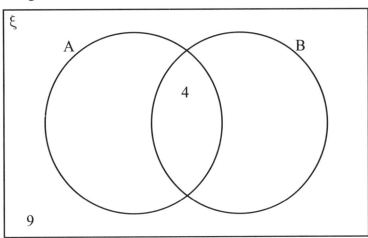

[2]

23 Chloe invests $300 in a bank account.
    The account pays 2% simple interest each year.

    Work out how much money she has in her account after 4 years.

    $ ....

    [3]

24 **Without using your calculator**, work out $1\frac{2}{3} \times 1\frac{5}{8}$.

    You must show all your working and give your answer as a mixed number in its simplest form.

    ....

    [3]

25 *AC* and *DG* are parallel lines.

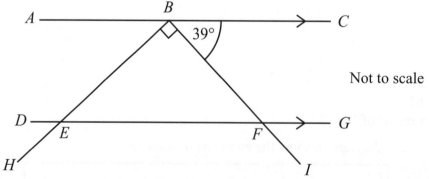

    Not to scale

    Work out the size of:
    (a) angle *BFG*,

    .... °

    [1]

    (b) angle *DEH*.

    .... °

    [2]

26 Solve the equation $3(2x – 4) = 2x + 8$

$x =$ ....

[3]

27 The diagram shows a right-angled triangle.

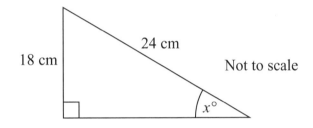

Calculate the value of x.

$x =$ ....

[2]

28 Solve the simultaneous equations

$$3x + 2y = 17$$
$$2x + y = 10$$

$x =$ ....

$y =$ ....

[3]

END OF QUESTIONS

Cambridge International GCSE Mathematics

Core Paper 2

In addition to this paper you should have:
• A pen and pencil.
• A ruler, protractor and pair of compasses.
• A calculator.

Centre name				
Centre number				
Candidate number				

Time allowed:
• 2 hours

Candidate name
Candidate signature

Instructions to candidates
• Write your name and other details in the spaces provided above.
• Use blue or black ink to write your answers.
• Answer all questions in the spaces provided.
• You may use tracing paper.
• In calculations, show clearly how you worked out your answers.
• Non-exact answers should be rounded to 3 significant figures or
  1 decimal place for angles, unless it is specified in the question.
• For π, use the button on your calculator or 3.142.

Information for candidates
• The marks available are given in brackets at the end of each question part.
• There are 104 marks available for this paper.

Answer ALL the questions.

Write your answers in the spaces provided.

You must show all of your working.

1 (a) (i) Write $\frac{3}{5}$ as a percentage.

.... %

[1]

(ii) Write down the reciprocal of $\frac{3}{5}$.

....

[1]

(iii) Kieron works out $4 \times \frac{3}{5}$ and gets the answer $\frac{12}{20}$.

Explain what mistake Kieron has made in calculating his answer.

....

....

[1]

(iv) Explain why $\frac{3}{5}$ is not a natural number.

....

....

[1]

(b) (i) Jeremy randomly picks a number from 1 to 10. The probability that it is **not** prime is $\frac{3}{5}$.
Work out the probability that it is prime. Give your answer as a decimal.

....

[2]

(ii) Jeremy repeats this experiment 300 times.
Estimate the number of times he will pick a number that is **not** prime.

....

[1]

(c) Write 300 as a product of its prime factors.

....

[2]

2   The diagram shows the first four patterns in a sequence.

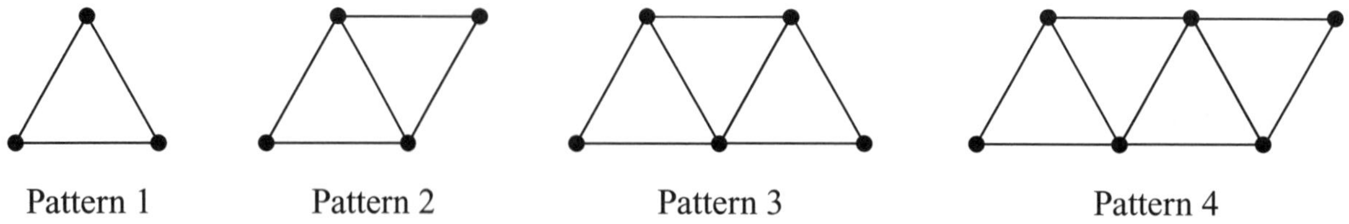

Pattern 1   Pattern 2   Pattern 3   Pattern 4

(a) Complete the table.

	Number of triangles	Number of dots	Number of lines
Pattern 1	1	3	3
Pattern 2	2	4	5
Pattern 3	3	5	7
Pattern 4	4	....	....
Pattern 5	5	....	....

[3]

(b) Work out the number of lines in Pattern 10.

....

[2]

(c) (i) Write down an expression for the number of dots in Pattern n.

....

[2]

(ii) Find the number of dots in Pattern 200.

....

[1]

(d) Write down the number of lines of symmetry in Pattern 2.

....

[1]

(e) In another pattern, the value for the number of dots in Pattern n is given by $6n^3 + 18n$.
Factorise the expression completely.

....

[2]

3 The scatter graph shows the maximum power (in kW) and the maximum speed (in km/h) of 11 cars.

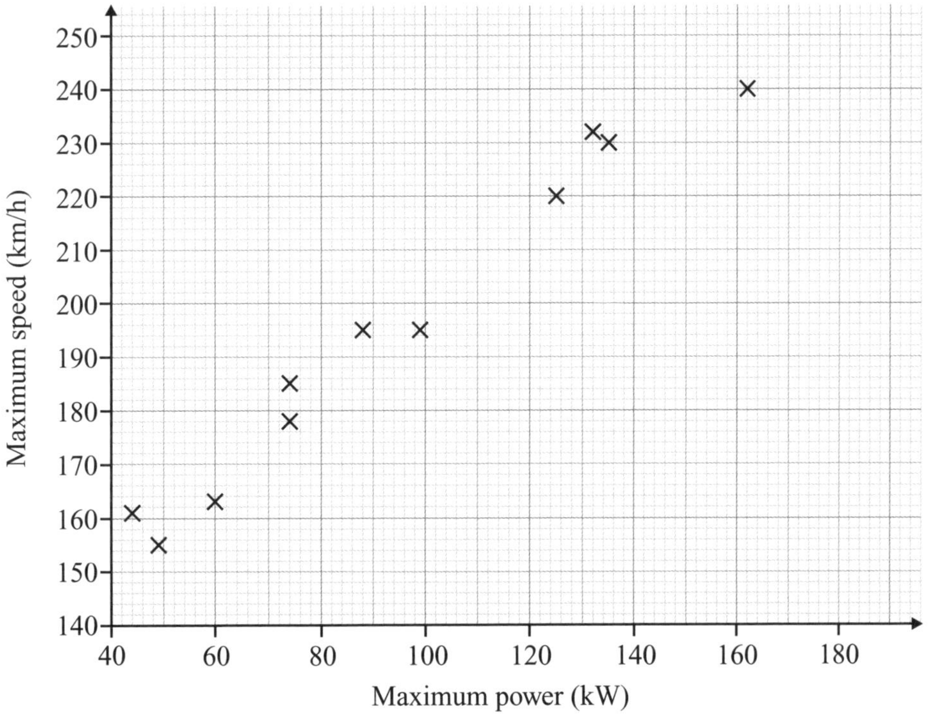

(a) (i) One of the cars has a maximum speed of 220 km/h.
Write down the maximum power of this car.

.... kW
[1]

(ii) Work out the fraction of the cars that have a maximum speed over 190 km/h.

....
[1]

(iii) Work out the percentage of the cars with a maximum power between 80 kW and 140 kW.

.... %
[2]

(b) Complete this statement.

The scatter graph shows .... correlation.
[1]

(c) A different car has a maximum power of 104 kW.
By drawing a suitable line on the scatter graph, estimate the maximum speed of this car.

.... km/h
[2]

(d) Explain why it may not be reliable to use the scatter graph to estimate
the maximum speed of a car with a maximum power of 190 kW.

....

....
[1]

4 (a) Two congruent trapeziums and two congruent triangles fit inside a square with side lengths of 12 cm as shown. $AB = 7$ cm

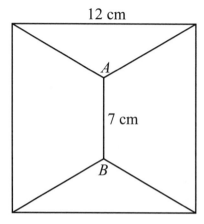

12 cm

Not to scale

7 cm

(i) Work out the area of each trapezium.

..........................cm²

[2]

(ii) Work out the area of each triangle.

..........................cm²

[2]

(b) Three congruent isosceles triangles fit together with three squares around a point *O*.

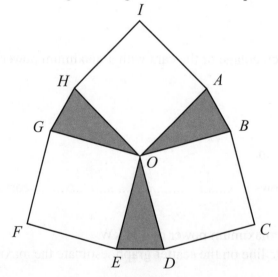

Show clearly that angle $OAB = 75°$. Do not measure any angles.

[4]

5   The scale drawing shows the gardens of a country house.

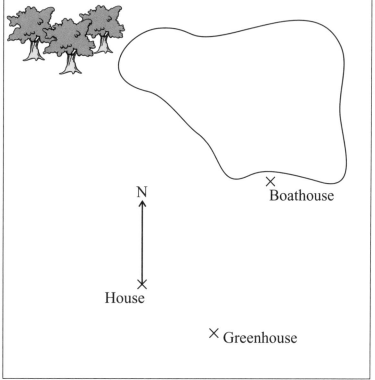

Scale: 1 cm = 100 metres

(a) (i)   Find the three-figure bearing of the boathouse from the house.

.... °

[1]

(ii)   Find the actual distance from the boathouse to the greenhouse.

.... metres

[2]

(iii)   A summerhouse is 600 metres from the house on a bearing of 335°.
Plot the position of the summerhouse on the map with a cross (×) .

[2]

(iv)   Sebastian is standing 30 m East and 40 m North of the greenhouse.
Use Pythagoras' theorem to show that he is exactly 50 m away from the greenhouse.

[2]

(b)   The house is 4 km away from the town centre.
(i)   Sebastian drove from the house to the town centre in 10 minutes.
Work out his average speed in km/h.

.... km/h

[2]

(ii)   Alice walked from the house to the town centre at an average speed of 5 km/h.
Work out how many minutes it took her.

.... minutes

[2]

6 A theatre sells three types of ticket.

Ticket type	Cost
Adult	$9
Child	$5
Senior	$6.50

The pictogram shows the number of tickets of each type sold for one performance.

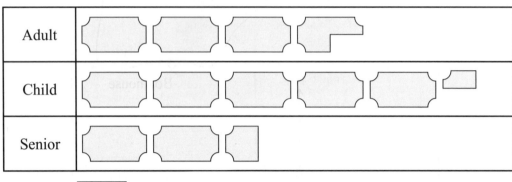

Key: = 8 tickets

(a) Work out how much money they made from all the ticket sales for this performance.

$ ....

[4]

(b) Give the following ratios in their simplest form:
   (i) adult tickets sold : senior tickets sold

....

[1]

   (ii) child tickets sold : total tickets sold

....

[2]

(c) The theatre sold 120 tickets for another performance. The ratio
   adult : child : senior tickets = 1 : 3 : 4. Work out the amounts of each ticket sold.

Adult Tickets: ....   Child Tickets: ....   Senior Tickets: ....

[3]

7 (a) On the grid, plot the points (0, 1) and (2, 7) and draw a straight line, *L*, passing through them.

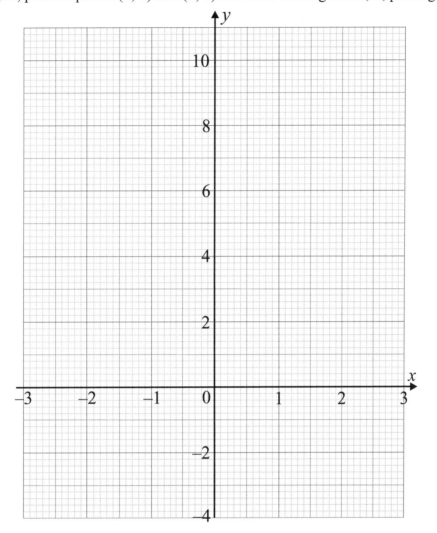

[2]

(b) (i) Work out the gradient of line *L*.

....
[2]

(ii) Give the equation of an example of a line parallel to line *L*.

....
[1]

(c) Complete the table of values for $y = x^2 + x - 3$.

x	-3	-2	-1	0	1	2	3
y		-1		-3			9

[3]

(d) Draw on the grid the graph of $y = x^2 + x - 3$ for values of *x* between -3 and 3.

[4]

(e) Use your graph to find approximate solutions to the equation $x^2 + x - 3 = 0$.

$x =$ .... and $x =$ ....
[2]

8   The diagram shows a solid aluminium cylinder and a solid silver cube.

Cylinder (aluminium)   Cube (silver)

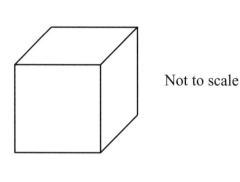

Not to scale

- The volume of the cylinder is 1180 cm³.
- The cylinder and the cube have the same mass.
- The density of aluminium is 2.7 g/cm³ and the density of silver is 10.5 g/cm³

(a) Write the volume of the cylinder in standard form.

.... cm³

[1]

(b) Work out the mass of the cylinder. [Density = $\frac{\text{Mass}}{\text{Volume}}$]

.... g

[2]

(c) Work out the side length of the cube in centimetres.

.... cm

[4]

(d) The surface area of another cube is 384 cm².
     (i) Work out the volume of the cube.

.... cm³

[3]

(ii) Convert the surface area of the cube to mm².

.... mm²

[1]

(iii) The mass of the cube, *m* grams, is 2100 g rounded to 2 significant figures.
       Complete this statement about the value of *m*.

.... ≤ *m* < ....

[2]

9 The values of four houses at the start of 2018 are shown.

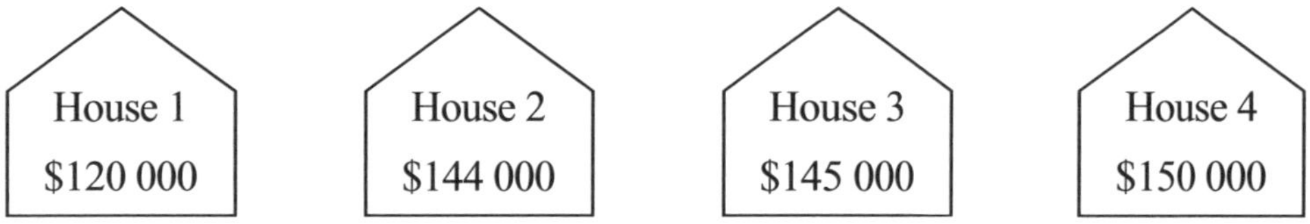

House 1	House 2	House 3	House 4
$120 000	$144 000	$145 000	$150 000

(a) Which house had a value 25% higher than House 1?

House ....

[1]

(b) Simone bought House 4 and received a 16% discount off the value.
Calculate how much she spent on House 4.

$ ....

[2]

(c) At the start of 2020, the value of House 2 was $161 280.
Find the percentage increase in the value of House 2 between 2018 and 2020.

.... %

[2]

(d) $2 = 15 Chinese Yuan (¥). Calculate the value of House 3 in Chinese Yuan.

¥ ....

[2]

(e) At the start of 2000, Abid invested $50 000 at a rate of 5% per year compound interest.
In 2018 he took the value of his investment and bought House 1.

Work out how much money Abid had left. Give your answer to the nearest dollar.

$ ....

[4]

10 The diagram shows a circle A and a sector B.

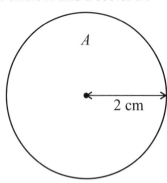 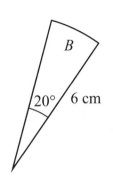

Not to scale

(a) Show that the area of A is twice the area of B.

[4]

(b) Find the perimeter of sector B. Give your answer in terms of π.

.... cm

[3]

(c) Sector B can be approximated by a triangle with side lengths 6 cm, 6 cm and 2 cm. **Using a ruler and pair of compasses only**, construct this triangle. Leave in your construction arcs.

[2]

END OF QUESTIONS

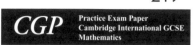

CGP Practice Exam Paper
Cambridge International GCSE
Mathematics

Cambridge International GCSE Mathematics

Extended Paper 1

In addition to this paper you should have:
- A pen and pencil.
- A ruler, protractor and pair of compasses.
- A calculator.

Centre name					
Centre number					
Candidate number					

Time allowed:
- 1 hour 30 minutes

Candidate name	
Candidate signature	

Instructions to candidates
- Write your name and other details in the spaces provided above.
- Use blue or black ink to write your answers.
- Answer all questions in the spaces provided.
- In calculations, show clearly how you worked out your answers.
- Non-exact answers should be rounded to 3 significant figures or 1 decimal place for angles, unless it is specified in the question.
- For π, use the button on your calculator or 3.142.

Information for candidates
- The marks available are given in brackets at the end of each question part.
- There are 70 marks available for this paper.

Answer ALL the questions.

Write your answers in the spaces provided.

You must show all of your working.

1   A is 60% of B.
     B is 30% of C.

     Work out A as a percentage of C.

     .... %

     [1]

2   A solid shape has a volume of 2680 mm³. Write its volume in cm³.

     .... cm³

     [1]

3   Two fair six-sided dice, numbered 1 to 6, are rolled.

     Put a ring around the probability that they both land on a 2.

     $$\frac{1}{3} \qquad \frac{1}{6} \qquad \frac{1}{12} \qquad \frac{1}{36}$$

     [1]

4   By rounding each number to 1 significant figure, estimate the value of

     $$\sqrt[3]{\frac{785.3 \times 2.156}{0.1972}}$$

     Show the numbers you used to work out your estimate.

     ....

     [2]

5   Put a ring around the number that is closest to $\frac{7}{9}$.

     0.77   0.7778   0.7   0.78   0.778

     [1]

6   A block of wood with a weight of 72 N is resting on a horizontal table top.
The base of the block is flat and has area 120 cm².

Find the pressure exerted by the block on the table, giving your answer in N/m². [Pressure = $\frac{\text{Force}}{\text{Area}}$]

.... N/m²
[2]

7   Find $(4 \times 10^6) \times (8 \times 10^{-3})$.
Give your answer in standard form.

....
[2]

8   144 people were asked what their favourite red food was.
The results are shown in the pie chart below.

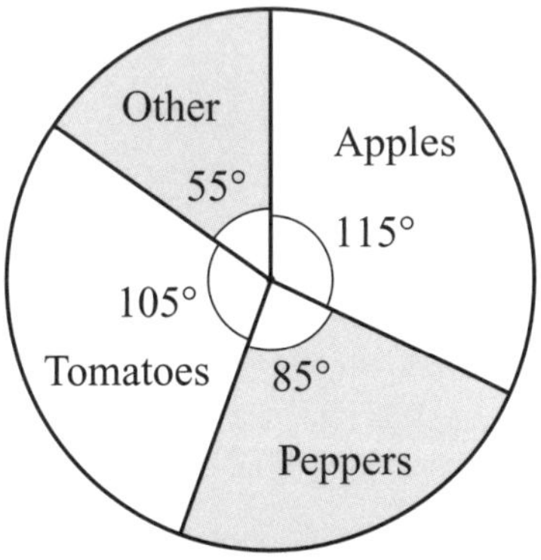

Work out how many people said that their favourite red food was tomatoes.

....
[2]

9   (a)   The length of a leaf is 11 cm to the nearest centimetre.
Calculate the upper bound for the length of the leaf.

.... cm
[1]

(b)   The mass of an apple is 0.080 kg to 3 decimal places.
Calculate the lower bound for the mass of the apple.

.... kg
[1]

10 Put a ring around the graph that matches the description.

(a) *y* is inversely proportional to *x*.

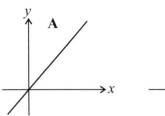 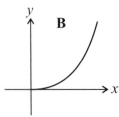 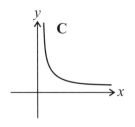 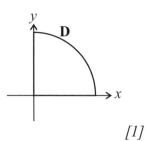

[1]

(b) $y = a^x$ where $a > 1$.

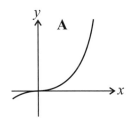 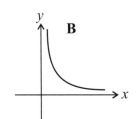 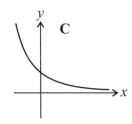 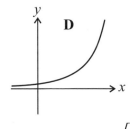

[1]

11 The diagram on the right shows a square-based pyramid.

Calculate the surface area of this pyramid.

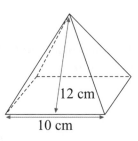

.... cm²

[3]

12 A drawer contains ties that are coloured red, green, white or black.
George picks a tie at random from the drawer. The table shows some of the probabilities.

Colour of tie	Red	Green	White	Black
Probability	0.35	0.20		

The drawer contains exactly twice as many black ties as white ties.

George says, "Half the ties are coloured either red or white."
Is George correct? Explain your answer.

....

....

....

....

[3]

13 Here are the equations of five straight lines.

$$y = 2 \qquad 2y = x \qquad y = 2x + 1 \qquad y - 2x = -3 \qquad 3y = 2x + 2$$

Write each of the equations in the correct position in this table.
The first equation has been put in for you.

	Gradient equal to 2	Gradient not equal to 2
Passes though the point (2, 1)		
Does not pass though the point (2, 1)		$y = 2$

[2]

14 Two functions are defined as $f : x \rightarrow 2x$ and $g : x \rightarrow x - 5$.

(a) Write down an expression for fg(x).

fg(x) = ...

[1]

(b) Find the value of a if gf(a) = 17.

a = ...

[3]

15 The grid shows a quadrilateral Q.

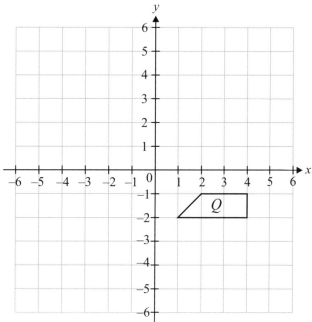

Draw the enlargement of Q using scale factor -2 and centre (2, 0). Label the image R.

[2]

16 These four number cards have a median value of 12 and a mean of 13.

7 12 ? ?

Work out the range of the four numbers. Show how you worked out your answer.

....
[3]

17 Find an expression for the *n*th term of the following sequences:
(a) 0.5, 1, 1.5, 2, 2.5, ...

....
[1]

(b) 2, 10, 50, 250, 1250, ...

....
[2]

18 Write the recurring decimal $0.34\dot{7}$ as a fraction. You must show all your working.

....
[2]

19 Farah's teacher asks her to draw a quadrilateral with these three properties:

- one line of symmetry
- exactly two sides that are equal in length
- two pairs of equal angles

Farah says, "There is no quadrilateral which has all these properties."

Draw a shape on the grid to show that Farah is wrong.

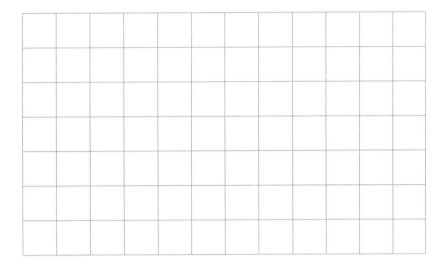

[2]

20 Solve the simultaneous equations

$$4x + 7 + 3y = 0$$
$$6x = 9 + 2y$$

$x =$ ....

$y =$ ....

[4]

21 The diagram shows a square *EFGH*.
    The square has been divided into smaller squares and isosceles triangles.

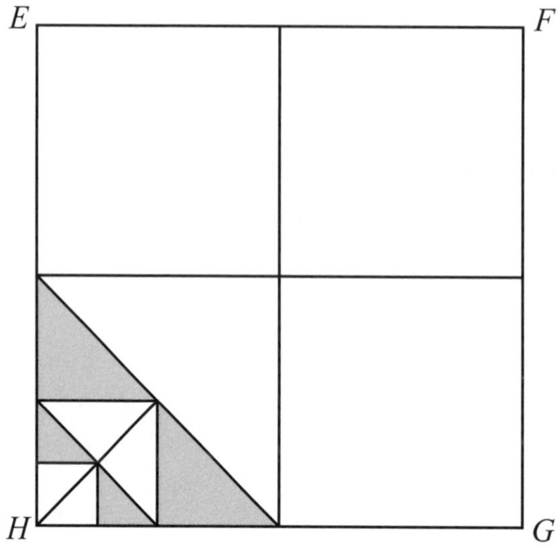

Work out the fraction of the square *EFGH* that is shaded.

....

[3]

22 Point *A* has coordinates (1, 1) and point *B* has coordinates (−3, 9).
    (a) Find the coordinates of the midpoint of *A* and *B*.

....

[2]

    (b) Find the equation of the straight line through *A* and *B*.

....

[3]

23 Amie has written this quadratic expression in completed square form.

$$(x + 4)^2 - 1$$

Write this quadratic expression in a factorised form.

....

[3]

24 The ratio of angles in a triangle is $2:3:5$.

Show that this a right-angled triangle.

[3]

25 The diagram shows a circle A and a sector B.

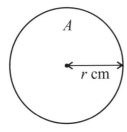 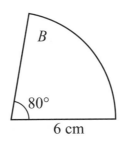

Not to scale

Given that these shapes have the same area, find the radius of circle A.

.... cm

[3]

26 Simplify the following:

(a) $(a^4)^3$

....
[1]

(b) $(2\sqrt{a})^3 \times \frac{1}{2}(a^{0.1})^5$

....
[3]

27 The diagram on the right shows a circle and a quadrilateral *ABCD*.

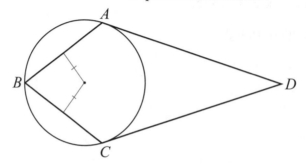

AD and *CD* are tangents to the circle.
AB and *BC* are equidistant from the centre of the circle.

Explain how you know that the quadrilateral *ABCD* is a kite.

....

....

....

[2]

28 Write $\dfrac{1}{x+3} + \dfrac{7}{(x+3)(x-4)}$ as a single fraction in its simplest form.

....

[3]

END OF QUESTIONS

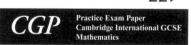

Cambridge International GCSE Mathematics

Extended Paper 2

In addition to this paper you should have:
- A pen and pencil.
- A ruler, protractor and pair of compasses.
- A calculator.

Centre name					
Centre number					
Candidate number					

Time allowed:
- 2 hours 30 minutes

Candidate name
Candidate signature

Instructions to candidates
- Write your name and other details in the spaces provided above.
- Use blue or black ink to write your answers.
- Answer all questions in the spaces provided.
- In calculations, show clearly how you worked out your answers.
- Non-exact answers should be rounded to 3 significant figures or 1 decimal place for angles, unless it is specified in the question.
- For π, use the button on your calculator or 3.142.

Information for candidates
- The marks available are given in brackets at the end of each question part.
- There are 130 marks available for this paper.

Answer ALL the questions.

Write your answers in the spaces provided.

You must show all of your working.

1   (a)   Azim has $6000, which he wants to invest for three years.
He is choosing between two savings accounts which each pay compound interest.

| **Account 1** |
| 2.5% each year |
| Fixed for 3 years |

| **Account 2** |
| Year 1: Interest rate 1.0% |
| Year 2: Interest rate 1.5% |
| Year 3: Interest rate 5.0% |

(i)   Calculate how much money Azim will have in his account after 3 years
if he chooses Account 1.

$ ....

[2]

(ii)   Calculate how much interest Azim will earn on his initial $6000
over the 3 years if he chooses Account 2.

$ ....

[2]

(b)   Sally invests a sum of money in an account that pays 2% compound interest each year.
Two years later, she has a total of $15 606 in the account.

Work out the amount of money she invested initially.

$ ....

[3]

(c)   Sally's classic car is worth $18 800. Its value increases in the ratio 5 : 4.
Work out the car's new value.

$ ....

[2]

(d) The value of Azim's car, V, is inversely proportional to the square root of its age, A, in years. After 1 year, the car is worth \$21 000. Calculate how much it will be worth after 9 years.

$ ....

[3]

(e) The graph below shows the conversions between US Dollars (\$) and Indian Rupees.

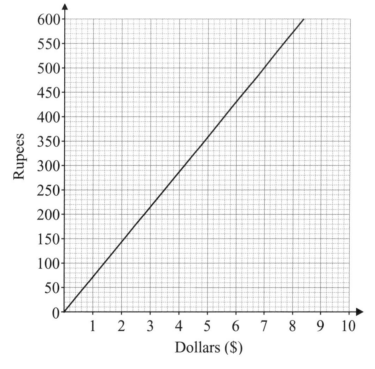

(i) Use the graph to estimate the value of \$6 in rupees.

.... rupees

[1]

(ii) Use the graph to estimate the value of 5000 rupees in dollars.

\$................................

[2]

2 A funfair stall runs a game played using this spinner. The rules of the game are shown below.

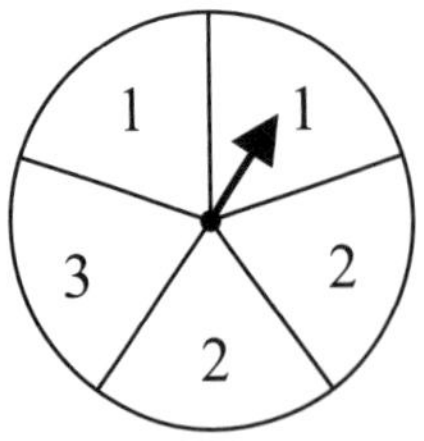

> **$0.50 a go**
> Spin this fair spinner twice.
> Win $2 if your total score
> is 5 or more.

(a) Complete the possibility diagram below showing the possible outcomes of the game.

First spin

		1	1	2	2	3
Second Spin	1	2	2	3	3	4
	1	2				4
	2	3				5
	2	3				5
	3	4	4	5	5	6

[1]

(b) Romesh plays the game once. Given that he gets a total of 4, what is the probability that his first spin landed on a 1?

....

[2]

(c) The game is played 200 times.
Estimate the profit that the stall will make. Show how you worked out your answer.

$ ....

[4]

(d) The result of each spin from the 200 games is shown in the table below.
  (i) Complete the table to show the relative frequency of each result.

Result	1	2	3	Total
Frequency	192	144	64	400
Relative Frequency				—

[2]

  (ii) Do you think these results support the claim that the spinner is fair? Explain your answer.

....

....

....

[1]

3   One day, a baker makes x rolls and y pastries.

(a)   The baker sells rolls for \$2 and pastries for \$3.

   (i)   Write a formula for the total amount of money, \$$M$,
         that the baker makes from selling x rolls and y pastries.

....

[2]

   (ii)   Find the number of rolls sold if the baker sold 20 pastries and made \$90.

.... rolls

[2]

(b)   The values of x and y must satisfy these inequalities:

$$y \le 25 \qquad y \le 50 - x \qquad x + 3y \le 90$$

   (i)   Rearrange the equation $x + 3y = 90$ to make y the subject.

$y =$ ....

[2]

   (ii)   Show on the grid below the region that satisfies the three inequalities above,
          shading the unwanted regions.

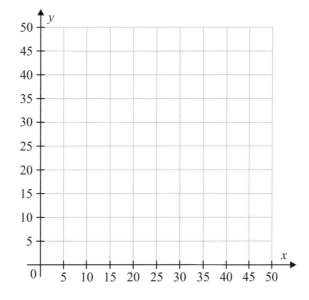

[4]

   (iii)   Find the values of x and y within this region that maximise the value of M.

$x =$ .... $y =$ ....

[3]

4   *OABC* is a parallelogram.

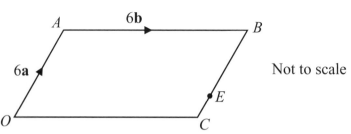

Not to scale

(a) $\overrightarrow{BE} : \overrightarrow{EC}$ is in the ratio $3:1$.
     Find the vector $\overrightarrow{AE}$ in terms of **a** and **b**.

     ....

     [3]

(b) The vectors **a** and **b** are written in column vectors as $\mathbf{a} = \begin{pmatrix} 1 \\ 2 \end{pmatrix}$ and $\mathbf{b} = \begin{pmatrix} 2 \\ 0 \end{pmatrix}$.
     Calculate the magnitude of the vector $(4\mathbf{a} + \mathbf{b})$.

     ....

     [3]

Some different parallelograms are drawn on the grid below.

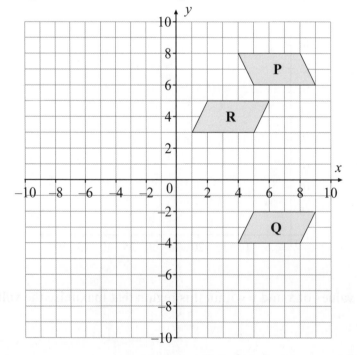

(c) Describe fully the single transformation that maps shape P onto shape Q.

....

....

     [2]

(d) Draw the rotation of shape R through $180°$ about the origin.

     [2]

5   Sixty people took part in a race in 2020. The cumulative frequency graph
    shows the times that the people took to complete the race.

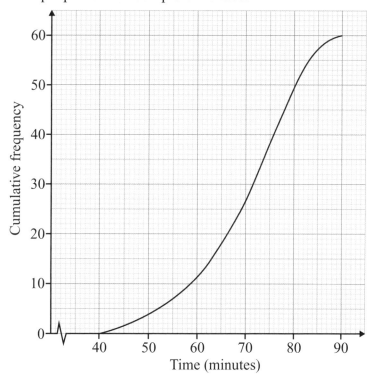

(a) (i)   Estimate how many people took over 75 minutes to finish the race.

....
[2]

     (ii) Estimate the 30th percentile of this data.

.... minutes
[2]

The table on the right summarises the times
that people took to complete the race in 2019.

(b) What is the smallest possible difference
     between the winning times in 2019 and 2020?

2019 Race Times	
Median	76 minutes
Interquartile range	18 minutes
Winning time	37 minutes

.... minutes
[2]

(c) On average, were people faster in 2019 or 2020? Explain your answer.

....

....
[2]

(d) Were the times more consistent in 2019 or 2020? Explain your answer.

....

....
[2]

6 (a) Complete the tables of values below for the graph of $y = \sin x$.
Give all values correct to 2 d.p. where appropriate.

x	0°	30°	60°	90°	120°	150°	180°
y	0	0.5	0.87	1	0.87	0.5	

x	210°	240°	270°	300°	330°	360°
y				−0.87	−0.5	0

[3]

(b) Use the tables of values to plot the graph of $y = \sin x$ for 0° to 360° on the axes below.

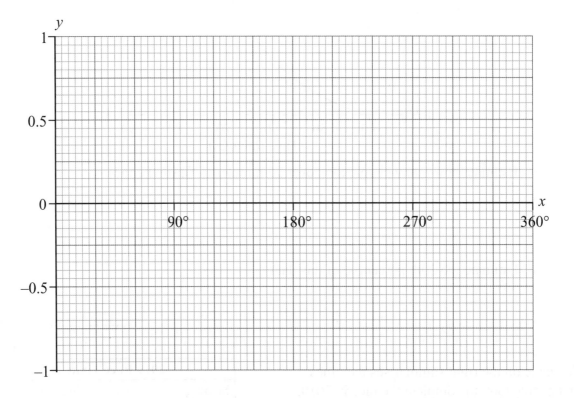

[4]

(c) Use your graph to approximate the two solutions of the equation
$2 - 5 \sin x = 0$ between 0° and 360°

$x = $ ....° $x = $ ....°

[3]

7   ξ = {20, 21, 22, 23, 24, 25, 26, 27, 28, 29, 30}
    A = {multiples of 3}
    B = {numbers with more than 4 factors}
    C = {x : 2x + 1 < 50}

(a) Fill in the four missing numbers in the Venn diagram below.

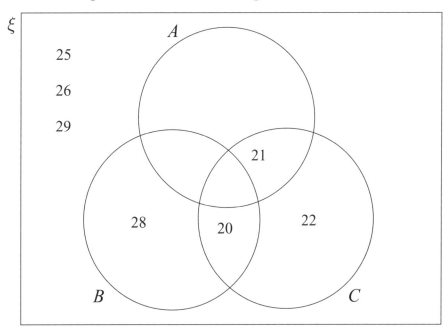

[3]

(b) For the sets above, find:
    (i) $A \cup B$

    ....
                                                                                [1]

    (ii) $B' \cap C'$

    ....
                                                                                [1]

    (iii) n($A \cap B \cap C$)

    ....
                                                                                [1]

(c) ξ = {all real numbers}
    D = {x : x is a rational number}
    Put a ring around the number that is a member of set D.

        $\sqrt{2}$ $\sqrt{3}$ $\sqrt{4}$ $\sqrt{5}$

                                                                                [1]

(d) ξ = {all natural numbers}
    E = {multiples of 24}
    F = {multiples of 32}

    Find the smallest positive number in $E \cap F$.

    ....
                                                                                [2]

8   (a)   The speed-time graph on the right shows
the first two minutes of a car journey.

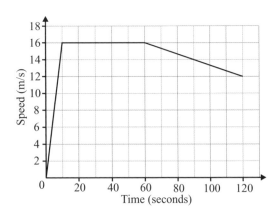

   (i)   Write down the speed of the car
90 seconds into its journey.

.... m/s
[1]

   (ii)   Calculate the distance the car travels
in the first two minutes of its journey.

.... m
[4]

(b)   The distance-time graph on the right
shows the distance a different car travels
during the same two minutes.

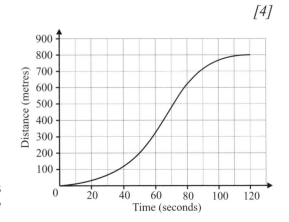

   (i)   Find the average speed of this car
over the whole two minute journey.

.... m/s
[2]

   (ii)   Estimate the speed of the car 50 seconds into its journey

.... m/s
[3]

(c)   A third car is travelling from point A to point B, as shown on the map below.

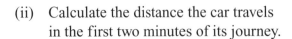

Not drawn
to scale

B

N

30°

C   A

   (i)   Use the information above to calculate the bearing of point A from point B.

.... °
[2]

   (ii)   Point C is 300 m south and 315 m west of point B.
Calculate the distance from point B to point C.

.... m
[2]

9   (a) A quadratic function f(x) is defined as f(x) = $x^2 - 10x + 10$.

      (i)   Write f(x) in completed square form.

f(x) = ...

[3]

      (ii)   Write down the coordinates of the turning point of the graph of y = f(x).

....

[1]

  (b) Another quadratic function g(x) is defined as g(x) = $3x^2 - 9x - 30$.

      (i)   Write g(x) in a fully factorised form.

g(x) = ...

[3]

      (ii)   Simplify $\dfrac{6x + 12}{3x^2 - 9x - 30}$.

....

[2]

10 (a) *ABC* is an isosceles triangle with *AB* = *AC* = 9 cm
and angle *BAC* = 40°.

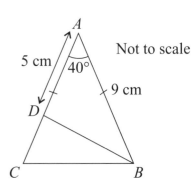

Not to scale

(i) Calculate the area of triangle *ABC*.

.... cm²

[3]

(ii) *D* is the point on *AC* such that *AD* = 5 cm. Calculate the length of the line *BD*.

.... cm

[4]

(b) The triangle *ABC* is the cross-section of a triangular prism, as shown.
Write down how many planes of symmetry this prism has.

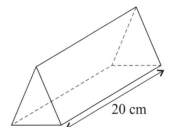

....

[1]

(c) The prism is made of a material with a density of 0.01 kg/cm³.
Calculate the mass of the prism. [Density = Mass ÷ Volume]

.... kg

[3]

(d) The prism is designed to fit inside a cuboid box
measuring 8 cm × 9 cm × 20 cm, as shown in the diagram.

(i) Calculate the distance *EK*.

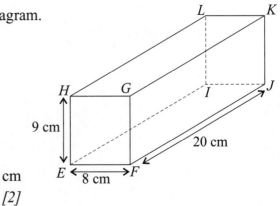

.... cm

[2]

(ii) Calculate the angle *KEJ*.

°

....

[2]

11 (a) Two cubic functions are given by the equations $f(x) = (x + 3)^3$ and $g(x) = x^3 - 3$.

    (i) Write $f(x)$ in the form $x^3 + ax^2 + bx + c$, where a, b and c are constants.

$$f(x) = \text{...}$$

[3]

    (ii) Find the difference in value between $g(5)$ and $g^{-1}(5)$.

....

[4]

(b) A different cubic function is plotted as a graph. The graph has the equation $y = x^3 - 12x + 5$.

    (i) Find $\dfrac{dy}{dx}$ for this graph.

$$\frac{dy}{dx} = \text{...}$$

[2]

    (ii) Find the coordinates of the turning points of the graph
       and identify the nature of each. Give reasons for your answers.

[6]

END OF QUESTIONS

Answers

Section One — Number

Page 7 (Warm-Up Questions)

1 a) 11 b) 37 c) 3

2 0.0253040584425048

Your answer might have more or fewer digits, depending on the number of figures displayed on your calculator.

3 One million, two hundred and thirty-four thousand, five hundred and thirty-one

4 a) 1, 10, −4, 7 b) $\sqrt{2}, 6\pi$

5 $n = 12$

The only square numbers between 10 and 50 are 16, 25, 36 and 49. Then only 36 is a multiple of 3.

6 11 and −11

Page 8 (Exam Questions)

3 −10.6419373361169 *[1 mark]*

Your answer might have more or fewer digits, depending on the number of figures displayed on your calculator.

4 Integers include all whole numbers, while natural numbers are just the positive integers (not including zero). *[1 mark]*

5 0.008, 0.09, 0.1, 0.2, 0.307, 0.37 *[1 mark]*

6 Try each number until you find the answer:
$1 \times 2 = 2, 2^2 = 4, \sqrt[3]{4} = 1.58...$
$2 \times 2 = 4, 4^2 = 16, \sqrt[3]{16} = 2.51...$
$3 \times 2 = 6, 6^2 = 36, \sqrt[3]{36} = 3.30...$
$4 \times 2 = 8, 8^2 = 64, \sqrt[3]{64} = 4$
So Juliette's number was 4.
[2 marks available — 1 mark for a correct method, 1 mark for the correct answer]

7 E.g. $6 = \sqrt{3x + 2y}$, so $36 = 3x + 2y$
Try different values of x and see what y-value each one gives:
$x = 2$: $3x = 6 \Rightarrow 2y = 36 - 6 = 30 \Rightarrow y = 15$
$x = 4$: $3x = 12 \Rightarrow 2y = 36 - 12 = 24 \Rightarrow y = 12$
[2 marks available — 1 mark for each correct pair of x and y values]
The only other possible solution is x = 6, y = 9.

Page 12 (Warm-Up Questions)

1 1, 2, 4, 5, 8, 10, 20, 40

2 34, 51, 68

3 $231 \div 3 = 77$ or $231 \div 7 = 33$ or $231 \div 11 = 21$.
So 231 has more than 2 factors.

4 $2 \times 2 \times 2 \times 5$ (or $2^3 \times 5$)

5 a) 36 b) 6

Page 13 (Exam Questions)

3 a) $30 = 1 \times 30$, 2×15, 3×10, $4 \times ...$, 5×6, 6×5, etc...
So the factors of 30 are: 1, 2, 3, 5, 6, 10, 15, 30 *[1 mark]*

  b) $48 = 1 \times 48$, 2×24, 3×16, 4×12, $5 \times ...$,
6×8, $7 \times ...$, 8×6, etc...
So the factors of 48 are: 1, 2, 3, 4, 6, 8, 12, 16, 24, 48
[1 mark]

  c) The HCF is the highest number in both lists, which is 6. *[1 mark]*

4 The first car takes 30 seconds to complete a circuit, the second car takes 70 seconds to complete a circuit.

Multiples of 30 are: 30, 60, 90, 120, 150, 180, ⃝210 240, ...

Multiples of 70 are: 70, 140, ⃝210 280, ...

So it will be 210 seconds or 3.5 minutes until they are side by side on the start line.
[2 marks available — 1 mark for a correct method, 1 mark for the correct answer]

5 $25 \times 10^2 - 1 = 2499$, so $x = 10$ *[1 mark]*
Substituting 10 into the factorised expression gives
$2499 = (5 \times 10 - 1)(5 \times 10 + 1) = 49 \times 51$ *[1 mark]*
$49 = 7^2$ and $51 = 17 \times 3$,
so 2499 as a product of its prime factors is $3 \times 7^2 \times 17$ *[1 mark]*
[3 marks available in total — as above]

Page 19 (Warm-Up Questions)

1 a) $\frac{4}{15}$ b) $\frac{3}{5}$ c) $\frac{16}{15}$ or $1\frac{1}{15}$

  d) $\frac{4}{15}$ e) 48 f) 80

2 a) $\frac{22}{5}$ b) $7\frac{1}{3}$

3 a) 40% b) 66.6...% or $66\frac{2}{3}$%

4 a) 0.7 b) 0.875

5 a) $\frac{4}{10}$ or $\frac{2}{5}$ b) $\frac{4}{9}$ c) $\frac{45}{99}$ or $\frac{5}{11}$

Page 20 (Exam Questions)

3 Number of chocolate muffins $= \frac{2}{5} \times 550$
$= (550 \div 5) \times 2 = 110 \times 2 = 220$ *[1 mark]*
Number of lemon muffins $= \frac{3}{11} \times 550$
$= (550 \div 11) \times 3 = 50 \times 3 = 150$ *[1 mark]*
So number of strawberry muffins
$= 550 - 220 - 150 = 180$ *[1 mark]*
[3 marks available in total — as above]
You could also have worked out the fraction of muffins that are strawberry, then multiplied that by 550.

4 a) $1\frac{1}{8} \times 2\frac{2}{5} = \frac{9}{8} \times \frac{12}{5}$ *[1 mark]* $= \frac{108}{40}$ *[1 mark]*
$= 2\frac{7}{10}$ *[1 mark]*
[3 marks available in total — as above]
You could also cancel a factor of 4 before multiplying.

  b) $1\frac{3}{4} \div \frac{7}{9} = \frac{7}{4} \times \frac{9}{7}$ *[1 mark]* $= \frac{63}{28}$ or $\frac{9}{4}$ *[1 mark]*
$= 2\frac{1}{4}$ *[1 mark]*
[3 marks available in total — as above]

5 $a = \frac{3}{4}, b = \frac{5}{2}$, so $\frac{1}{a} + \frac{1}{b} = \frac{4}{3} + \frac{2}{5} = \frac{20}{15} + \frac{6}{15} = \frac{26}{15}$ or $1\frac{11}{15}$
[3 marks available — 1 mark for reciprocal fractions, 1 mark for rewriting over a common denominator, 1 mark for the correct answer]

6 Let $10r = 5.9\dot{0}$, so $1000r = 590.9\dot{0}$
$990r = 585$ *[1 mark]* $\Rightarrow r = \frac{585}{990} = \frac{13}{22}$ *[1 mark]*
[2 marks available in total — as above]

Page 25 (Warm-Up Questions)

1 $17 2 74%
3 9 4 $138
5 $205 6 25%
7 $610 8 $3376.53

Page 26 (Exam Questions)

2 20% increase $= 1 + 0.2 = 1.2$
20% increase of $33.25 = 1.2 \times \$33.25 = \$39.90$
[2 marks available — 1 mark for a correct method, 1 mark for the correct answer]

3 He normally gets $240 \div 40 = 6$ packs *[1 mark]*
40% cheaper $= 1 - 0.4 = 0.6$
So the stickers are $\$0.40 \times 0.6 = \$0.24$ per pack this week *[1 mark]*
He can buy $240 \div 24 = 10$ packs this week *[1 mark]*
So he can get $10 - 6 = 4$ more packs *[1 mark]*
[4 marks available in total — as above]

4 Multiplier = 1 + 0.06 = 1.06
After 3 years she will owe: $750 × 1.06³
= $893.26 (to the nearest cent)
*[3 marks available — 1 mark for working out the multiplier,
1 mark for using the formula, 1 mark for the correct answer]*

5 Multiplier = 1 − 0.25 = 0.75 *[1 mark]*
$N_0 × (0.75)^{35 − 31} = 2\,000\,000$ *[1 mark]*
$N_0 = 2\,000\,000 ÷ 0.75^4 = 6\,320\,987.654...$
= $6\,300\,000 (to the nearest $100\,000) *[1 mark]*
[3 marks available in total — as above]

Page 31 (Warm-Up Questions)

1 a) 1:2   b) 4:9   c) 2:9   d) 16:7   e) 5:4
2 1:4.4
3 300 g ÷ 2 = 150 g; 150 g × 3 = 450 g of flour
4 a) 12:6 = 2:1   b) $\frac{12}{18} = \frac{2}{3}$
5 84
6 $1000, $1400
7 45, 60, 75
(3 + 4 + 5 = 12 parts, so 180 ÷ 12 = 15 per part.)
8 $150
9 6 hours

Page 32 (Exam Questions)

2 a) Shortest side of shape A = 3 units
Shortest side of shape B = 6 units
Ratio of shortest sides = 3:6 = 1:2
*[2 marks available — 1 mark for finding the shortest sides of
the triangles, 1 mark for the correct answer]*

b) Area of shape A = $\frac{1}{2} × 3 × 4 = 6$ square units *[1 mark]*
Area of shape B = $\frac{1}{2} × 6 × 8 = 24$ square units *[1 mark]*
Ratio of areas = 6:24 = 1:4 *[1 mark]*
[3 marks available in total — as above]

3 Mr Appleseed's Supercompost is made up of 4 + 3 + 1 = 8 parts,
so contains: $\frac{4}{8}$ soil, $\frac{3}{8}$ compost and $\frac{1}{8}$ grit.

16 kg of Mr Appleseed's Supercompost contains:
$\frac{4}{8} × 16 = 8$ kg of soil
$\frac{3}{8} × 16 = 6$ kg of compost
$\frac{1}{8} × 16 = 2$ kg of grit
Soil costs $8 ÷ 40 = $0.20 per kg.
Compost costs $15 ÷ 25 = $0.60 per kg.
Grit costs $12 ÷ 15 = $0.80 per kg.
16 kg of Mr Appleseed's Supercompost costs:
(8 × 0.2) + (6 × 0.6) + (2 × 0.8) = $6.80
*[5 marks available — 1 mark for finding the fractions of each
material in the mix, 1 mark for the correct mass of one
material, 1 mark for the correct masses for the other two
materials, 1 mark for working out the price per kg for each
material, 1 mark for the correct answer]*

4 a) 12 litres of petrol will keep 8 go-karts going for 20 minutes.
16 = 2 × 8, so 12 litres will keep 16 go-karts going for:
20 minutes ÷ 2 = 10 minutes
*[2 marks available — 2 marks for the correct answer,
otherwise 1 mark for using a correct method]*

b) In 1 minute, 8 go-karts will use 12 ÷ 20 = 0.6 litres *[1 mark]*
In 45 minutes, 8 go-karts will use
0.6 × 45 = 27 litres *[1 mark]*
27 litres of petrol cost: $1.37 × 27 = $36.99 *[1 mark]*
[3 marks available in total — as above]

Page 38 (Warm-Up Questions)

1 a) 40.22   b) 1070   c) 39.9   d) 28
2 $\frac{94 × 1.9}{0.328 + 0.201} ≈ \frac{90 × 2}{0.3 + 0.2} = \frac{180}{0.5} = 360$

---

3 Upper bound = 14.5 km. Lower bound = 13.5 km
4 a) Maximum = 9.3, minimum = 9.1
b) Maximum = 3.5, minimum = 3.3
c) Maximum = 18.7325, minimum = 17.8125
d) Maximum = 2.23 (3 s.f.), minimum = 2.12 (3 s.f.)
5 $2.7 × 10^{-6}$ seconds
6 a) $2.4 × 10^{11}$ b) $2 × 10^4$ c) $7.797 × 10^6$

Page 39 (Exam Questions)

3 a) $\frac{215.7 × 44.8}{460} ≈ \frac{200 × 40}{500} = \frac{8000}{500} = 16$
*[2 marks available — 2 marks for correct answer,
otherwise 1 mark for correctly rounding at least two numbers
to 1 significant figure]*

b) The answer to a) will be smaller than the exact answer because
in the rounded fraction the numerator is smaller and the
denominator is larger compared to the exact calculation.
[1 mark]

4 a) $2.1 × 10^5 = 0.021 × 10^7$ *[1 mark]*
$7.59 × 10^7 + 0.021 × 10^7 = 7.611 × 10^7$ kg *[1 mark]*
[2 marks available in total — as above]

b) $(2.1 × 10^5) ÷ (7.611 × 10^7) = 0.002759...$ *[1 mark]*
$0.002759 × 100 = 0.28\%$ (2 d.p.) *[1 mark]*
[2 marks available in total — as above]

5 Upper bound for x = 57.5 mm *[1 mark]*
Upper bound for y = 32.5 mm *[1 mark]*
Upper bound for area = 57.5 mm × 32.5 mm = 1868.75 mm²
= 1870 mm² to 3 s.f. *[1 mark]*
[3 marks available in total — as above]

Page 45 (Warm-Up Questions)

1 Peter is a member of the sports club but does not play badminton.
2 Trees that are over 3 m tall.
3 a) $K ∩ L = \{2, 3\}$
b) 2
c) Yes, the statement is true.
*$J ∪ K = \{2, 3, 4, 5, 6, 7, 8, 9, 11, 12\}$,
and $L = \{2, 3, 5, 7, 11\}$*
d)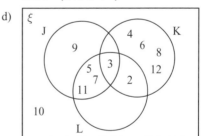

*You might have drawn your circles differently to how
they're shown here — as long as all of the numbers
are inside the right circles, you'll get the marks.*

Page 46 (Exam Questions)

3 a) There are no students who are in both the basketball
and football clubs. *[1 mark]*
b) There are 25 students who are in either the cycling
or the football club (or both). *[1 mark]*

4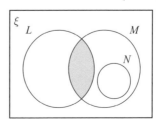

a) *[1 mark for the correct shaded area]*
b) *[1 mark for correct N]*

5 3, 9, 15
[2 marks available — 2 marks for the correct answer,
otherwise 1 mark for one or more elements correct]

Page 47 (Revision Questions)

1 a) 16   b) 2

2 9, 23, 87, 345, 493, 1029, 3004

3 a) −16   b) 7   c) 20

4 a) Whole numbers — either positive or negative, or zero
   b) Numbers that can be written as fractions
   c) Whole numbers which will only divide by themselves or 1

5 a) 169   b) 7   c) 3   d) 125

6 a) $1050 = 2 \times 3 \times 5^2 \times 7$
   b) $360 = 2^3 \times 3^2 \times 5$

7 a) 42   b) 8

8 a) $8\frac{2}{9}$ b) $\frac{33}{7}$

9 a) $\frac{14}{99}$ b) $\frac{22}{7} = 3\frac{1}{7}$
   c) $\frac{11}{24}$ d) $\frac{151}{20} = 7\frac{11}{20}$

10 a) Divide the top by the bottom.
    b) Put the digits after the decimal point on the top, and a power of
        10 with the same number of zeros as there were decimal places
        on the bottom.

11 a) (i) $\frac{4}{100} = \frac{1}{25}$ (ii) 4%
    b) (i) $\frac{65}{100} = \frac{13}{20}$ (ii) 0.65

12 Let $r = 0.5\dot{1}$.
    Then $100r - r = 51.\dot{5}\dot{1} - 0.\dot{5}\dot{1}$
    $\Rightarrow 99r = 51 \Rightarrow r = \frac{51}{99} = \frac{17}{33}$

13 To find x as a percentage of y, make sure both amounts are
    in the same units, then divide x by y and multiply by 100.

14 17.6 m

15 6% simple interest pays $59.62 more (to the nearest cent)

16 240

17 1. Add up the parts.
    2. Divide to find one part.
    3. Multiply to find the amounts.

18 600, 960, 1440

19 $1.41

20 a) 427.96   b) 428.0
    c) 430   d) 428.0

21 Estimates should be in the range 20-24

22 132.2425 m²

23 1. The front number must always be between 1 and 10.
    2. The power of 10, n, is how far the decimal point moves.
    3. n is positive for big numbers, and negative for small numbers.

24 a) 9.7×10^5 b) 3.56×10^9 c) 2.75×10^{-6}

25 a) 1.5875×10^3 b) 2.739×10^{12}

26 a) 5 and 10
    b)

    c) 7

Section Two — Algebra

Page 53 (Warm-Up Questions)

1 a) $2a - 5c$ b) $7r^2 - 5r - 1$ c) $-60rs$

2 a) $4^3 = 64$ b) $\frac{81}{49}$ or $1\frac{32}{49}$ c) 9   d) $\frac{9}{4}$

3 a) $3x^5$ b) $2y^3$ c) $10a^{11}$ d) x^{12}

4 $5a^{10}b^5c^{\frac{5}{2}}$

5 a) $8p + 28$ b) $8x^2 - 2$ c) $5a^2 - 3a$

6 a) $x^2 - 6x + 9$ b) $16y^2 + 40y + 25$

7 a) $2(3p - 6q + 2)$ b) $2cd(2d - 1 + 5cd^2)$

8 a) $(2m + 5n)(1 + p)$ b) $(z + 4)^2$ c) $(x + 2y)(x - 2y)$

Page 54 (Exam Questions)

3 a) $(y + 3)(y - 3) = y^2 - 3y + 3y - 9 = y^2 - 9$
       [2 marks available — 1 mark for expanding the brackets
       correctly, 1 mark for simplifying]
    b) $(2z - 1)(z - 5) = 2z^2 - 10z - z + 5 = 2z^2 - 11z + 5$
       [2 marks available — 1 mark for expanding the brackets
       correctly, 1 mark for simplifying]

4 $2v^3w + 8v^2w^2 = 2(v^3w + 4v^2w^2)$
   $= 2v^2w(v + 4w)$
   [2 marks available — 2 marks for the correct factorisation,
   otherwise 1 mark for a correct partial factorisation]

5 $(9a^4)^{\frac{1}{2}} = \sqrt{9a^4} = 3a^2$ *[1 mark]*
   $\frac{2ab^2}{6a^3b} = \frac{2}{6} \times \frac{a}{a^3} \times \frac{b^2}{b} = \frac{1}{3} \times \frac{1}{a^2} \times b = \frac{b}{3a^2}$ *[1 mark]*
   so $(9a^4)^{\frac{1}{2}} \times \frac{2ab^2}{6a^3b} = 3a^2 \times \frac{b}{3a^2} = b$ *[1 mark]*
   [3 marks available in total — as above]

6 a) $9x^2 - 100 = (3x)^2 - 10^2 = (3x + 10)(3x - 10)$
       [2 marks available — 2 marks for the correct final answer,
       otherwise 1 mark for attempting to use the difference
       of two squares]
    b) $12m + 3ml - 4n - ln = 3m(4 + l) - n(4 + l)$ *[1 mark]*
                          $= (3m - n)(4 + l)$ *[1 mark]*
       [2 marks available in total — as above]

7 $(x - 1)(2x + 3)(2x - 3) = (x - 1)(4x^2 - 6x + 6x - 9)$
                          $= (x - 1)(4x^2 - 9)$
                          $= 4x^3 - 4x^2 - 9x + 9$
   [3 marks available — 3 marks for the correct answer, otherwise
   1 mark for correctly multiplying two sets of brackets together,
   1 mark for attempting to multiply this product by the third set
   of brackets]
   The trick here is spotting that the second pair of brackets multiply
   out to give just two terms (a difference of two squares), which makes
   the second multiplication much easier.

Page 61 (Warm-Up Questions)

1 a) $x = 3$ b) $x = -3$ c) $x = 5$

2 $C = 12d + 18$

3 $q = 7(p - 2r)$ or $q = 7p - 14r$

4 $z = \frac{3x - y}{2}$

5 a) $\frac{2(2abc + 1)}{c^3}$ b) $\frac{x^2 + 2y}{x}$
   You could give your answers in slightly different forms, as long as the
   common factors have been cancelled correctly.

Page 62 (Exam Questions)

3 $\frac{a + 2}{3} = b - 1 \Rightarrow a + 2 = 3b - 3$ *[1 mark]*
   $\Rightarrow a = 3b - 5$ *[1 mark]*
   [2 marks available in total — as above]

4 a) $40 - 3x = 17x \Rightarrow 40 = 20x$ *[1 mark]*
       $\Rightarrow x = 40 \div 20 = 2$ *[1 mark]*
       [2 marks available in total — as above]

b) $2y - 5 = 3y - 12 \Rightarrow -5 + 12 = 3y - 2y$ *[1 mark]*
$\Rightarrow y = 7$ *[1 mark]*
[2 marks available in total — as above]

5 Area = ½ × base × height
= ½ × (3x + 5) × (2x − 4) = ½ (3x + 5)(2x − 4) *[1 mark]*
= ½ × ((3x × 2x) + (3x × −4) + (5 × 2x) + (5 × −4))
= ½ × (6x² − 12x + 10x − 20)
= ½ × (6x² − 2x − 20) *[1 mark]*
= 3x² − x − 10 *[1 mark]*
[3 marks available in total — as above]
You could also have multiplied (2x − 4) by ½ first of all. The area would then just be (3x + 5)(x − 2), which is a bit simpler to multiply out.

6 $\dfrac{1}{x-5} + \dfrac{2}{x-2} = \dfrac{x-2}{(x-5)(x-2)} + \dfrac{2(x-5)}{(x-5)(x-2)}$

$= \dfrac{(x-2)+2(x-5)}{(x-5)(x-2)} = \dfrac{x-2+2x-10}{(x-5)(x-2)} = \dfrac{3x-12}{(x-5)(x-2)}$

[3 marks available — 1 mark for finding the common denominator, 1 mark for a correct method for addition, 1 mark for the correct final answer]

7 $x = \sqrt{\dfrac{(1+n)}{(1-n)}}$, so $x^2 = \dfrac{(1+n)}{(1-n)}$ *[1 mark]* $\Rightarrow x^2(1-n) = 1 + n$

$\Rightarrow x^2 - x^2n = 1 + n$ *[1 mark]* $\Rightarrow x^2 - 1 = n + x^2n$ *[1 mark]*

$\Rightarrow x^2 - 1 = n(1 + x^2)$ *[1 mark]*

$\Rightarrow n = \dfrac{x^2-1}{1+x^2}$ *[1 mark]*

[5 marks available in total — as above]

Page 68 (Warm-Up Questions)

1 a) $(x + 4)(x + 7)$ b) $(x + 14)(x + 2)$
c) $(x + 14)(x − 2)$

2 a) $x = −3$ or $x = −5$ *(it factorises to (x + 3)(x + 5) = 0)*
b) $x = 2$ or $x = −7$ *(it factorises to (x − 2)(x + 7) = 0)*
c) $x = 3$ or $x = 4$
Rearrange to give x² − 7x + 12 = 0, then factorise to give (x − 3)(x − 4) = 0, so x = 3 or x = 4.

3 $(3x + 2)(x + 10)$

4 $x = 1.46$ or $x = −0.46$
Use the quadratic formula, with a = 3, b = −3 and c = −2.

5 $(x − 5)^2 − 16$, so $x = 9$ or $x = 1$
(x − 5)² gives x² − 10x + 25
so complete the square by subtracting 16:
(x − 5)² − 16 = 0 ⇒ (x − 5)² = 16
⇒ (x − 5) = ±√16 ⇒ (x − 5) = 4 or (x − 5) = −4
⇒ x = 9 or x = 1

6 $2(x + 4)^2 + 7$
2(x + 4)² = 2x² + 16x + 32, so add +7 to complete the square.

Page 69 (Exam Questions)

3 $3x^2 + 18x + 24 = 0 \Rightarrow x^2 + 6x + 8 = 0$ *[1 mark]*
$(x + 4)(x + 2) = 0$ *[1 mark]*
$x + 4 = 0$ or $x + 2 = 0$
$x = −4$ or $x = −2$
[1 mark for both solutions]
[3 marks available in total — as above]

4 The area of the square is $(x + 3)(x + 3) = x^2 + 6x + 9$. *[1 mark]*
The area of the triangle is $\frac{1}{2}(2x + 2)(x + 3)$

$= \frac{1}{2}(2x^2 + 6x + 2x + 6) = \frac{1}{2}(2x^2 + 8x + 6)$
$= x^2 + 4x + 3$ *[1 mark]*
So the area of the whole shape is $x^2 + 6x + 9 + x^2 + 4x + 3$
$= 2x^2 + 10x + 12$ *[1 mark]*
$2x^2 + 10x + 12 = 60$, so $2x^2 + 10x − 48 = 0$ *[1 mark]*
Dividing by 2 here will make a = 1 and the quadratic easier to solve.
So $x^2 + 5x − 24 = 0 \Rightarrow (x − 3)(x + 8) = 0$ *[1 mark]*
$x − 3 = 0$ or $x + 8 = 0$
$x = 3$ or $x = −8$
[1 mark for both solutions]

A length can't have a negative value
so the answer must be $x = 3$. *[1 mark]*
[7 marks available in total — as above]
If x = −8 then the square would have sides of length −8 + 3 = −5 cm and the triangle would have a height of 2×−8 + 2 = −14 cm, neither of which are possible.

5 a) $2(x^2 − 4x) + 19$ *[1 mark]*
$4 ÷ 2 = 2$, so the first bit is $2[(x − 2)^2]$
Expanding the brackets: $2(x^2 − 4x + 4) = 2x^2 − 8x + 8$
To complete the square: $19 − 8 = 11$ *[1 mark]*
So $2x^2 − 8x + 19 = 2(x − 2)^2 + 11$ *[1 mark]*
[3 marks available in total — as above]

b) Minimum value = 11, which occurs at $x = 2$, so the coordinates of the minimum point are $(2, 11)$ *[1 mark]*

c) This quadratic is u-shaped and its minimum value is 11, so it's always greater than 0. This means it never crosses the x-axis. *[1 mark]*

Page 75 (Warm-Up Questions)

1 a) $x = 3, y = 3$ b) $x = 1, y = 2$ c) $x = 3, y = 2$
2 $x = 2, y = 5$
3 $x = 3, y = −1$
4 $x = 1, y = −1$ and $x = −4, y = 14$
5 $x = 2, y = 4$
6 a) $q \leq 5$ b) $p > 4.5$

7 a) and b)

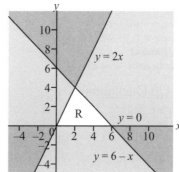

Page 76 (Exam Questions)

3 $2x + 3y = 12$ (1) $\xrightarrow{\times 5}$ $10x + 15y = 60$ (3) *[1 mark]*
$5x + 4y = 9$ (2) $\xrightarrow{\times 2}$ $10x + 8y = 18$ (4) *[1 mark]*

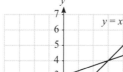

(3) − (4): $10x + 15y = 60$ $2x + 3y = 12$
         $\underline{-\ 10x + \ 8y = 18}$ $2x = 12 − (3 × 6)$
             $7y = 42$ $2x = −6$
               $y = 6$ *[1 mark]* $x = −3$ *[1 mark]*

[4 marks available in total — as above]
Simultaneous equations usually have a few different ways to solve them. E.g. you could substitute y into equation (2) instead of (1) to find x. So long as you get the right solution, you'll get the marks.

4

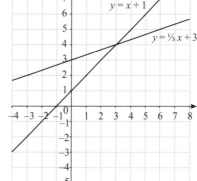

$x = 3, y = 4$
[3 marks available — 1 mark for correctly drawing the line y = x + 1, 1 mark for correctly drawing the line y = ⅓x + 3, 1 mark for the correct solution]

5 a)

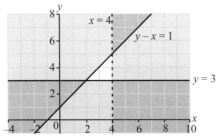

[4 marks available — 1 mark for drawing each line correctly, 1 mark for shading the correct areas]

b) The points in the region that satisfy all three inequalities are at (2, 3), (3, 3) and (3, 4). *[1 mark]*
Find the value of D at these three points:
At (2, 3), $D = 9 - 8 = 1$
At (3, 3), $D = 9 - 12 = -3$
At (3, 4), $D = 12 - 12 = 0$ *[1 mark for all 3 correct]*
So the minimum value of D is -3,
when $x = 3$ and $y = 3$. *[1 mark]*
[3 marks available in total — as above]

6 $y = (x + 6)^2$, so $2x^2 + (x + 6)^2 = 51$ *[1 mark]*
$2x^2 + x^2 + 12x + 36 = 51$
$3x^2 + 12x - 15 = 0$ *[1 mark]*
Dividing by 3: $x^2 + 4x - 5 = 0$
$(x - 1)(x + 5) = 0$ *[1 mark]*
$x = 1$ or $x = -5$ *[1 mark]*
When $x = 1$, $y = (1 + 6)^2 = 49$
When $x = -5$, $y = (-5 + 6)^2 = 1$
So the solutions are $x = 1$, $y = 49$ *[1 mark]*
and $x = -5$, $y = 1$ *[1 mark]*
[6 marks available in total — as above]

Page 81 (Warm-Up Questions)

1 a) 18, 22 b) 81, 243 c) 17, 23
2 a) $n + 1$ b) $2n^2$
3 $2 \times 3^{(n-1)}$
4 a) $A = kr^2$ b) $D = \dfrac{k}{R}$ c) $H = \dfrac{k}{D^3}$ d) $V = kS^3$

Page 82 (Exam Questions)

3 a)

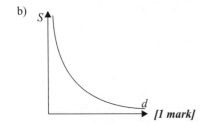

[1 mark]

b) The number of circles added increases by one each time, so the tenth triangle number is:
$1 + 2 + 3 + 4 + 5 + 6 + 7 + 8 + 9 + 10 = 55$.
[2 marks available — 1 mark for 55, 1 mark for correct reasoning]

4
2   6   12   20
  +4 +6 +8

The difference is increasing by 2, so the next term is: $20 + 10 = 30$
[2 marks available — 1 mark for spotting the pattern, 1 mark for the correct answer]

5 a) $S \propto \dfrac{1}{d}$, so $S = \dfrac{k}{d}$ *[1 mark]*
When $S = 6000$ and $d = 15$, $6000 = \dfrac{k}{15}$, so $k = 90\,000$ *[1 mark]*
So $S = \dfrac{90\,000}{d}$ *[1 mark]*
[3 marks available in total — as above]

b)

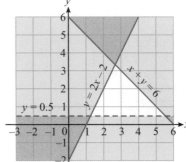

[1 mark]

6 $x_{n+1} = (n + 1)^3 - 3(n + 1) + 2$
$= (n^2 + 2n + 1)(n + 1) - (3n + 3) + 2$ *[1 mark]*
$= (n^3 + 3n^2 + 3n + 1) - 3n - 3 + 2$ *[1 mark]*
$= n^3 + 3n^2$ *[1 mark]*
$y_n = x_{n+1} - x_n$
$= (n^3 + 3n^2) - (n^3 - 3n + 2)$ *[1 mark]*
$= 3n^2 + 3n - 2$ *[1 mark]*
[5 marks available in total — as above]
Alternatively you could have worked out the first few values of the y_n sequence (4, 16, 34, 58...) and then found the nth term of this quadratic sequence in the normal way.

Page 83 (Revision Questions)

1 $5x - 4y - 5$
2 a) x^9 b) y^2 c) z^{-12} d) $t^{-\frac{2}{5}}$
3 a) $6x + 3$ b) $x^2 - x - 6$ c) $x^3 + 7x^2 + 7x - 15$
4 a) $2x(5y + 2x)$ b) $7x(xy + 3z^2)$
5 a) $(7 + 9pq)(7 - 9pq)$ b) $(x + 4y)^2$
6 a) $x = 2$ b) $x = \pm 3$
7 $P = 7d + 5c$
8 a) $p = \dfrac{1}{r - 3q}$ b) $p = -\dfrac{4y}{3}$
9 $\dfrac{3x + 1}{(x + 3)(x - 1)}$
10 a) $x = -3$ or $x = -6$ b) $x = 4$ or $x = -\dfrac{3}{5}$
11 a) $x = 1.56$ or $x = -2.56$
b) $x = 0.27$ or $x = -1.47$
c) $x = 0.44$ or $x = -3.44$
12 a) $x = -1.42$ (3 s.f.) or $x = -10.6$ (3 s.f.)
b) $x = 3$ or $x = -\dfrac{1}{2}$
13 $x = 2, y = 3$
14 $x = -2, y = -2$ or $x = -4, y = -8$
15 a) $x \geq -2$ b) $-1 < x \leq 6$
16

17 a) 31, rule is add 7
b) 256, rule is multiply by 4
c) 19, rule is add two previous terms.
18 a) $4n + 1$ b) $-3n + 14$
19 Yes (it's the 5th term)
20 $n^2 - 1$
21 a) $7 \times 10^{(n-1)}$ b) $n^3 + 2n$
22 $y = kx^2$
23 $p = 72$

Section Three — Graphs, Functions and Calculus

Page 90 (Warm-Up Questions)

1 a) $y = x$
b) Horizontal line ($y = 4$)
c) Vertical line ($x = -1$)
d) $y = -x$

2 a)

x	0	2	3
y	−4	2	5

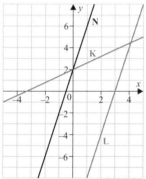

b) $y = 3x + 2$ has the same gradient as $y = 3x - 4$ (the lines are parallel) and the y-intercept is 6 units higher (it's at $y = 2$).

3 a) $y = -5x + 4$ **b)** $\dfrac{1}{5}$

Page 91 (Exam Questions)

2 a) Pick two points on the line, e.g. (0, 2) and (5, 5).

Gradient = $m = \dfrac{\text{change in } y}{\text{change in } x} = \dfrac{5 - 2}{5 - 0} = \dfrac{3}{5}$ *[1 mark]*

y-intercept = $c = 2$ *[1 mark]*

So the equation of the line is $y = \dfrac{3}{5}x + 2$ *[1 mark]*

[3 marks available in total — as above]

b) **N** goes through (0, 2). It has a gradient of 4, so every time you go across 1, you go up 4. So draw a line through points (0, 2) and (1, 6).

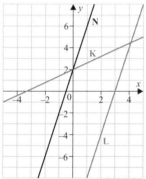

[2 marks available — 2 marks for the correct line, otherwise 1 mark for a line with gradient 4 or a line with y-intercept 2]

c) **L** has a gradient of 4 (you can either work this out or see that it's parallel to **N**). So it's equation is of the form $y = 4x + c$. The point (3, 0) is on the line, so $0 = 4 \times 3 + c \Rightarrow c = -12$. So the y-intercept is (0, −12).

[2 marks available — 1 mark for a correct method, 1 mark for the correct answer]

Alternatively, you can see that (1, −8) is on the line. Then, since the gradient is 4, you can go left 1 and down 4 to reach (0, −12).

3 a) $\left(\dfrac{(6 + (-4))}{2}, \dfrac{(2 + 1)}{2} \right)$ *[1 mark]*

$= (1, 1.5)$ *[1 mark]*

[2 marks available in total — as above]

b) $\dfrac{(6 + a)}{2} = 3 \Rightarrow a = 6 - 6 \Rightarrow a = 0$

$\dfrac{2 + b}{2} = 5 \Rightarrow b = 10 - 2 \Rightarrow b = 8$

[3 marks available — 1 mark for a correct method, 1 mark for each correct a and b value]

4 Midpoint of line AB: $\left(\dfrac{5 + 1}{2}, \dfrac{7 - 1}{2} \right) = (3, 3)$

Midpoint of line CD: $\left(\dfrac{13 + 3}{2}, \dfrac{4 - 2}{2} \right) = (8, 1)$

Gradient of line AB: $\dfrac{7 - (-1)}{5 - 1} = \dfrac{8}{4} = 2$,

so gradient of the line perpendicular to AB = $\dfrac{-1}{2}$

Gradient of the line joining the midpoints of AB and CD:

Gradient = $\dfrac{1 - 3}{8 - 3} = \dfrac{-2}{5}$

$\dfrac{-1}{2} \neq \dfrac{-2}{5}$, therefore James is incorrect.

[4 marks available — 1 mark for saying James is wrong, 1 mark for finding both midpoints, 1 mark for finding both gradients, 1 mark for comparing gradients to show that the lines aren't perpendicular]

Alternatively, you could have found the equation of the perpendicular line that goes through the midpoint of AB and show that it does not pass through the midpoint of CD.

Page 97 (Warm-Up Questions)

1 a)

x	−2	−1	0	1	2	3	4	5
y	7	2	−1	−2	−1	2	7	14

b)

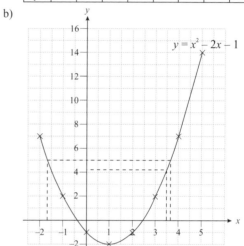

c) 4.25 *Allow answers between 4 and 4.5.*

d) $x = -1.65$ and 3.65

Allow answers between −1.6 and −1.7, and between 3.6 and 3.7.

2

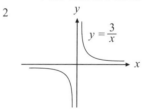

3 $x = 310°$ *Allow answers between 308° and 312°.*

Pages 98-99 (Exam Questions)

2 a)

x	1	2	3
y	1	0	1

[3 marks available — 1 mark for each correct value]

b)

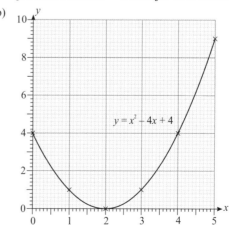

[4 marks available — 4 marks for a correct curve with all points plotted correctly, 3 marks for at least 5 points plotted correctly, 2 marks for at least 3 points plotted correctly, 1 mark for at least 1 point plotted correctly]

c) Draw the line $y = 2$ on the graph.

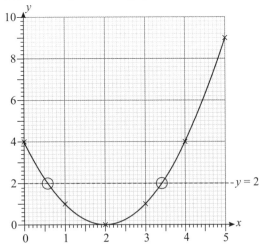

The solutions to $2 = x^2 - 4x + 4$ occur where the line
and the curve intersect: $x = 0.6$ and $x = 3.4$ (both 1 d.p.)
*[2 marks available — 1 mark for using y = 2,
1 mark for both correct solutions]*
Allow solutions between 0.5 and 0.7, and between 3.3 and 3.5.

3 a) B *[1 mark]*   b) C *[1 mark]*   c) A *[1 mark]*

4 a)

x	30°	90°	...	270°	330°
y	0.5	1	...	−1	−0.5

[4 marks available — 1 mark for each correct answer]

b)

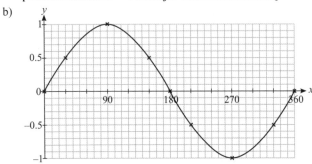

*[4 marks available — 4 marks for a correct curve with all
points plotted correctly, 3 marks for at least 8 points plotted
correctly, 2 marks for at least 5 points plotted correctly,
1 mark for at least 2 points plotted correctly]*

c) Draw the line of $y = 0.3$ on the graph:

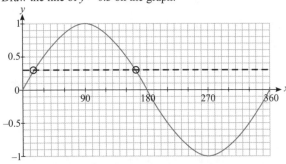

The solutions are at the intersections: $x = 17°$ or $x = 163°$.
*[2 marks available — 1 mark for drawing the line y = 0.3
on the graph, 1 mark for the correct solutions]*
Allow solutions within 5° of the correct answer.

5 a)

x	0.2	5
y	17.2	2.8

[2 marks available — 1 mark for each correct value]

b)

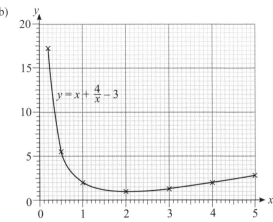

*[4 marks available — 4 marks for a correct curve with all
points plotted correctly, 3 marks for at least 6 points plotted
correctly, 2 marks for at least 4 points plotted correctly,
1 mark for at least 2 points plotted correctly]*

c) Draw the line of $y = 5x + 5$ on the graph.

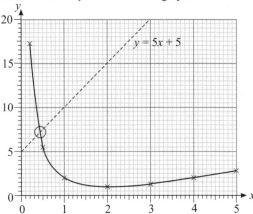

The solutions to the equation occur where the line
and the curve intersect: $x = 0.4$ (1 d.p.)
*[3 marks available — 2 marks for drawing the line $y = 5x + 5$
correctly on the graph, otherwise 1 mark for drawing a
straight line with gradient 5 or y-intercept 5;
1 mark for the correct solution]*

Page 104 (Warm-Up Questions)

1 a) 36 litres (allow 35.5-36.5 litres)
   b) 4.4 gallons (allow 4.3-4.5 gallons)

2 a) Ben drove faster on his way home.   b) 15 minutes

3 a) 25 seconds   b) 235 m

Page 105 (Exam Questions)

2 a) 1 hour *[1 mark]*

b) Tyrone. He reaches 30 km after 5 hours, whereas Selby
reaches 30 km after 6 hours. *[1 mark]*

c) Gradient $= \dfrac{\text{change in } y}{\text{change in } x} = \dfrac{25 - 15}{3 - 1.5} = \dfrac{10}{1.5} = 6.67$ km/h (2 d.p.)
*[2 marks available — 2 marks for correct answer,
otherwise 1 mark for choosing correct x and y values]*

3 a) Gradient $= \dfrac{\text{change in } y}{\text{change in } x} = \dfrac{7.6 - 6.2}{4 - 2} = \dfrac{1.4}{2} = 0.7$ m/s^2
*[2 marks available — 2 marks for correct answer,
otherwise 1 mark for choosing correct x and y values]*

b)

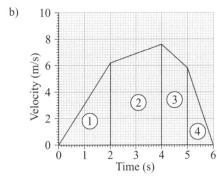

Area of triangle ①: $\frac{1}{2} \times 2 \times 6.2 = 6.2$ m

Area of trapezium ②: $\frac{1}{2} \times (6.2 + 7.6) \times 2 = 13.8$ m

Area of trapezium ③: $\frac{1}{2} \times (7.6 + 5.8) \times 1 = 6.7$ m

Area of triangle ④: $\frac{1}{2} \times 5.8 \times 1 = 2.9$ m

Distance travelled = 6.2 + 13.8 + 6.7 + 2.9 = 29.6 m

[3 marks available — 1 mark for a correct method to split the area up, 1 mark for at least two correct areas found, 1 mark for correct answer]

c) Average speed = 29.6 ÷ 6 *[1 mark]*

= 4.9333... = 4.93 m/s (3 s.f.) *[1 mark]*

[2 marks available in total — as above]

Page 109 (Warm-Up Questions)

1 a) 19   b) 7

   c) $10 - 10x$ d) $5x^2 + 14$

   e) -16 f) $f^{-1}(x) = \frac{x+1}{5}$

2 a) $7a^6$ b) $50t^4$ c) 1   d) $-4w^5$

3 $36x^3 + 3x^2 + 8x$

4 a) -2 b) 24   c) -6 d) -0.5

5 a) $(0, 0)$ minimum

   b) $(2, -4)$ maximum

   c) $(-4, 33)$ maximum, $(0, 1)$ minimum

Page 110 (Exam Questions)

3 a) $f(7.5) = \frac{3}{2(7.5) + 5} = \frac{3}{20} = 0.15$ *[1 mark]*

   b) Write out $x = f(y)$, $x = \frac{3}{2y + 5}$ *[1 mark]*

   Rearrange to make y the subject:

   $2y + 5 = \frac{3}{x} \Rightarrow 2y = \frac{3}{x} - 5$ *[1 mark]*

   $\Rightarrow y = \frac{3}{2x} - \frac{5}{2}$ so $f^{-1}(x) = \frac{3}{2x} - \frac{5}{2}$ *[1 mark]*

   [3 marks available in total — as above]

   c) $ff^{-1}(x) = \frac{3}{2\left(\frac{3}{2x} - \frac{5}{2}\right) + 5}$ *[1 mark]*

   $= \frac{3}{\left(\frac{3}{x} - 5 + 5\right)} = \frac{3}{\left(\frac{3}{x}\right)}$ *[1 mark]*

   $= 3 \times \frac{x}{3} = x$ *[1 mark]*

   [3 marks available in total — as above]

4 a) $A = (5x + 1)(5 - 2x)$ *[1 mark]*

   $= -10x^2 + 25x - 2x + 5$

   $= -10x^2 + 23x + 5$ *[1 mark]*

   [2 marks available in total — as above]

   b) $\frac{dA}{dx} = -20x + 23$

   [2 marks available — 1 mark for each correct term]

   c) Maximum is at $\frac{dA}{dx} = 0$, so

   $-20x + 23 = 0$ *[1 mark]*

   $\Rightarrow -20x = -23 \Rightarrow x = 1.15$ *[1 mark]*

   $A = -10 \times 1.15^2 + (23 \times 1.15) + 5 = 18.225$ km^2 *[1 mark]*

   [3 marks available in total — as above]

5 $y = x^3 - 12x - 2 \Rightarrow \frac{dy}{dx} = 3x^2 - 12$

   [2 marks — 1 for each correct term]

   At turning points, $\frac{dy}{dx} = 0 \Rightarrow 3x^2 - 12 = 0$ *[1 mark]*

   $\Rightarrow x^2 - 4 = 0$

   $\Rightarrow x^2 = 4 \Rightarrow x = \pm 2$ *[1 mark]*

   $\frac{d^2y}{dx^2} = 6x$ *[1 mark]*

   When $x = 2$, $\frac{d^2y}{dx^2} = 12 > 0$, so this is a minimum point. *[1 mark]*

   When $x = -2$, $\frac{d^2y}{dx^2} = -12 < 0$, so this is a maximum point. *[1 mark]*

   [7 marks available in total — as above]

Page 111 (Revision Questions)

1 A(5, −3), B(4, 0), C(0, 3), D(−4, 5), E(−2, −3)

2 (2, 1.5)

3 (6, 9)

4

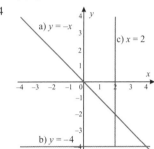

5 E.g.

x	−2	0	2
y	−2.4	0	2.4

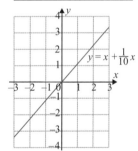

6 When $x = 0$, $y = 3(0) + 5 \Rightarrow y = 5$

   When $y = 0$, $0 = 3x + 5 \Rightarrow 3x = -5 \Rightarrow x = \frac{-5}{3}$

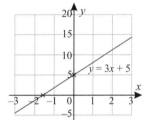

7 2

8 'm' is the gradient and 'c' is the y-intercept.

9 $y = 2x + 10$

10 a) 5   b) $-\frac{1}{5}$

11

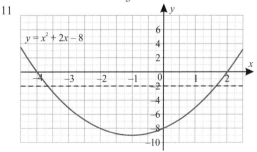

$x = -3.6$ (allow −3.8 to −3.5) or $x = 1.6$ (allow 1.5 to 1.8)

12 a)
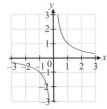

b)
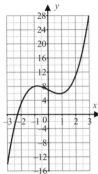

13 a) A graph that goes through (0, 1). To the left, it gets closer and closer to the *x*-axis without ever touching it. To the right, it curves upwards towards infinity.

b) A graph that and crosses the *x*-axis at (0, 0). To the left, it curves downwards to minus infinity as it approaches $x = -90°$. To the right, it curves upwards to infinity as it approaches $x = 90°$. It repeats every 180°.

14
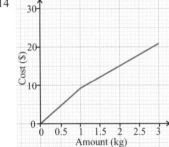

15 The object has stopped.

16 a) Allow 470 metres to 530 metres

b) 1.25 m/s²

c) 1.5 m/s² (Allow 1.25 m/s² to 1.75 m/s²)

17 5

18 0.04 or $\frac{1}{25}$

19 Write out the equation $x = f(y)$, then rearrange the equation to make *y* the subject.

20 $15x^4 + 2$
Gradient = 1217

21 a) (1, –1) minimum   b) (–1, 1) maximum

Section Four — Geometry and Measures

Page 118 (Warm-Up Questions)

1 $a = 115°$, angles on a straight line add to 180°, so $a = 180° - 65°$
$b = 115°$, *a* and *b* are corresponding angles, so $a = b$
$c = 65°$, *c* and 65° are also corresponding angles
$d = 115°$, angles on a line add to 180°, so $d = 180° - c$
There are often different ways of going about angle questions. Just keep scribbling down angles as you find them. It can make it easier to get the angle you want.

2 300°   3 6 sides   4 Pentagon

5 24°   6 Kite

Page 119 (Exam Questions)

2 $a = 75°$ *[1 mark]*
because vertically opposite angles are equal. *[1 mark]*
[2 marks available in total — as above]

3 $70° + 90° + 97° = 257°$
Angle ADC = $360° - 257° = 103°$
(angles in a quadrilateral add up to 360°)
[2 marks available — 1 mark for a correct method, 1 mark for the correct answer]

4 Exterior angle = $180° - 150° = 30°$ *[1 mark]*
Number of sides = $360° \div 30°$ *[1 mark]* = 12 *[1 mark]*
[3 marks available in total — as above]

5 Angle BCG = Angle CGF = *x* (alternate angles)
So $78° + x = 180°$ *[1 mark]*
$x = 180° - 78°$
$x = 102°$ *[1 mark]*
[2 marks available in total — as above]
There are other ways to find x. For instance angles ACB and CGF are corresponding angles. You can then use angles on a straight line to find x.

6 The polygon is split into 5 triangles.
Angles in a triangle add up to 180°, *[1 mark]*
so the angles in the polygon = $5 \times 180° = 900°$ *[1 mark]*
[2 marks available in total — as above]

Page 123 (Warm-Up Questions)

1 14°
(DF is a diameter so angle DEF = 90°. Angles in a triangle add to 180°, so x = 180° – 90° – 76° = 14°.)

2 $m = n = 64°$
(Angles m and n are equal to the 64° angle given, using the alternate segment theorem.)
$l = 52°$
(Angles in a triangle add to 180°, so 180° – 64° – 64° = 52°.)

Page 124 (Exam Questions)

2 *JK* and *KL* are tangents, so $ONK = OMK = 90°$. *[1 mark]*
OMKN is a quadrilateral, and angles in a quadrilateral add up to 360°, so $JKL = 360° - 90° - 90° - 128° = 52°$ *[1 mark]*
[2 marks available in total — as above]

3 Angle in a semicircle = 90°, so $QPR = 90°$. *[1 mark]*
QS is a straight line, so $RPS = 180° - 90° = 90°$. *[1 mark]*
PRS is a triangle, and angles in a triangle add up to 180°, so angle $PSR = 180° - 90° - 32° = 58°$ *[1 mark]*
[3 marks available in total — as above]

4 Angle DBC = 62° *[1 mark]* (angles in the same segment are equal)
Angle ABC = 90° *[1 mark]* (the angle in a semicircle is 90°)
Angle $x = 90° - 62° = 28°$ *[1 mark]*
[3 marks available in total — as above]

5 Angle DEG = 53° and angle AEF = 37°
(alternate segment theorem) *[1 mark]*
Angle $AED = 180° - 53° - 37° = 90°$
(angles on a straight line) *[1 mark]*
The chord *AD* must be a diameter of the circle (angle in a semicircle is 90°), so *AD* must pass through the centre of the circle. *[1 mark]*
[3 marks available in total — as above]

Page 130 (Warm-Up Questions)

1 a) A and E   b) B and F

2 a) 0.222... or $\frac{2}{9}$ b) 2.6 cm
Note that the enlargement scale factor is less than one — so the 'enlargement' actually makes the shape smaller.

3 $\begin{pmatrix} -3 \\ 3 \end{pmatrix}$ 4 (–3, 5)

Page 131 (Exam Questions)

2 a) Rotation 90° anticlockwise around the point (0, 0)
[3 marks available — 1 mark for rotation, 1 mark for correct angle and direction of rotation, 1 mark for correct centre of rotation]

b)

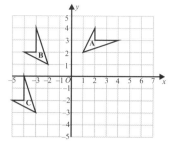

[1 mark for correct translation]

3 a) Scale factor from *EFGH* to *ABCD* = 9 ÷ 6 = 1.5 *[1 mark]*
EF = 6 ÷ 1.5 = 4 cm *[1 mark]*
[2 marks available in total — as above]

   b) BC = 4 × 1.5 = 6 cm *[1 mark]*

4 a) Scale factor from **A** to **C**:
$n^2 = 108\pi ÷ 12\pi = 9$ *[1 mark]* ⇒ n = 3 *[1 mark]*
Volume of **A** = 135π cm³ ÷ 3³ *[1 mark]*
= 5π cm³ *[1 mark]*
[4 marks available in total — as above]

   b) Scale factor from **A** to **B**:
$m^2 = 48\pi ÷ 12\pi = 4$ *[1 mark]* ⇒ m = 2 *[1 mark]*
Perpendicular height of B = 4 cm × 2 *[1 mark]*
= 8 cm *[1 mark]*
[4 marks available in total — as above]

Page 137 (Warm-Up Questions)

1 a) 12 700 g   b) 14.3 m

2 3 000 000 000 mm³

3 90 km/h *(Speed in m/s = 100 ÷ 4 = 25 m/s.*
Multiply by 3600 to get m/h, then divide by 1000 to get km/h.)

4 9 km   5 11.3 g/cm³

6 96 g *(Volume = 5 × 4 × 6 = 120 cm³.*
Then use mass = density × volume.)

Page 138 (Exam Questions)

3 4.30 pm till 5.00 pm is 30 minutes.
5.00 pm till 7.00 pm is 2 hours.
7.00 pm till 7.15 pm is 15 minutes.
So they spend:
2 hours + 30 minutes + 15 minutes = 2 hours 45 minutes
2 hours 45 minutes = 2.75 hours
2.75 × 12 = 33 hours
33 hours + 7 hours 10 minutes = 40 hours 10 minutes
[4 marks available — 1 mark for a correct method to find the
time from 4.30 pm till 7.15 pm, 1 mark for finding the correct
time from 4.30 pm till 7.15 pm, 1 mark for the correct total time
for the first 12 days, 1 mark for the correct answer]

4 a) E.g. 2500 m = 2.5 km.
102 s ÷ 60 = 1.7 minutes ÷ 60 = 0.02833... hours.
Speed = 2.5 km ÷ 0.02833... hours = 88 km/h (to nearest km/h)
[2 marks available — 1 mark for converting into
km and hours, 1 mark for the correct answer]

   b) Time = 2.5 km ÷ 80 km/h = 0.03125 hours
0.03125 hours × 60 × 60 = 113 s (to nearest second)
[2 marks available — 1 mark for dividing the distance
by the speed limit, 1 mark for the correct answer]

5 a) Volume = 360 ÷ 1800 *[1 mark]* = 0.2 m³ *[1 mark]*
[2 marks available in total — as above]

   b) 80 000 cm³ = 80 000 ÷ (100 × 100 × 100) = 0.08 m³ *[1 mark]*
Density = 360 ÷ 0.08 *[1 mark]* = 4500 kg/m³ *[1 mark]*
[3 marks available in total — as above]

Page 143 (Warm-Up Questions)

1 42 cm

2 a) area = length × width, A = l × w

   b) circumference = π × diameter, C = π × D (or C = 2πr)

   c) area = base × vertical height, A = b × h

3 201 cm² (3 s.f.) *(Area = πr² = π × 8²)*

4 40 cm (Allow answers between 38 cm and 42 cm)

5 E.g.

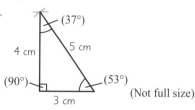

(Not full size)

Page 144 (Exam Questions)

3 a) Area of trapezium = ½(8 + 11) × 6 = ½ × 19 × 6 = 57 cm²
Area of triangle = area of trapezium ÷ 3 = 57 ÷ 3 = 19 cm²
Total area of the shape = area of trapezium + area of triangle
= 57 + 19 = 76 cm²
[3 marks available — 1 mark for the area of the trapezium,
1 mark for the area of the triangle, 1 mark for the correct
final answer]

   b) Area of triangle = ½ × base × height
19 = ½ × 8 × height *[1 mark]*
height = 19 ÷ 4 = 4.75 cm *[1 mark]*
[2 marks available in total — as above]

4 E.g.

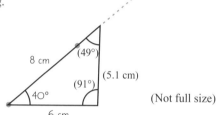

(Not full size)

[2 marks available — 2 marks for a fully correct diagram,
otherwise 1 mark for either correct angle and one correct side,
or both correct sides]

5 Circumference of full circle = 2 × π × 6 = 12π cm
Length of arc = $\frac{50}{360}$ × circumference of circle
= $\frac{50}{360}$ × 12π = $\frac{5\pi}{3}$ cm
Perimeter of sector = $\frac{5\pi}{3}$ + 6 + 6 = 17.235... = 17.2 cm (3 s.f.)
Area of full circle = π × 6² = 36π cm²
Area of sector = $\frac{50}{360}$ × area of circle = $\frac{50}{360}$ × 36π
= 5π cm² = 15.707... = 15.7 cm² (3 s.f.)
[5 marks available — 1 mark for a correct method for calculating
the length of the arc, 1 mark for correct arc length, 1 mark for
correct perimeter of sector, 1 mark for a correct method for
finding the area of the sector, 1 mark for correct area of sector]

Page 149 (Warm-Up Questions)

1 a) Square-based pyramid   b) 5   c) 4

2 a) Net B
   b) 2bh (4 × area of triangle = 4 × $\frac{1}{2}$ × b × h)

3 672 cm³

4 1440 m³

Page 150 (Exam Questions)

2 a) Volume = 90 × 40 × 30 *[1 mark]*
= 108 000 cm³ *[1 mark]*
[2 marks available in total — as above]

   b) Volume of cuboid = length × width × height
108 000 = 120 × width × 18
108 000 = 2160 × width
width = 108 000 ÷ 2160 = 50 cm
[2 marks available — 1 mark for correctly rearranging the
formula to find the width, 1 mark for the correct answer]

3 Area of L-shaped face = $(4 \times 9) + (3 \times 2) = 42$ cm^2 *[1 mark]*
Total surface area = $(6 \times 3) + (3 \times 3) + (2 \times 3) + (6 \times 3)$
$\qquad\qquad\qquad + (4 \times 3) + (9 \times 3) + 42 + 42$ *[1 mark]*
$= 18 + 9 + 6 + 18 + 12 + 27 + 42 + 42 = 174$ cm^2 *[1 mark]*
[3 marks available in total — as above]

4 Surface area of curved part of hemisphere
$= \frac{1}{2} \times$ surface area of a sphere $= \frac{1}{2} \times 4 \times \pi \times 7^2$
$\qquad\qquad\qquad\qquad\qquad = 307.876...$ cm^2 *[1 mark]*

Surface area of curved part of cone $= \pi \times 2 \times 12$
$\qquad\qquad\qquad\qquad\qquad = 75.398...$ cm^2 *[1 mark]*

Surface area of flat top of hemisphere $= (\pi \times 7^2) - (\pi \times 2^2)$
$\qquad\qquad\qquad\qquad\qquad = 141.371...$ cm^2 *[1 mark]*

Total surface area $= 307.876... + 75.398... + 141.371...$
$\qquad\qquad\qquad = 525$ cm^2 (3 s.f.) *[1 mark]*

[4 marks available in total — as above]

Page 151 (Revision Questions)

1 An obtuse angle
2 360°   3 58°
4 295°   5 162°
6 a) 3   b) 3
7 90°   8 53°

9 Congruent shapes are exactly the same size and same shape.
Similar shapes are the same shape but different sizes.

10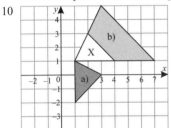

11 80 cm^2
12 a) 5600 cm^3 b) 0.083 kg
    c) 5 690 000 cm^2 d) 10.8 km/h

13 9:48 pm

14 11 m^2

15 36 cm^2

16 52 cm^2

17 Area = 7.07 cm^2 (3 s.f.)
    Perimeter = 10.7 cm (3 s.f.)

18 Multiply by the map scale to go from map distance to real life.
Divide by the map scale to go from real life to map distance.
The scale needs to be in the form 1 cm = ...

19 E.g.

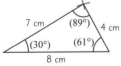
                    (Not full size)

20 75π cm^2

21 396 cm^3

Section Five — Pythagoras, Trigonometry and Vectors

Page 155 (Warm-Up Questions)

1 314 m (3 s.f.)
The diagonal of the field is the hypotenuse of a right-angled triangle with shorter sides of length 250 m and 190 m.

2 a) 0.292   0.956   0.306
   b) 0.993   0.122   8.14
   c) 0.0872   0.996   0.0875
   d) 0.469   0.883   0.532
   e) 0.707   0.707   1.00

3 a) 13.1 cm (3 s.f.)   b) 40° (nearest degree)
4 3 cm

Page 156 (Exam Questions)

3 $3.5^2 = x^2 + 2.1^2$ *[1 mark]*
$x = \sqrt{12.25 - 4.41} = \sqrt{7.84}$ *[1 mark]* = 2.8 m *[1 mark]*
[3 marks available in total — as above]

4 Length of EA:
$28.3^2 = 20^2 + EA^2$ *[1 mark]*
$EA = \sqrt{800.89 - 400} = 20.02...$ cm *[1 mark]*
Length of CE:
$54.3^2 = 20^2 + CE^2$ *[1 mark]*
$CE = \sqrt{2948.49 - 400} = 50.48...$ cm *[1 mark]*
Perimeter $= 28.3 + 54.3 + EA + CE = 153.1$ cm (1 d.p.) *[1 mark]*
[5 marks available in total — as above]

5 a) $\sin 34° = \frac{h}{10}$ *[1 mark]*
      $h = 10 \times \sin 34° = 5.59$ m (2 d.p.) *[1 mark]*
      [2 marks available in total — as above]

   b) Split ABC into two right-angled triangles,
       and find half of AC (call it x).
       $\cos 34° = \frac{x}{10}$ *[1 mark]*
       $x = 10 \times \cos 34° = 8.29...$ m *[1 mark]*
       $AC = 8.29... \times 2 = 16.58$ m (2 d.p.) *[1 mark]*
       [3 marks available in total — as above]
       Alternatively, you could find x by using Pythagoras' theorem and the length h you found in part a).

6 Let the angle of elevation $= x$.
$\tan x = \frac{94}{19}$ *[1 mark]* $\Rightarrow x = \tan^{-1}\left(\frac{94}{19}\right) = 78.572...°$ *[1 mark]*
Angle of elevation = angle of depression = 78.6° (1 d.p.) *[1 mark]*
[3 marks available in total — as above]

Page 164 (Warm-Up Questions)

1 $AC = 9.6$ cm (1 d.p.)

2 104.5° (1 d.p.)

3 $FDG = 31.2°$ (1 d.p.)

4 a) 122.9°   b) 170.0°   c) 135.0°   d) 94.0°

5 a) $\begin{pmatrix} 21 \\ -9 \end{pmatrix}$ b) $\begin{pmatrix} 9 \\ -4 \end{pmatrix}$ c) $\sqrt{29}$ or 5.39 (3 s.f.)

6 a) $\overrightarrow{CD} = -2\mathbf{a}$ *(since ABCD is a parallelogram, $\overrightarrow{AB} = \overrightarrow{DC}$)*
   b) $\overrightarrow{AC} = 2\mathbf{d} + 2\mathbf{a}$
   c) $\overrightarrow{BL} = \mathbf{d} - \mathbf{a}$ *(you could find this in a few different ways — for example $\overrightarrow{BL} = \overrightarrow{BC} + \frac{1}{2}\overrightarrow{CA} = 2\mathbf{d} - (\mathbf{d} + \mathbf{a}) = \mathbf{d} - \mathbf{a}$)*

Page 165 (Exam Questions)

2 $2\mathbf{p} = \begin{pmatrix} 5 \\ -9 \end{pmatrix} \times 2 = \begin{pmatrix} 10 \\ -18 \end{pmatrix}$ *[1 mark]*

   $\mathbf{q} - \mathbf{r} = \begin{pmatrix} -3 \\ 6 \end{pmatrix} - \begin{pmatrix} 8 \\ 1 \end{pmatrix} = \begin{pmatrix} -11 \\ 5 \end{pmatrix}$

   so $3(\mathbf{q} - \mathbf{r}) = \begin{pmatrix} -11 \\ 5 \end{pmatrix} \times 3 = \begin{pmatrix} -33 \\ 15 \end{pmatrix}$ *[1 mark]*

   $2\mathbf{p} + 3(\mathbf{q} - \mathbf{r}) = \begin{pmatrix} 10 \\ -18 \end{pmatrix} + \begin{pmatrix} -33 \\ 15 \end{pmatrix} = \begin{pmatrix} -23 \\ -3 \end{pmatrix}$ *[1 mark]*
   [3 marks available in total — as above]

3 Angle $ABD = 180° - 90° - 31° - 12° = 47°$
   Angle $ACB = 180° - 12° - 47° = 121°$ *[1 mark]*
   Use the sine rule: $\frac{3.3}{\sin 12°} = \frac{AB}{\sin 121°}$ *[1 mark]*
   $AB = \frac{3.3}{\sin 12°} \times \sin 121°$ *[1 mark]*
   $AB = 13.6050...$ m *[1 mark]*
   Find length BD: $\cos 47° = \frac{BD}{13.6050...}$ *[1 mark]*
   $BD = \cos 47° \times 13.6050...$
   $BD = 9.2786... = 9.28$ m (3 s.f.) *[1 mark]*
   [6 marks available in total — as above]
   There's more than one way of doing this question. As long as you've used a correct method to get the right answer you'll still get the marks.

4 Find length DC: $5^2 - (7-4)^2 = DC^2$ *[1 mark]*
   $DC^2 = 16 \Rightarrow DC = 4$ cm
   Find length DG: $4^2 + 11^2 = DG^2$ *[1 mark]*
   $DG^2 = 137 \Rightarrow DG = 11.704...$ cm *[1 mark]*
   Find angle AGD: $\tan AGD = \dfrac{7}{11.704...}$ *[1 mark]*
   $AGD = \tan^{-1}\left(\dfrac{7}{11.704...}\right) = 30.9°$ (1 d.p.) *[1 mark]*
   [5 marks available in total — as above]

5 a) $\overrightarrow{BX} = \overrightarrow{BC} + \overrightarrow{CX} = \overrightarrow{BC} - \overrightarrow{XC}$ *[1 mark]*
       $\overrightarrow{BC} = 6\overrightarrow{BW} = 6\mathbf{b}$

       As $AX = 2XC$, XC must be one third of AC, so:
       $\overrightarrow{CX} = -\overrightarrow{XC} = -\dfrac{1}{3}\overrightarrow{AC}$ (or $\overrightarrow{CX} = \dfrac{1}{3}\overrightarrow{CA}$) *[1 mark]*
       $\overrightarrow{AC} = \overrightarrow{AB} + \overrightarrow{BC} = 3\mathbf{a} + 6\mathbf{b}$ (or $\overrightarrow{CA} = -3\mathbf{a} - 6\mathbf{b}$)
       $\overrightarrow{CX} = -\dfrac{1}{3}(3\mathbf{a} + 6\mathbf{b}) = -\mathbf{a} - 2\mathbf{b}$
       $\overrightarrow{BX} = 6\mathbf{b} - \mathbf{a} - 2\mathbf{b} = 4\mathbf{b} - \mathbf{a}$ *[1 mark]*
       [3 marks available in total — as above]
       You could have solved this a little differently,
       for instance starting by writing $\overrightarrow{BX} = \overrightarrow{BA} + \overrightarrow{AX}$

   b) From part a), $\overrightarrow{BX} = 4\mathbf{b} - \mathbf{a}$. $ABCD$ is a parallelogram, so:
       $\overrightarrow{CD} = \overrightarrow{BA} = -\overrightarrow{AB} = -3\mathbf{a}$, so $\overrightarrow{CM} = \dfrac{1}{2}\overrightarrow{CD} = -\dfrac{3}{2}\mathbf{a}$
       $\overrightarrow{BM} = \overrightarrow{BC} + \overrightarrow{CM}$ *[1 mark]* $= 6\mathbf{b} - \dfrac{3}{2}\mathbf{a} = \dfrac{3}{2}(4\mathbf{b} - \mathbf{a})$ *[1 mark]*

       B, X and M must be three points on a straight line because the lines BM and BX are both scalar multiples of the vector $4\mathbf{b} - \mathbf{a}$.
       [2 marks available in total — as above]

Page 166 (Revision Questions)

1 $a^2 + b^2 = c^2$
   You use Pythagoras' theorem to find
   the missing side of a right-angled triangle.

2 4.72 m (3 s.f.)

3 7.8 (1 d.p.)

4

5 33.4° (1 d.p.)

6 21.5° (1 d.p.)

7 11.8 cm (3 s.f.)

8 Sine rule: $\dfrac{a}{\sin A} = \dfrac{b}{\sin B} = \dfrac{c}{\sin C}$
   Cosine rule: $a^2 = b^2 + c^2 - 2bc\cos A$
   Area $= \dfrac{1}{2}ab\sin C$

9 Two angles given plus any side — sine rule.
   Two sides given plus an angle not enclosed by them — sine rule.
   Two sides given plus the angle enclosed by them — cosine rule.
   All three sides given but no angles — cosine rule.

10 6.84 cm (3 s.f.)

11 48.1 cm² (3 s.f.)

12 120.6° (1 d.p.)

13 $a^2 + b^2 + c^2 = d^2$

14 11.9 m (3 s.f.)

15 15.2° (3 s.f.)

16 54° (nearest degree)

17 a) $\mathbf{d} + \mathbf{e} = \begin{pmatrix} 6 \\ 5 \end{pmatrix} + \begin{pmatrix} -8 \\ 3 \end{pmatrix} = \begin{pmatrix} -2 \\ 8 \end{pmatrix}$

    b) $4\mathbf{d} = 4 \times \begin{pmatrix} 6 \\ 5 \end{pmatrix} = \begin{pmatrix} 24 \\ 20 \end{pmatrix}$

18 7.21 (3 s.f.)

19 a) $\overrightarrow{OX} = \dfrac{1}{3}\mathbf{a}$

    b) $\overrightarrow{DX} = \dfrac{4}{3}\mathbf{a} - \mathbf{b}$ $\overrightarrow{XB} = \dfrac{8}{3}\mathbf{a} - 2\mathbf{b}$

    c) $\overrightarrow{XB} = 2\overrightarrow{DX}$, so DXB is a straight line.

Section Six — Probability and Statistics

Page 170 (Warm-Up Questions)

1 $\dfrac{3}{10}$ or 0.3   2 0.2

3 a) $\dfrac{1}{6}$ b) Approximately 50 times

4 $\dfrac{8}{26}$ or $\dfrac{4}{13}$

Page 171 (Exam Questions)

2 a) Number of red balls $= 10 - 4 = 6$ *[1 mark]*
       Probability of getting a red ball $= \dfrac{6}{10} = \dfrac{3}{5}$ *[1 mark]*
       [2 marks available in total — as above]

    b) No green balls so probability of getting a green $= 0$ *[1 mark]*

3 P(being born on a Tuesday) $= \dfrac{1}{7}$ *[1 mark]*
   Expected frequency $= \dfrac{1}{7} \times 834$ *[1 mark]*
   $= 119.1428... \approx 119$ students *[1 mark]*
   [3 marks available in total — as above]

4 a) P(fewer than 3 dots) $=$ P(1 or 2 dots) $= \dfrac{2}{6}$ or $\dfrac{1}{3}$ *[1 mark]*

    b)

	1	2	3	4	5	6
1	2	3	4	5	6	7
2	3	4	5	6	7	8
3	4	5	6	7	8	9
4	5	6	7	8	9	10
5	6	7	8	9	10	11
6	7	8	9	10	11	12

       [2 marks available — 2 marks for a fully correct table, otherwise 1 mark for a table with at most two mistakes]

    c) $6 \times 6 = 36$ possible outcomes
       Looking at the possibility diagram from part b), there are three ways to get a total of 4 dots *[1 mark]*.
       So P(total is 4) $= \dfrac{3}{36}$ or $\dfrac{1}{12}$ *[1 mark]*
       [2 marks available in total — as above]

Page 176 (Warm-Up Questions)

1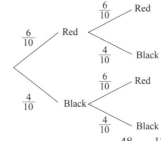
   P(different colours) $= \dfrac{48}{100}$ or $\dfrac{12}{25}$

2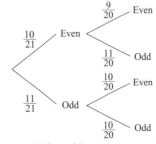
   a) $\dfrac{310}{420}$ or $\dfrac{31}{42}$ b) $\dfrac{220}{420}$ or $\dfrac{11}{21}$

3 a)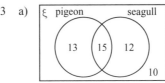

    b) P(saw seagull) $= \dfrac{27}{50}$

4

Score	1	2	3	4	5	6
Relative freq.	0.14	0.137	0.138	0.259	0.161	0.165

E.g. Expected probability of each is $\frac{1}{6} = 0.1666...$

P(4) is much higher than expected, so the dice is probably biased.

Page 177 (Exam Questions)

2   a)

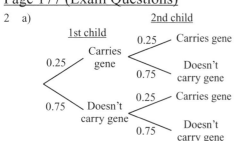

[2 marks available in total — 2 marks for a fully correct diagram, otherwise 1 mark for at least two correct branches]

b)   P(both children carry the gene) = 0.25 × 0.25 *[1 mark]*
= 0.0625 *[1 mark]*
[2 marks available in total — as above]

3   a)   Total = 26 + 33 + 21 + 20 = 100
n(not a singer) = 26 + 20 = 46
So P(not a singer) = $\frac{46}{100}$ or $\frac{23}{50}$ *[1 mark]*

b)   n(singers) = 33 + 21 = 54, n(singer and not female) = 21
So P(not female, given singer) = $\frac{21}{54}$ or $\frac{7}{18}$ *[1 mark]*

4   a)   P(2nd is milk given 1st is milk) = $\frac{6}{11}$ *[1 mark]*

1 milk chocolate has been taken, so there are 6 milk chocolates left out of 11 remaining chocolates.

b)   P(milk and white) = P(milk then white) + P(white then milk)
= $\left(\frac{7}{12} \times \frac{5}{11}\right) + \left(\frac{5}{12} \times \frac{7}{11}\right)$ *[1 mark]* = $\frac{35}{66}$ *[1 mark]*
[2 marks available in total — as above]
You might find it helpful to draw a tree diagram for this question.

Page 182 (Warm-Up Questions)

1   a)   Discrete   b)   Qualitative   c)   Continuous

2   Mode = 2, median = 1.5, mean = 1.333..., range = 11

3

Number of cars	0	1	2	3	4	5	6	Total
Frequency	1	24	36	31	22	9	1	124
No. of cars × F	0	24	72	93	88	45	6	328

a)   Mean = 328 ÷ 124 = 2.645 (3 d.p.)

b)   Median is halfway between the 62nd and 63rd values,
so median = 3

c)   Mode = 2   d)   Range = 6 − 0 = 6

4

Height (cm)	$145 \le x < 155$	$155 \le x < 165$	$165 \le x < 175$	$175 \le x < 185$	Total
Frequency	18	22	24	15	79
Midpoint	150	160	170	180	—
Midpoint × F	2700	3520	4080	2700	13 000

a)   Mean = 13000 ÷ 79 = 164.56 cm (2 d.p.)

b)   Modal Group = $165 \le x < 175$

Page 183 (Exam Questions)

2   Total mark for boys = 15b *[1 mark]*,
total mark for girls = 13g *[1 mark]*

So mean mark for all pupils = $\frac{15b + 13g}{28}$ *[1 mark]*

[3 marks available in total — as above]

3   $(0 \times 2) + (2 \times 4) + (3 \times 7) + (5 \times 11)$
$+ (7 \times 6) + (8 \times 3) + (10 \times 3) = 180$

$180 \div 36 = 5$

[3 marks available — 1 mark for finding the total number of messages, 1 mark for the correct calculation to find the mean, 1 mark for the correct answer]
You could have done this question by adding an extra column to the table for 'number of messages × frequency'.

4   a)   The modal class is the one with
the highest frequency — $4 \le x \le 6$ *[1 mark]*

b)

Growth in cm	Number of plants	Mid-interval value in cm	Mid-interval value × Number of plants
$1 \le x \le 3$	2	2	4
$4 \le x \le 6$	4	5	20
$7 \le x \le 9$	3	8	24
$10 \le x \le 12$	1	11	11
Total:	10	—	59

Mean = 59 ÷ 10 = 5.9 cm
[4 marks available — 1 mark for finding the mid-interval values, 1 mark for multiplying together the mid-interval values and number of plants, 1 mark for the correct calculation to find the mean, 1 mark for the correct answer]

Page 189 (Warm-Up Questions)

1   a)   15   b)

Rock	●
Blues	●●
Opera	◖
Jazz	●◖

2
```
0 | 2 4 9
1 | 2 2 7 9      Key: 1|7 represents 17
2 | 3 5 9
3 | 1 9
```

3   Comedy = 23 × 6° = 138°   Western = 25 × 6° = 150°
Action = 12 × 6° = 72°

4   a)   Graph 1 shows positive correlation.
b)   Graph 2 shows negative correlation.

Page 190 (Exam Questions)

2

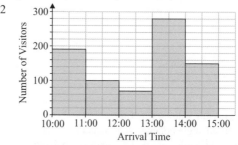

[4 marks available — 1 mark for a suitable scale starting from zero with a correct label on the vertical axis, 1 mark for a correctly labelled horizontal axis, 1 mark for all bars with equal width and no gaps in between, 1 mark for all heights correct]

3   a)

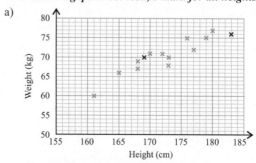

[1 mark for both points plotted correctly]

b)   E.g. In general, as the height increases,
the weight also increases.
[1 mark for any answer indicating a positive correlation]

4

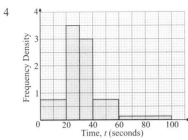

[3 marks available — 1 mark for finding frequency densities, 2 marks for all bars drawn correctly, otherwise 1 mark for one bar drawn correctly]

Page 196 (Warm-Up Questions)

1

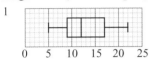

2 a)

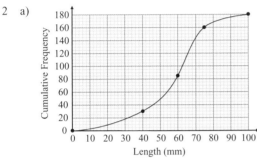

b) Median = 61 mm (accept answers of 60-62 mm)

3 The mode is 30°C but most of the temperatures are less than 20°C, so it's not representative of all the data.

Page 197 (Exam Questions)

2 a) Max value = 63 mm, min value = 8 mm *[1 mark for both]*, so range = 63 − 8 = 55 mm *[1 mark]*
E.g. a range of 55 mm isn't a good reflection of the spread of the data because most of the data is much closer together.
[1 mark for a correct comment]
[3 marks available in total — as above]
Or you could say that the single value of 63 mm has a big effect on increasing the value of the range so that it doesn't represent the spread of the rest of the data.

b) Median rainfall in June = (12 + 1) ÷ 2 = 6.5th value
= (29 + 30) ÷ 2 = 29.5 mm
E.g. The rainfall was generally higher in June, as the median was higher. The rainfall in June was much more varied than in November as the range was much bigger.
[3 marks available — 1 mark for calculating the median rainfall in June, 1 mark for a correct statement comparing the medians and 1 mark for a correct statement comparing the ranges]

3 a)

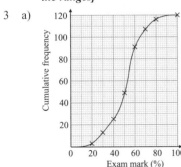

[3 marks available — 1 mark for all points plotted at correct class boundaries, 1 mark for all points plotted at correct heights, 1 mark for joining them with a smooth curve or straight lines]
Be careful — a common mistake in exams is not plotting the points at the top end of the interval.

b) Median at 60 gives a value of 53%
[1 mark, accept answers ± 1%]

c) Lower quartile at 30 gives a value of 43%
Upper quartile at 90 gives a value of 60%
Interquartile range = 60 − 43 = 17%
[2 marks available — 1 mark for correct method, 1 mark for correct answer, accept answers ± 2%]

d) $\frac{1}{5}$ of pupils got lower than grade 5,
$\frac{1}{5}$ of 120 = 24 pupils
Reading from the graph at a cumulative frequency of 24 gives 39%, so the mark needed to get a grade 5 was about 39%.
[3 marks available — 1 mark for finding the number of pupils who got lower than grade 5, 1 mark for drawing a line across from 24 on the cumulative frequency axis, 1 mark for an answer in the range 37-40%]

Page 198 (Revision Questions)

1 $\frac{8}{50}$ or $\frac{4}{25}$

2 1

3 a)

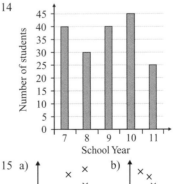

	Second flip	
First flip	Heads	Tails
Heads	HH	HT
Tails	TH	TT

b) $\frac{1}{4}$

4 Expected times outcome will happen = probability × n

5 $\frac{1}{12}$

6 $\frac{1}{2}$

7 $\frac{1}{169}$

8 a)

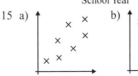

b) $\frac{64}{100} = \frac{16}{25}$

9 When you can't tell what the probabilities of different outcomes are 'just by looking', e.g. when you have a biased dice/spinner etc.

10 Qualitative data

11 Mode = 31, Median = 24, Mean = 22, Range = 39

12 a) Modal class is: $1.5 \leq y < 1.6$.

b) Estimated mean = 1.58 m (2 d.p.)

13 You need to look at the key to see what each symbol represents.

14

15 a)

b)

c)

16 Frequency Density = Frequency ÷ Class Width.

17 a)

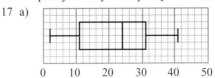

b)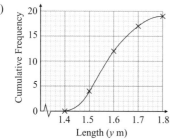

18 Outliers can have a big effect on increasing or decreasing the value of the mean or range, so that it doesn't represent the rest of the data set very well.

19 Black cars were only owned by men and silver cars were only owned by women. So black cars were more popular amongst men and silver cars were more popular amongst women.
There are similar proportions of men and women owning blue and green cars. So blue and green cars are equally popular amongst men and women.
The proportion of men owning red cars was nearly double the proportion of women owning red cards. So red cars were almost twice as popular amongst men as women.

Exam Papers

Core Paper 1

1 $7\% < 0.7$ *[1 mark]*

2 $40 : 25 = 8 : 5$ *[1 mark]*

3 a) F *[1 mark]*
 b) $x = 3$ *[1 mark]*

4 a) $-12, -8, -6, 2, 6$ *[1 mark]*
 b) $2 - -8 = 10$ *[1 mark]*

5 a) $3.97 \times 1000 = 3970$ m *[1 mark]*
 b) $4 \times 100 \times 100 \times 100 = 4\,000\,000$ cm³ *[1 mark]*

6 $\begin{pmatrix} -5 \\ 0 \end{pmatrix}$ *[1 mark]*

7 a)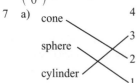

 [2 marks available — 2 marks for all lines correct, otherwise 1 mark for two lines correct]
 b) 6 *[1 mark]*

8 E.g. 6 (multiple of 3) + 6 (multiple of 6) = 12 (not a multiple of 9) *[1 mark]*

9 a) $9a + 7b$ *[1 mark]*
 b) $6a^2$ *[1 mark]*

10 64 (8^2 and 4^3) *[1 mark]*

11 a) Rewrite data in order: 5, 6, 6, 7, 9, 11, 12
 Median is the middle (4th) value = 7 years *[1 mark]*
 b) Mean = $\dfrac{6 + 12 + 9 + 6 + 5 + 7 + 11}{7}$ *[1 mark]*
 $= \dfrac{56}{7} = 8$ years *[1 mark]*
 [2 marks available in total — as above]

12 $594\,000\,000\,000 = 5.94 \times 10^{11}$ *[1 mark]*

13 a) 107.3158498 *[1 mark]*
 Your calculator may display more or fewer digits than this.
 b) 107.32 *[1 mark]*
 If you got a) wrong but rounded it correctly, you'll still get the mark for part b).

14 a) Trapezium *[1 mark]*   b) Parallelogram *[1 mark]*

15 AB is a tangent and AO is a radius, so BAO is 90° since a tangent and radius always meet at 90°.
 So $OBA = 180° - 50° - 90° = 40°$. *[1 mark]*

16 -2 *[1 mark]*

17 Radius of sphere $= 6 \div 2 = 3$ cm
 $V = \dfrac{4}{3}\pi r^3 = \dfrac{4}{3} \times \pi \times 3^3$ *[1 mark]* $= 36\pi$ cm³ *[1 mark]*
 [2 marks available in total — as above]

18 $\dfrac{113}{1000}$ *[1 mark]*

19 $3^{-2} = \dfrac{1}{9}$ *[1 mark]* $\Rightarrow k \times \dfrac{1}{9} = 4$, so $k = 4 \times 9 = 36$ *[1 mark]*
 [2 marks available in total — as above]

20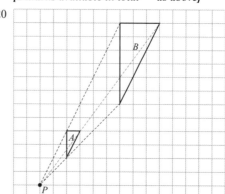

[2 marks available — 2 marks for the fully correct image, otherwise 1 mark for two vertices in the correct position or for an image of the correct size but positioned incorrectly on the grid]

21 a)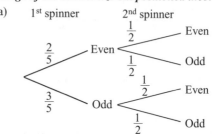

 [2 marks available — 1 mark for the correct probabilities for the first spinner, 1 mark for the correct probabilities for the second spinner]
 b) P(two odd numbers) $= \dfrac{3}{5} \times \dfrac{1}{2}$ *[1 mark]* $= \dfrac{3}{10}$ *[1 mark]*
 [2 marks available in total — as above]

22 Elements of B are 1, 2, 3, 4, 6
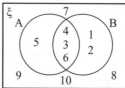

 [2 marks available — 2 marks for a completely correct diagram, otherwise 1 mark for correct elements in the intersection]

23 1% of \$300 = \$3, so 2% = \$3 × 2 = \$6 *[1 mark]*
 Interest for 4 years = \$6 × 4 = \$24 *[1 mark]*
 \$300 + \$24 = \$324 *[1 mark]*
 [3 marks available in total — as above]

24 $1\dfrac{2}{3} \times 1\dfrac{5}{8} = \dfrac{5}{3} \times \dfrac{13}{8} = \dfrac{65}{24} = 2\dfrac{17}{24}$
 [3 marks available — 1 mark for converting both numbers to improper fractions, 1 mark for multiplying, 1 mark for the correct answer]

25 a) Angles CBF and BFG are allied angles, so angle $BFG = 180° - 39° = 141°$ *[1 mark]*
 b) Angles on a straight line add up to 180°, so angle $ABE = 180 - 90 - 39 = 51°$ *[1 mark]*
 Angles ABE and DEH are corresponding angles, so angle $DEH = 51°$ *[1 mark]*
 [2 marks available in total — as above]
 You could have also found angle DEH using other methods.

26 $3(2x - 4) = 2x + 8 \Rightarrow 6x - 12 = 2x + 8$ *[1 mark]*
$\Rightarrow 4x = 20$ *[1 mark]* $\Rightarrow x = 5$ *[1 mark]*
[3 marks available in total — as above]

27 $\sin x = \dfrac{18}{24}$ *[1 mark]*

$x = \sin^{-1}\left(\dfrac{18}{24}\right) = 48.590... = 48.6$ (1 d.p.) *[1 mark]*
[2 marks available in total — as above]

28 $2x + y = 10 \xrightarrow{\times 2} 4x + 2y = 20$ *[1 mark]*

$\begin{array}{ll} 4x + 2y = 20 & 2(3) + y = 10 \\ \underline{-\ 3x + 2y = 17} & y = 10 - 6 \\ x = 3 \ \textbf{\textit{[1 mark]}} & y = 4 \ \textbf{\textit{[1 mark]}} \end{array}$

[3 marks available in total — as above]
You could have found the value of y first then used it to find x.

Core Paper 2

1 a) (i) $\dfrac{3}{5} = 60\%$ *[1 mark]*   **(ii)** $\dfrac{5}{3}$ *[1 mark]*

(iii) He has multiplied the denominator and numerator by 4, but he should have just multiplied the numerator by 4 (so the answer should have been $\dfrac{12}{5}$, or $2\dfrac{2}{5}$). *[1 mark]*

(iv) E.g. Natural numbers are the positive integers, but $\dfrac{3}{5} = 0.6$ which is not an integer.
[1 mark for a sensible explanation]

b) (i) P(prime) $= 1 - \dfrac{3}{5}$ *[1 mark]* $= \dfrac{2}{5} = 0.4$ *[1 mark]*
[2 marks available in total — as above]

(ii) $300 \times \dfrac{3}{5} = 180$ *[1 mark]*

c) E.g.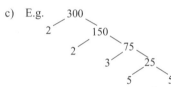

$300 = 2 \times 2 \times 3 \times 5 \times 5 = 2^2 \times 3 \times 5^2$
[2 marks available — 2 marks for the correct answer, otherwise 1 mark for finding that 2, 3 and 5 are the prime factors]

2 a)

	Number of triangles	Number of dots	Number of lines
Pattern 1	1	3	3
Pattern 2	2	4	5
Pattern 3	3	5	7
Pattern 4	4	6	9
Pattern 5	5	7	11

[3 marks available — 1 mark for both values correct for Pattern 4, 1 mark for the correct number of dots in Pattern 5, 1 mark for the correct number of lines in Pattern 5]

b) The 'Number of lines' column increases by 2 each time.
The column would continue: 13, 15, 17, 19, 21...
So Pattern 10 has 21 lines.
[2 marks available — 1 mark for finding the sequence, 1 mark for the correct number of lines in Pattern 10]
You could also find an expression for the nth term (2n + 1) and work out the value when n = 10: (2 × 10) + 1 = 21.

c) (i) The number of dots is 2 more than the pattern number, so the number of dots is given by $n + 2$
[2 marks available — 2 marks for n + 2, otherwise 1 mark for '2 more than the pattern number']

(ii) Number of dots in Pattern 200 = 200 + 2 = 202 *[1 mark]*

d) 2 *[1 mark]*

e) $6n(n^2 + 3)$
[2 marks available — 2 marks for the correct answer, otherwise 1 mark for taking out a factor of '6' or 'n']

3 a) (i) 125 kW *[1 mark]*

(ii) 6 cars have a maximum speed over 190 km/h which is $\dfrac{6}{11}$ of the cars. *[1 mark]*

(iii) 5 cars have a maximum power between 80 kW and 140 kW which is $\dfrac{5}{11}$ of the cars.
$\dfrac{5}{11} \times 100\%$ *[1 mark]* $= 45.454545...\%$
$= 45.5\%$ (3 s.f.) *[1 mark]*
[2 marks available in total — as above]

b) The scatter graph shows (strong) positive correlation. *[1 mark]*

c)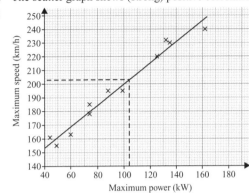

Maximum speed = 203 km/h (allow ± 3).
[2 marks available — 1 mark for drawing a line of best fit, 1 mark for accurately reading from your graph the speed corresponding to a power of 104 kW]

d) 190 kW lies outside of the range of data plotted on the scatter graph. *[1 mark]*

4 a) (i) Each trapezium has these dimensions:
Parallel sides: 12 cm and 7 cm   Height: 12 ÷ 2 = 6 cm
So area $= \dfrac{1}{2}(12 + 7) \times 6$ *[1 mark]*
$= 9.5 \times 6 = 57$ cm² *[1 mark]*
[2 marks available in total — as above]

(ii) The area of the square is $12 \times 12 = 144$ cm²
So the area of both triangles is $144 - 57 - 57 = 30$ cm²
So the area of one triangle is $30 \div 2 = 15$ cm²
[2 marks available — 1 mark for a correct method, 1 mark for the correct answer]
You could also have found that the height of each triangle is (12 − 7) ÷ 2 = 2.5 cm and then used the area of a triangle formula to get the answer.

b) Angles in a square are 90°.
There are three squares around O, so $90° \times 3 = 270°$. *[1 mark]*
Angles around a point add to 360°,
so angle $AOB = (360° - 270°) \div 3 = 30°$ *[1 mark]*
The two base angles in an isosceles triangle are equal,
so angle $OAB = (180° - 30°) \div 2$ *[1 mark]* $= 75°$ *[1 mark]*
[4 marks available in total — as above]

5 a) (i) 052° (Accept answer between 050° and 054°) *[1 mark]*

(ii) Distance on map = 4.3 cm
Actual distance = 4.3 × 100 = 430 metres
[2 marks available — 2 marks for an answer in the range 420 m-440 m, otherwise 1 mark for a measurement in the range 4.2 cm-4.4 cm]

(iii) $360° - 335° = 25°$

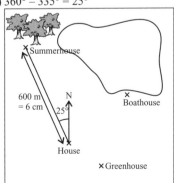

[2 marks available — 2 marks for summerhouse plotted in the correct position, otherwise 1 mark for a point marked that is on a bearing of 335° or 6 cm from the house]

(iv) $\sqrt{30^2 + 40^2}$ *[1 mark]* $= \sqrt{2500} = 50$ m *[1 mark]*
[2 marks available in total — as above]

b) (i) 10 minutes $= \frac{1}{6}$ of an hour *[1 mark]*
Speed = Distance ÷ Time $= 4 \div \frac{1}{6} = 24$ km/h *[1 mark]*
[2 marks available in total — as above]

(ii) Time = Distance ÷ Speed $= 4 \div 5 = 0.8$ hours *[1 mark]*
$0.8 \times 60 = 48$ minutes *[1 mark]*
[2 marks available in total — as above]

6 a) The number of tickets sold was:
Adults: $(8 \times 3) + 6 = 30$
Child: $(8 \times 5) + 2 = 42$
Senior: $(8 \times 2) + 4 = 20$
Adult tickets: $30 \times \$9 = \$270$
Child tickets: $42 \times \$5 = \$210$
Senior tickets: $20 \times \$6.50 = \$130$
Total sales = $\$270 + \$210 + \$130 = \$610$
[4 marks available — 1 mark for the correct number of each type of ticket sold (adult, child, senior), 1 mark for multiplying number of tickets sold by cost, 1 mark for attempting to add up the total sales, 1 mark for the correct answer]

b) (i) $30 : 20 = 3 : 2$ *[1 mark]*
(ii) $42 : 30 + 42 + 20$ *[1 mark]* $= 42 : 92 = 21 : 46$ *[1 mark]*
[2 marks available in total — as above]

c) There are a total of $1 + 3 + 4 = 8$ parts
So 1 part is $120 \div 8 = 15$ tickets
Adult tickets: 15 tickets *[1 mark]*
Child Tickets: $3 \times 15 = 45$ tickets *[1 mark]*
Senior Tickets: $4 \times 15 = 60$ tickets *[1 mark]*
[3 marks available in total — as above]

7 a) See graph in part d).
[2 marks available — 2 marks for both points plotted correctly with a straight line going through them, otherwise 1 mark for one point plotted correctly and one point plotted incorrectly but with a straight line going through both points]

b) (i) E.g. $\frac{7-1}{2-0} = \frac{6}{2} = 3$
[2 marks available — 1 mark for using a correct method, 1 mark for the correct answer]

(ii) E.g. $y = 3x + 4$
[1 mark for any line of the form $y = 3x + a$ or any rearrangement]

c)

x	-3	-2	-1	0	1	2	3
y	3	-1	-3	-3	-1	3	9

[3 marks available — 3 marks for all four correct, otherwise 2 marks for three correct or 1 mark for two correct]

d)

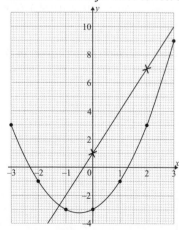

[4 marks available — 4 marks for a correct curve with all points plotted correctly, 3 marks for at least 6 points plotted correctly, 2 marks for at least 4 points plotted correctly, 1 mark for at least 2 points plotted correctly]

e) $x = -2.3$ and $x = 1.3$
[2 marks available — 1 mark for an answer between −2.4 and −2.2, 1 mark for an answer between 1.2 and 1.4]

8 a) 1.18×10^3 cm³ *[1 mark]*
b) Mass = Density × Volume $= 2.7 \times 1180$ *[1 mark]*
$= 3186$ g *[1 mark]*
[2 marks available in total — as above]

c) Mass of cube = mass of cylinder = 3186 g
Volume of cube = mass ÷ density $= 3186 \div 10.5$ *[1 mark]*
$= 303.428...$ cm³ *[1 mark]*
Side length $= \sqrt[3]{303.428...}$ *[1 mark]*
$= 6.719... $ cm $= 6.72$ cm (3 s.f.) *[1 mark]*
[4 marks available in total — as above]

d) (i) Area of one face $= 384 \div 6 = 64$ cm² *[1 mark]*
Side length of cube $= \sqrt{64} = 8$ cm *[1 mark]*
Volume $= 8 \times 8 \times 8 = 512$ cm³ *[1 mark]*
[3 marks available in total — as above]

(ii) $384 \times 10 \times 10 = 38\,400$ mm² *[1 mark]*

(iii) The actual amount could be $100 \div 2 = 50$ g below or up to 50 g above the rounded value: $2050 \le m < 2150$
[2 marks available — 1 mark for each correct value]

9 a) 25% higher than £120 000 $= 1.25 \times £120\,000$
$= £150\,000$, so House 4 *[1 mark]*

b) 16% discount $= 1 - 0.16 = 0.84$ *[1 mark]*
$0.84 \times £150\,000 = £126\,000$ *[1 mark]*
[2 marks available in total — as above]

c) $£161\,280 - £144\,000 = £17\,280$ *[1 mark]*
% change $= \frac{17\,280}{144\,000} \times 100 = 12\%$ *[1 mark]*
[2 marks available in total — as above]

d) $\$2 = ¥15$ so $\$1 = ¥15 \div 2 = ¥7.5$
$\$145\,000 \times 7.5 = ¥1\,087\,500$
[2 marks available — 1 mark for a correct method, 1 mark for the correct answer]

e) $2018 - 2000 = 18$ years *[1 mark]*
$\$50\,000 \times 1.05^{18}$ *[1 mark]* $= \$120\,330.9617...$ *[1 mark]*
$\$120\,330.9617... - \$120\,000 = \$330.9617...$
$= \$331$ (nearest dollar) *[1 mark]*
[4 marks available in total — as above]

10 a) Shape A: Area $= \pi \times 2^2 = 4\pi$ cm² *[1 mark]*
Shape B: Area $= \frac{20}{360} \times \pi \times 6^2$ *[1 mark]* $= 2\pi$ cm² *[1 mark]*
$4\pi = 2 \times 2\pi$ so the area of A is twice the area of B. *[1 mark]*
[4 marks available in total — as above]

b) Arc length of shape $B = \frac{20}{360} \times 2 \times \pi \times 6$ *[1 mark]*
$= \frac{240}{360} \times \pi = \frac{2}{3}\pi$ cm *[1 mark]*
Perimeter $= 6 + 6 + \frac{2}{3}\pi = 12 + \frac{2}{3}\pi$ cm *[1 mark]*
[3 marks available in total — as above]

c)

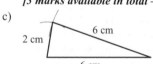

[2 marks available — 2 marks for a correct triangle with construction arcs, otherwise 1 mark for at least one correct side and a correctly drawn arc]

Extended Paper 1

1 A = 60% of B $= 0.6 \times$ B, B = 30% of C $= 0.3 \times$ C
A $= 0.6 \times (0.3 \times$ C$) = 0.18 \times$ C $= 18\%$ of C *[1 mark]*

2 2680 mm³ $= (2680 \div 10 \div 10 \div 10)$ cm³ $= 2.68$ cm³ *[1 mark]*

3 Probability of landing on a $2 = \frac{1}{6}$
Probability that they both land on a $2 = \frac{1}{6} \times \frac{1}{6} = \frac{1}{36}$ *[1 mark]*

4 Round all numbers to 1 significant figure.
$\sqrt[3]{\frac{785.3 \times 2.156}{0.1972}} = \sqrt[3]{\frac{800 \times 2}{0.2}}$ *[1 mark]*
$= \sqrt[3]{\frac{1600}{0.2}} = \sqrt[3]{\frac{16000}{2}} = \sqrt[3]{8000} = 20$ *[1 mark]*
[2 marks available in total — as above]

5 $\frac{7}{9} = 0.777777...$ so 0.7778 is closest. *[1 mark]*

6   Convert area to m²: 120 cm² = 0.012 m² *[1 mark]*
Pressure = Force ÷ Area = $\frac{72}{0.012}$ = 6000 N/m² *[1 mark]*
[2 marks available in total — as above]

7   $(4 \times 10^6) \times (8 \times 10^{-3}) = (4 \times 8) \times 10^{6-3}$ *[1 mark]*
$= 32 \times 10^3 = 3.2 \times 10^4$ *[1 mark]*
[2 marks available in total — as above]

8   There are 144 people, so 1 person is represented by
360° ÷ 144 = 2.5°
The angle for 'Tomatoes' is 105°, and 105 ÷ 2.5 = 42,
so 42 people said 'Tomatoes'.
*[2 marks available — 1 mark for a correct method,
1 mark for the correct answer]*
Alternatively, you could have done 105 ÷ 360 × 144.

9   a)   The upper bound is 11 + 0.5 = 11.5 cm *[1 mark]*
b)   The lower bound is 0.080 – 0.0005 = 0.0795 kg *[1 mark]*

10 a) y is inversely proportional to $x \Rightarrow y = \frac{k}{x}$
This is shown by graph C. *[1 mark]*
b)   The graph of $y = a^x$ crosses the y-axis at $y = 1$.
$a > 1$, so the graph increases as x gets larger.
This is shown by graph D. *[1 mark]*

11 Area of base = 10 × 10 = 100 cm² *[1 mark]*
Area of each triangular face = $\frac{1}{2}$ × 10 × 12 = 60 cm² *[1 mark]*
Total surface area = 100 + (4 × 60) = 340 cm² *[1 mark]*
[3 marks available in total — as above]

12 Probability of getting a white or a black tie = 1 – 0.35 – 0.2
= 0.45 *[1 mark]*
The ratio of black to white ties is 2 : 1, so
the probability of getting a white tie = 0.45 ÷ 3 = 0.15 *[1 mark]*
So the probability of getting a red or a white tie
= 0.35 + 0.15 = 0.5, so she is correct *[1 mark]*
[3 marks available in total — as above]

13

	Gradient equal to 2	Gradient not equal to 2
Passes though the point (2, 1)	$y - 2x = -3$	$2y = x$
Does not pass though the point (2, 1)	$y = 2x + 1$	$y = 2$ $3y = 2x + 2$

*[2 marks available — 2 marks if all equations are in the correct
places, otherwise 1 mark if 2 or 3 lines are in the correct place]*

14 a)   fg(x) = f(g(x)) = f(x – 5) = 2(x – 5) or 2x – 10 *[1 mark]*
b)   gf(x) = g(f(x)) = g(2x) = 2x – 5 *[1 mark]*
gf(a) = 17 ⇒ 2a – 5 = 17 *[1 mark]*
⇒ 2a = 22 ⇒ a = 11 *[1 mark]*
[3 marks available in total — as above]

15
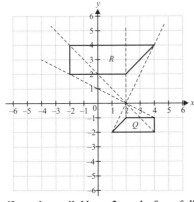
*[2 marks available — 2 marks for a fully correct shape, otherwise
1 mark for a shape the correct size but positioned incorrectly]*

16 The median is 12, so one of the unknown cards must be
another 12. *[1 mark]*
The mean is 13 so the sum of the cards is 13 × 4 = 52.
The last card must be 52 – 7 – 12 – 12 = 21 *[1 mark]*
The range is 21 – 7 = 14 *[1 mark]*
[3 marks available in total — as above]

17 a)   Common difference = 0.5, so the *n*th term = 0.5*n* *[1 mark]*
b)   The first term is 2, and you multiply by 5 each time. *[1 mark]*
So the *n*th term is $2 \times 5^{(n-1)}$ *[1 mark]*
[2 marks available in total — as above]

18 Let r = 0.34$\dot{7}$
Then 100r = 34.$\dot{7}$ and 1000r = 347.$\dot{7}$
So 900r = 347.7 – 34.7 *[1 mark]* = 313
So r = $\frac{313}{900}$ *[1 mark]*
[2 marks available in total — as above]

19 E.g.
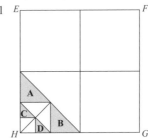
*[2 marks available — 2 marks for drawing an isosceles
trapezium, otherwise 1 mark for drawing a shape that
has two of the listed properties]*

20 Rearrange into the same form, e.g.:
4x + 3y = –7 (1)   6x – 2y = 9 (2)

4x + 3y = –7 $\xrightarrow{\times 3}$ 12x + 9y = –21 (3) *[1 mark]*
6x – 2y = 9 $\xrightarrow{\times 2}$ 12x – 4y = 18 (4) *[1 mark]*

(3) – (4)   12x + 9y = –21
            − 12x − 4y = 18
                   13y = –39
                     y = –3 *[1 mark]*
4x + 3y = –7 ⇒ 4x + 3(–3) = –7 ⇒ 4x – 9 = –7
                          ⇒ 4x = 2 ⇒ x = 0.5 *[1 mark]*
[4 marks available in total — as above]
*There are other methods you could use to solve these equations
— for example, the substitution method.*

21 Work out the fraction of the square made up by each shaded region:
Region A = region B = $\frac{1}{4} \times \frac{1}{2} \times \frac{1}{2} \times \frac{1}{2} = \frac{1}{32}$

Region C = region D = $\frac{1}{4} \times \frac{1}{4} \times \frac{1}{4} \times \frac{1}{2} = \frac{1}{128}$

Overall fraction shaded = $\left(2 \times \frac{1}{32}\right) + \left(2 \times \frac{1}{128}\right)$

$= \frac{2}{32} + \frac{2}{128} = \frac{4}{64} + \frac{1}{64} = \frac{5}{64}$

*[3 marks available — 1 mark for identifying the fraction of the
square regions A and B make up, 1 mark for identifying the
fraction of the square regions C and D make up, 1 mark for the
correct answer]*
*Alternatively, you could have assumed an appropriate area for the large
square and used it to find the total area of the shaded regions.*

22 a)   Midpoint = $\left(\frac{1 + (-3)}{2}, \frac{1 + 9}{2}\right) = \left(\frac{-2}{2}, \frac{10}{2}\right) = (-1, 5)$
[2 marks available — 1 mark for each correct coordinate]
b)   Gradient = $\frac{\text{Change in } y}{\text{Change in } x} = \frac{9 - 1}{(-3) - 1} = \frac{8}{-4} = -2$ *[1 mark]*
$y = mx + c \Rightarrow y = -2x + c$
At (1, 1): 1 = –2(1) + c *[1 mark]* ⇒ c = 3
So the equation of the line is y = –2x + 3 *[1 mark]*
[3 marks available in total — as above]

23 $(x + 4)^2 - 1 = (x + 4)(x + 4) - 1 = x^2 + 4x + 4x + 16 - 1$ *[1 mark]*
$= x^2 + 8x + 15$ *[1 mark]* $= (x + 5)(x + 3)$ *[1 mark]*
[3 marks available in total — as above]

24 $2 + 3 + 5 = 10$ 'parts' in the ratio. Angles in a triangle add to 180°, so 10 parts = 180° and 1 part = 18°.
So, the three angles in the triangle are $(2 \times 18°) = 36°$,
$(3 \times 18°) = 54°$ and $(5 \times 18°) = 90°$.
One angle is 90°, so the triangle is a right-angled triangle.
[3 marks available — 1 mark for finding the size of one part of the ratio, 1 mark for finding the size of at least one angle in the triangle and 1 mark for showing that one angle is 90°]

25 Shape B: Area $= \dfrac{80}{360} \times \pi \times 6^2 = 8\pi$ *[1 mark]*
Shape A: Area $= \pi \times r^2 = 8\pi$ *[1 mark]*
$\Rightarrow r^2 = 8 \Rightarrow r = \sqrt{8} = 2.828... = 2.83$ cm (3 s.f.) *[1 mark]*
[3 marks available in total — as above]

26 a) $(a^4)^3 = a^{4 \times 3} = a^{12}$ *[1 mark]*

b) $(2\sqrt{a})^3 \times \dfrac{1}{2}(a^{0.1})^5 = 2^3(a^{0.5})^3 \times \dfrac{1}{2}(a^{0.1})^5$
$= 8a^{0.5 \times 3} \times \dfrac{1}{2}a^{0.1 \times 5} = 8a^{1.5} \times \dfrac{1}{2}a^{0.5}$
$= \dfrac{8}{2}a^{1.5 + 0.5} = 4a^2$
[3 marks available — 3 marks for the correct answer, otherwise 2 marks for either 4 or a^2, or 1 mark for some correct application of power rules]

27 The lines AD and CD are both tangents to the same point, so these lines have the same length. The chords AB and BC are equidistant from the centre of the circle, so they are also the same length. So the quadrilateral has two adjacent pairs of equal sides, so it is a kite.
[2 marks available — 2 marks for stating both circle theorems correctly with a suitable explanation, otherwise 1 mark for stating at least one circle theorem correctly]

28 $\dfrac{1}{x+3} + \dfrac{7}{(x+3)(x-4)}$
$= \dfrac{1(x-4)}{(x+3)(x-4)} + \dfrac{7}{(x+3)(x-4)}$ *[1 mark]*
$= \dfrac{x-4+7}{(x+3)(x-4)} = \dfrac{x+3}{(x+3)(x-4)}$ *[1 mark]* $= \dfrac{1}{x-4}$ *[1 mark]*
[3 marks available in total — as above]

Extended Paper 2

1 a) (i) The multiplier for an increase of 2.5% is 1.025. *[1 mark]*
Balance after 3 years = 6000×1.025^3
= \$6461.34375 = \$6461.34 (nearest cent) *[1 mark]*
[2 marks available in total — as above]

(ii) Balance after 3 years = $6000 \times 1.01 \times 1.015 \times 1.05$
= \$6458.445 = \$6458.45 (nearest cent) *[1 mark]*
So the interest is \$6458.45 – \$6000 = \$458.45 *[1 mark]*
[2 marks available in total — as above]

b) Let the initial balance be \$$x$. Then the balance after 2 years is:
$x \times 1.02^2$ *[1 mark]* = \$15 606
$\Rightarrow x = \$15\,606 \div 1.02^2$ *[1 mark]* = \$15 000 *[1 mark]*
[3 marks available in total — as above]

c) New value = $\$18\,800 \times \dfrac{5}{4}$ *[1 mark]* = \$23 500 *[1 mark]*
[2 marks available in total — as above]

d) $V \propto \dfrac{1}{\sqrt{A}} \Rightarrow V = \dfrac{k}{\sqrt{A}}$ *[1 mark]*
When $A = 1$, $V = \$21\,000 \Rightarrow 21\,000 = \dfrac{k}{\sqrt{1}}$
$\Rightarrow k = 21\,000$ *[1 mark]*
When $A = 9$, $V = \dfrac{21\,000}{\sqrt{9}} = \dfrac{21\,000}{3} = \$7000$ *[1 mark]*
[3 marks available in total — as above]

e) (i) Read off the graph: \$6 ≈ 430 rupees
(Allow any answer between 425 and 435 rupees) *[1 mark]*

(ii) E.g. 500 rupees ≈ \$7 $\Rightarrow$ 5000 rupees ≈ \$70
(Allow any answer between \$65 and \$75)
[2 marks available — 1 mark for a correct method, 1 mark for the correct answer]

2 a)

		First spin				
		1	1	2	2	3
Second Spin	1	2	2	3	3	4
	1	2	2	3	3	4
	2	3	3	4	4	5
	2	3	3	4	4	5
	3	4	4	5	5	6

[1 mark]

b) From the possibility diagram, there are 8 ways that Romesh can get a total of 4. Of these, there are 2 where his first spin landed on a 1. *[1 mark]*
So P(first spin was a 1 given total is 4) $= \dfrac{2}{8} = \dfrac{1}{4}$ *[1 mark]*
[2 marks available in total — as above]

c) Total cost to play = $200 \times \$0.50 = \$100$ *[1 mark]*
From the possibility diagram, there are 5 ways to get a 5 or more. So the probability of getting a total score of 5 or more is $\dfrac{5}{25} = \dfrac{1}{5}$ *[1 mark]*
So the player is expected to win $\dfrac{1}{5} \times 200 = 40$ times *[1 mark]*
Expected prize money = $40 \times \$2 = \$80$
So the expected profit is $\$100 - \$80 = \$20$ *[1 mark]*
[4 marks available in total — as above]

d) (i)

Result	1	2	3	Total
Frequency	192	144	64	400
Relative Frequency	0.48	0.36	0.16	—

[2 marks available — 2 marks for all three values correct, otherwise 1 mark for at least one value correct]

(ii) E.g. No — if the spinner was fair, then the relative frequencies of 1 and 2 should be roughly equal (close to 0.4), but the relative frequency of 1 is much higher than 2, so the spinner seems to be biased. *[1 mark]*
You could have argued that the spinner is fair as the relative frequencies are fairly close to what you would expect — as long as you give a sensible answer, you'll get the mark.

3 a) (i) $M = 2x + 3y$
[2 marks available — 1 mark for each correct term]

(ii) $2x + 3(20) = 90$ *[1 mark]*
$\Rightarrow 2x = 90 - 60 = 30 \Rightarrow x = 15$ *[1 mark]*
[2 marks available in total — as above]

b) (i) $x + 3y = 90 \Rightarrow 3y = 90 - x$ *[1 mark]*
$\Rightarrow y = \dfrac{90 - x}{3} = 30 - \dfrac{1}{3}x$ *[1 mark]*
[2 marks available in total — as above]

(ii)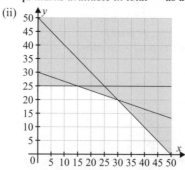

[4 marks available — 1 mark for each line plotted correctly, 1 mark for the correct regions shaded]

(iii) The corners of the region are at:
(0, 0), (0, 25), (15, 25), (30, 20) and (50, 0) *[1 mark]*
Test the value of M at these points:
At (0, 0): $M = 2(0) + 3(0) = 0 + 0 = 0$
At (0, 25): $M = 2(0) + 3(25) = 0 + 75 = 75$
At (15, 25): $M = 2(15) + 3(25) = 30 + 75 = 105$
At (30, 20): $M = 2(30) + 3(20) = 60 + 60 = 120$
At (50, 0): $M = 2(50) + 3(0) = 100 + 0 = 100$
[1 mark for a correct method]
So the maximum value is 120, at $x = 30$, $y = 20$ *[1 mark]*
[3 marks available in total — as above]

4 a) $\overrightarrow{AE} = \overrightarrow{AB} + \overrightarrow{BE}$ *[1 mark]*
$\overrightarrow{AB} = 6\mathbf{b}$, and since the shape is a parallelogram, $\overrightarrow{BC} = -6\mathbf{a}$.
As the ratio is 3 : 1, E is $\frac{3}{4}$ of the way from B to C,
so $\overrightarrow{BE} = \frac{3}{4}\overrightarrow{BA} = \frac{3}{4}(-6\mathbf{a}) = -4.5\mathbf{a}$ *[1 mark]*
So $\overrightarrow{AE} = 6\mathbf{b} - 4.5\mathbf{a}$ *[1 mark]*
[3 marks available in total — as above]

b) $4\mathbf{a} + \mathbf{b} = \begin{pmatrix} 4 \times 1 \\ 4 \times 2 \end{pmatrix} + \begin{pmatrix} 2 \\ 0 \end{pmatrix} = \begin{pmatrix} 4 + 2 \\ 8 + 0 \end{pmatrix} = \begin{pmatrix} 6 \\ 8 \end{pmatrix}$ *[1 mark]*
Magnitude $= \sqrt{6^2 + 8^2}$ *[1 mark]*
$= \sqrt{36 + 64} = \sqrt{100} = 10$ *[1 mark]*
[3 marks available in total — as above]

c) Reflection *[1 mark]* in the line $y = 2$ *[1 mark]*
[2 marks available in total — as above]

d)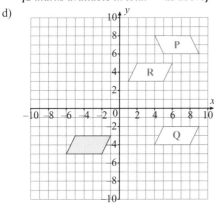
*[2 marks available — 1 mark for a shape of the correct size
and rotation, 1 mark for the shape in the correct position]*

5 a) (i) Read up and across at 75 minutes — the corresponding
cumulative frequency is 38. *[1 mark]*
This means roughly 38 people took 75 minutes
or less, meaning that $60 - 38 = 22$ people took
over 75 minutes. *[1 mark]*
[2 marks available in total — as above]

(ii) 30% of $60 = 18$ *[1 mark]*
So read across and down at 18:
30th percentile = 65 minutes. *[1 mark]*
[2 marks available in total — as above]

b) The cumulative frequency diagram starts at 40 minutes,
so that is the quickest possible winning time in 2020.
Difference: $40 - 37 = 3$ minutes
*[2 marks available — 1 mark for finding the quickest
possible winning time in 2020, 1 mark for the correct answer]*

c) To find the median, read across at 30 and then read down:
Median for 2020 $\approx$ 71.5 minutes (Allow 71-72 minutes).
[1 mark]
The teams were faster on average in 2020 than in 2019
as the median was lower. *[1 mark]*
[2 marks available in total — as above]

d) To find the upper quartile read across and down at 45,
to find the lower quartile read across and down at 15:
Upper quartile = 78 and lower quartile = 63
Interquartile range = $78 - 63 = 15$ minutes *[1 mark]*
The times of the teams were less spread out in 2020
than in 2019 as the interquartile range was smaller,
so times were more consistent in 2020. *[1 mark]*
[2 marks available in total — as above]

6 a)

x	...	180°	210°	240°	270°	...
y	...	0	–0.5	–0.87	–1	...

*[3 marks available — 3 marks for all four values correct,
otherwise 2 marks for three values correct or 1 mark
for two values correct]*

b)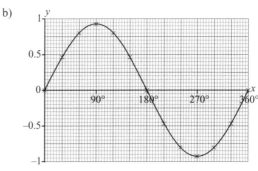
*[4 marks available — 4 marks for a correct curve with all
points plotted correctly, 3 marks for at least 10 points plotted
correctly, 2 marks for at least 8 points plotted correctly,
1 mark for at least 6 points plotted correctly]*

c) $2 - 5\sin x = 0 \Rightarrow 2 = 5\sin x \Rightarrow \sin x = \frac{2}{5}$ *[1 mark]*
Draw a line on the graph:

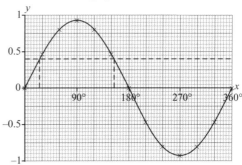

So the solutions are roughly 24° (allow 20°-28°) *[1 mark]*
and 156° (allow 152°-160°) *[1 mark]*
[3 marks available in total — as above]

7 a)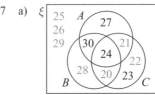
*[3 marks available — 3 marks for all four numbers in the
correct places, otherwise 2 marks for three numbers in the
correct places or 1 mark for two numbers in the correct places]*

b) (i) $A \cup B = \{20, 21, 24, 27, 28, 30\}$ *[1 mark]*
(ii) $B' \cap C' = \{25, 26, 27, 29\}$ *[1 mark]*
(iii) $A \cap B \cap C = \{24\}$, so $n(A \cap B \cap C) = 1$ *[1 mark]*

c) $\sqrt{4} = 2$ which is a rational number, so $\sqrt{4} \in D$ *[1 mark]*

d) The smallest positive number in $E \cap F$ is the lowest common
multiple of 24 and 32.
Multiples of 24: 24, 48, 72, 96, 120, 144, ...
Multiples of 32: 32, 64, 96, 128, 160, 192, ...
So the lowest common multiple is 96.
*[2 marks available — 1 mark for a correct method,
1 mark for the correct answer]*

8 a) (i) Read off the graph — at 90 seconds,
the car's speed is 14 m/s *[1 mark]*
(ii) Distance travelled in first 10 seconds $= 0.5 \times 10 \times 16$
$= 80$ m *[1 mark]*
Distance between 10 and 60 seconds $= 16 \times (60 - 10)$
$= 800$ m *[1 mark]*
Distance in final 60 seconds $= 0.5 \times (16 + 12) \times 60$
$= 840$ m *[1 mark]*
Total distance $= 80 + 800 + 840 = 1720$ m *[1 mark]*
[4 marks available in total — as above]

b) (i) Distance travelled = 800 m, time taken = 120 s
Average speed $= \frac{800}{120}$ *[1 mark]*
$= 6.67$ m/s (3 s.f.) *[1 mark]*
[2 marks available in total — as above]

(ii) Draw a tangent on the graph at 50 seconds:

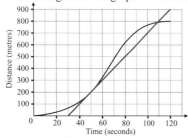

$$\text{Speed} \approx \frac{900}{120-30} = \frac{900}{90}$$
$$= 10 \text{ m/s (Allow 7 m/s - 15 m/s)}$$

[3 marks available — 1 mark for drawing a tangent on the graph at 50 seconds, 1 mark for using two points on the tangent to calculate its gradient, 1 mark for the correct answer]

c) (i) Draw a sketch:

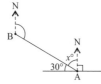

The angle marked $x = 90° - 30° = 60°$
So the bearing of point A from point B
$= 180° - 60° = 120°$ (as these are allied angles).
[2 marks available — 1 mark for a correct method, 1 mark for the correct answer]

(ii) Draw a sketch:

Using Pythagoras' theorem:
$BC^2 = 300^2 + 315^2$ *[1 mark]*
$\Rightarrow BC^2 = 90\,000 + 99\,225 = 189\,225$
$\Rightarrow BC = \sqrt{189\,225} = 435$ m *[1 mark]*
[2 marks available in total — as above]

9 a) (i) $10 \div 2 = 5$, so the bracket is $(x-5)^2$ *[1 mark]*
Expanding the bracket: $x^2 - 10x + 25$
To complete the square: $10 - 25 = -15$ *[1 mark]*
So $x^2 - 10x + 10 = (x-5)^2 - 15$ *[1 mark]*
[3 marks available in total — as above]

(ii) The minimum value of $(x-5)^2 - 15$ is -15,
which happens when $x - 5 = 0 \Rightarrow x = 5$
So the turning point is at $(5, -15)$ *[1 mark]*

b) (i) $3x^2 - 9x - 30 = 3(x^2 - 3x - 10)$
Factor pairs of 10 are 1×10 and 2×5
$2 - 5 = -3$, so:
$3(x^2 - 3x - 10) = 3(x+2)(x-5)$
[3 marks available — 1 mark for a correct method to factorise the quadratic, 1 mark for a correct double bracket, 1 mark for taking out a factor of 3]

(ii) $\dfrac{6x+12}{3x^2-9x-30} = \dfrac{6(x+2)}{3(x+2)(x-5)}$ *[1 mark]*

$= \dfrac{6}{3(x-5)} = \dfrac{2}{x-5}$ *[1 mark]*
[2 marks available in total — as above]

10 a) (i) Area of triangle $ABC = \frac{1}{2} \times AB \times AC \times \sin BAC$ *[1 mark]*

$= \frac{1}{2} \times 9 \times 9 \times \sin 40°$ *[1 mark]*

$= 26.032...$
$= 26.0$ cm² (3 s.f.) *[1 mark]*
[3 marks available in total — as above]

(ii) Using the cosine rule:
$BD^2 = 5^2 + 9^2 - (2 \times 5 \times 9 \times \cos 40°)$ *[1 mark]*
$= 25 + 81 - 90\cos 40° = 37.056...$ *[1 mark]*
$BD = \sqrt{37.056...}$ *[1 mark]*
$= 6.0873... = 6.09$ cm (3 s.f.) *[1 mark]*
[4 marks available in total — as above]
There are alternative methods you could use to get the correct answer — as long as you show your working and get the right answer, you'll get full marks.

b) The prism has two planes of symmetry:

[1 mark]

c) Volume of prism = area of triangle $ABC \times 20$
$= 26.032... \times 20 = 520.65...$ cm³ *[1 mark]*
Mass = Density × Volume *[1 mark]*
$= 0.01 \times 520.65... = 5.2065... = 5.21$ kg (3 s.f.) *[1 mark]*
[3 marks available in total — as above]

d) (i) $EK^2 = EF^2 + FJ^2 + JK^2 = 8^2 + 20^2 + 9^2$ *[1 mark]*
$= 64 + 400 + 81 = 545$
$\Rightarrow EK = \sqrt{545} = 23.345... = 23.3$ cm (3 s.f.) *[1 mark]*
[2 marks available in total — as above]

(ii) Sketch a right-angled triangle:

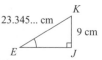

So $\sin KEJ = \dfrac{9}{23.345...}$ *[1 mark]* $= 0.3855...$
$\Rightarrow$ Angle $KEJ = 22.675... = 22.7°$ (1 d.p.) *[1 mark]*
[2 marks available in total — as above]

11 a) (i) $f(x) = (x+3)^3 = (x+3)(x+3)(x+3)$
$= (x^2 + 6x + 9)(x+3)$ *[1 mark]*
$= x^3 + 6x^2 + 9x + 3x^2 + 18x + 27$ *[1 mark]*
$= x^3 + 9x^2 + 27x + 27$ *[1 mark]*
[3 marks available in total — as above]

(ii) $g(5) = 5^3 - 3 = 125 - 3 = 122$ *[1 mark]*
Let $g^{-1}(5) = a$, then $a^3 - 3 = 5$ *[1 mark]*
$\Rightarrow a^3 = 8 \Rightarrow a = 2$. So $g^{-1}(5) = 2$ *[1 mark]*
Then the difference in value between $g(5)$ and $g^{-1}(5)$
is $122 - 2 = 120$ *[1 mark]*
[4 marks available in total — as above]

b) (i) $y = x^3 - 12x + 5 \Rightarrow \dfrac{dy}{dx} = 3x^2 - 12$
[2 marks available — 1 mark for each correct term]

(ii) The stationary points are when $\dfrac{dy}{dx} = 0$
$\Rightarrow 3x^2 - 12 = 0$ *[1 mark]*
$\Rightarrow 3x^2 = 12 \Rightarrow x^2 = 4 \Rightarrow x = \pm 2$ *[1 mark]*
When $x = 2$, $y = (2)^3 - 12(2) + 5 = 8 - 24 + 5 = -11$
When $x = -2$, $y = (-2)^3 - 12(-2) + 5 = -8 + 24 + 5 = 21$
[1 mark for both]
E.g. To identify the nature, find $\dfrac{d^2y}{dx^2}$:
$\dfrac{dy}{dx} = 3x^2 - 12 \Rightarrow \dfrac{d^2y}{dx^2} = 6x$
[1 mark for a suitable method]
When $x = 2$, $\dfrac{d^2y}{dx^2} = 6(2) = 12 > 0$
So the stationary point at $(2, -11)$ is a minimum *[1 mark]*
When $x = -2$, $\dfrac{d^2y}{dx^2} = 6(-2) = -12 < 0$
So the stationary point at $(-2, 21)$ is a maximum *[1 mark]*
[6 marks available in total — as above]

Glossary

acute angle	An angle that is less than 90°.
adjacent side	In trigonometry, the side of a right-angled triangle next to the angle being used.
allied angles	Found in a C- or U-shape between parallel lines. The two angles add up to 180°.
alternate angles	Found in a Z-shape between parallel lines. The two angles are the same.
angle of depression	The downwards angle between the horizontal and a diagonal line.
angle of elevation	The upwards angle between the horizontal and a diagonal line.
arc	Part of the circumference of a circle.
biased	When one or more outcomes of an experiment have a higher probability of happening.
BODMAS	The order in which these operations should be done: Brackets, Other, Division & Multiplication, Addition & Subtraction.
chord	A straight line drawn across the inside of a circle.
circumference	The distance all the way around the outside of a circle.
complement (of a set)	All the elements of the universal set that aren't in the given set, written as A'.
conditional probability	The probability of one event happening, given that another event happens.
congruent shapes	Two or more shapes that are exactly the same size and shape.
continuous data	Quantitative data where the numbers can take any value in a range.
correlation	A relationship between two sets of data — as one variable increases, the other variable tends to increase (positive correlation) or decrease (negative correlation).
corresponding angles	Found in an F-shape next to parallel lines. The two angles are the same.
cube number	The result of multiplying a whole number by itself twice — $a \times a \times a$.
cubic	An expression where x^3 is the highest power of x.
cumulative frequency	The sum of the frequencies in a data set up to a given point.
denominator	The number on the bottom of a fraction.
density	The mass per unit volume of a substance.
direct proportion	As one quantity increases, the other quantity increases proportionally.
discrete data	Quantitative data where the numbers can only take certain exact values.
equation	An expression with an = sign in it.
expected frequency	The expected number of times an outcome will happen in an experiment.
exponential	An expression of the form k^x, where k is a positive number.
expression	A collection of terms which doesn't have an = sign.
factor (of a number)	A number which the given number can be divided by (to give a whole number).

Glossary

fair	When all outcomes of an experiment are equally likely.
formula	A rule that helps you to work something out (it will have an = sign in it).
frequency density	The frequency of a class divided by the class width.
gradient	A measure of a line's slope. The bigger the number, the steeper the line.
highest common factor	The biggest number that the two (or more) given numbers can be divided by (also HCF).
hypotenuse	The longest side of a right-angled triangle, found opposite the right angle.
improper fraction	A fraction where the numerator is larger than the denominator.
integer	A whole number — it can be positive, negative or zero.
intersection (of two sets)	A set that only contains objects that are elements of both sets, written as A ∩ B.
inverse proportion	As one quantity increases, the other quantity decreases proportionally.
irrational number	A number that can't be written as a fraction.
lowest common multiple	The smallest number that can be divided by the two (or more) given numbers (also LCM).
magnitude	The length of a vector (magnitude has no direction).
mean	The total of all items in a data set, divided by the number of items in that set.
median	The middle value of a data set when the values are in order of size.
mixed number	A number that has an integer part and a fraction part.
mode	The most common value in a data set.
multiple (of a number)	A number that is in the times table of the given number.
natural number	A positive integer — not negative or zero.
numerator	The number on the top of a fraction.
obtuse angle	An angle that is between 90° and 180°.
opposite side	In trigonometry, the side of a right-angled triangle that is opposite the angle being used.
parallel lines	Lines that have the same gradient.
perpendicular lines	Lines that cross at a right angle. Their gradients multiply together to give –1.
plane of symmetry	A flat surface that splits a 3D shape into two symmetrical pieces.
polygon	A many-sided 2D shape that has only straight sides.
possibility diagram	A diagram that shows all the possible outcomes of two activities.
pressure	The amount of force acting per unit area.
prime number	A number that can only be divided exactly by two whole numbers — 1 and itself.
prism	A 3D object which is the same shape all the way through — it has a constant cross-section.

Glossary

proper subset	A subset with fewer elements than the set which contains it.
quadratic	An expression where x^2 is the highest power of x.
qualitative data	Descriptive data — it uses words, not numbers.
quantitative data	Data that measures quantities using numbers.
range	The difference between the highest and lowest values in a data set.
rational number	A number that can be written as a fraction.
real number	Every type of number — rational and irrational.
reciprocal (algebra)	An expression of the form $\frac{A}{x}$, where A is a number.
reciprocal (of a number)	1 divided by the given number.
recurring decimal	A decimal number that has a pattern of numbers which repeats forever.
reflex angle	An angle that is more than 180°.
regular polygon	A polygon where all the sides are the same length and all angles are equal.
relative frequency	The frequency of an event divided by the number of times the experiment is done.
right angle	An angle that is exactly 90°.
sector	A wedge-shaped area in a circle cut from the centre.
segment	The area between a chord and the outside of the circle.
similar shapes	Shapes that are the same shape (with the same angles) but different sizes.
speed	The distance travelled per unit time.
square number	The result of multiplying a whole number by itself — $a \times a$.
standard form	A number in the form $A \times 10^n$ (where $1 \leq A < 10$).
stationary point	A point on a graph where the gradient equals zero.
subset	A set entirely contained within another set.
tangent	A straight line which just touches a curve without crossing it.
term (algebra)	A collection of numbers and letters, all multiplied/divided together.
terminating decimal	A decimal number that has an end — it doesn't go on forever.
turning point	A type of stationary point on a graph — it can be a maximum or a minimum.
union (of two sets)	A set containing all the elements that are in either set, written as A ∪ B.
vector	A way of representing a movement of a certain size in a given direction. Can be used to describe a translation on a coordinate grid.
vertically opposite angles	Found opposite each other when two lines cross over. The two angles are equal.

Index

Index

Formulas in the Exams

International GCSE Maths uses a lot of formulas — and you'll have a difficult time trying to answer a question without the proper formula to start you off. Thankfully, CGP is here to solve all your formula problems.

You're Given These Formulas

Fortunately, those lovely examiners give you some of the formulas you need to use.

Volume of sphere $= \frac{4}{3}\pi r^3$

Surface area of sphere $= 4\pi r^2$

Volume of cone $= \frac{1}{3}\pi r^2 h$

Curved surface area of cone $= \pi r l$

Volume of pyramid $= \frac{1}{3} \times$ base area $\times$ height

Compound Measures:

$\text{Density} = \dfrac{\text{Mass}}{\text{Volume}}$ $\qquad$ $\text{Pressure} = \dfrac{\text{Force}}{\text{Area}}$

These are all the formulas you'll be given, I'm afraid — as for the rest of them...

Learn All the Other Formulas

Sadly, there are lots of formulas which you're expected to be able to remember for the exam.
Basically, any formulas in this book that aren't above, you need to learn.
There isn't space to write them all out below, but here are some of the main ones:

Compound Growth and Decay:

$N = N_0(\text{multiplier})^n$

Where P(A) and P(B) are the probabilities of events A and B respectively:

P(A or B) = P(A) + P(B) $\quad$ (If A and B can't both happen at the same time.)

P(A and B) = P(A) × P(B) $\quad$ (If the result of one event doesn't affect the probability of the other.)

For a right-angled triangle:

Pythagoras' theorem: $\quad a^2 + b^2 = c^2$

Trigonometry ratios:

$\sin x = \dfrac{O}{H}, \quad \cos x = \dfrac{A}{H}, \quad \tan x = \dfrac{O}{A}$

Area of trapezium $= \frac{1}{2}(a+b)h_v$

Extended

For any triangle *ABC*:

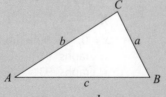

Sine rule: $\quad \dfrac{a}{\sin A} = \dfrac{b}{\sin B} = \dfrac{c}{\sin C}$

Cosine rule: $\quad a^2 = b^2 + c^2 - 2bc\cos A$

Area of triangle $= \frac{1}{2}ab\sin C$

Compound Measures:

$\text{Speed} = \dfrac{\text{Distance}}{\text{Time}}$

Extended

The Quadratic Formula:

The solutions of $ax^2 + bx + c = 0$, where $a \neq 0$

$x = \dfrac{-b \pm \sqrt{(b^2 - 4ac)}}{2a}$